**statistical
quality control
handbook**

This Handbook, as indicated in the "Foreword," was prepared to assist Western Electric people in performing Western Electric Company work. Others elsewhere may also think it useful as a guide for applying statistical quality control. The Handbook is not for sale through ordinary commercial channels.

Inquiries may be made to the following address:
AT&T Technologies
Commercial Sales Clerk
Select Code 700-444
P.O. Box 19901
Indianapolis, Indiana 46219
1-800-432-6600

First Edition 1956

Second Edition 1958

Second Printing—August 1964

Third Printing—June 1967

Fourth Printing—September 1970

Fifth Printing—November 1977

Sixth Printing—April 1982

Seventh Printing—June 1983

Eighth Printing—October 1983

Ninth Printing—March 1984

Tenth Printing—May 1984

Eleventh Printing—May 1985

PRINTED IN THE UNITED STATES OF AMERICA
BY DELMAR PRINTING COMPANY, CHARLOTTE, NORTH CAROLINA

Foreword

This book is a working Handbook prepared by Western Electric people for Western Electric use. Its primary purpose is to provide a guide for applying statistical quality control principles to the company's manufacturing and other operations.

The book was prepared under the guidance of a Handbook Committee appointed by the Manufacturing Division's Engineering Staff. The following persons have served, during all or part of the time, as members of the formal Committee:

D. W. Thomas, *Chairman*

C. S. Barrett	C. W. LeSage
E. E. Blankenstein	A. S. Ordecki
A. T. Chapman	R. Schin
C. C. Cole	Miss Bonnie B. Small
F. H. Drummond	F. Stonehill

The chairman of the Writing Committee was Miss Bonnie B. Small.

Many engineers and supervisors have assisted in the writing, assembling and checking of this material. The names are so numerous that it is not possible to list them all. The Committee wishes to express its appreciation to all these individuals for contributing so much of their time, effort and material, and also for the excellent spirit of cooperation in which the work was done.

————— ✦ —————

It is with deep regret that it must be recorded here that two very active members of this group, Mr. Claude E. Adair and Mr. Fred H. Drummond, of the Indianapolis Works, lost their lives in an airplane accident on April 1, 1956 while on their way to a Handbook meeting. Both had made important contributions to the writing and planning. For this, as well as personal reasons, their loss has been keenly felt.

————— ✦ —————

A preliminary edition of this book was issued in September 1956. Many members of the Western Electric Company, and also of the Bell Telephone Laboratories, were kind enough to read it. The Committee wishes to express its appreciation for the many helpful comments, suggestions and criticisms. The contents of this volume, however, are entirely the responsibility of the Committee.

Preface by the Writing Committee

This book is not a textbook on Statistical Quality Control. It does not attempt to discuss quality control theory, nor is it a book of examples of quality control applications. It is intended primarily to be a description of those procedures which, if followed, will tend to preserve the essential features of the quality control programs at Western Electric. To a certain extent it may be looked upon as a compendium of the techniques and methods which have been found to contribute most to making these programs successful. Much of the material is based on training courses which have been given during the past six or seven years to Engineers, key people in the Shop and people at all levels of Management.

The book is written in non-technical language, and no attempt has been made to write for the professional statistician or the mathematician. The techniques described are essentially those which have been used in all types of industry since their development during the 1920's by Dr. Shewhart. Perhaps the most distinctive features of the Western Electric program are (a) the emphasis on Engineering and Operating applications rather than Inspection, and (b) emphasis on the control chart, and particularly the process capability study, as the foundation of the entire program.

The book also stresses the importance of the Quality Control Team as a means of putting the quality control methods to direct practical use.

On certain subjects, such as designed experiments and correlation, it has not been possible to give more than a brief discussion of principles and an explanation of some of the terminology. It was thought best to include this, however briefly, rather than to omit these subjects entirely. The material on acceptance sampling has purposely been kept brief, partly because of the emphasis on Operating and Engineering, and partly because the subject has been covered adequately elsewhere.

Much of this book has been written in the imperative form. This is to facilitate its use as a practical working Handbook. The fact that the book states that "samples should be taken this way" or that "patterns should be marked this way" should not be taken to imply that this is the only way to do it.

It should also be kept in mind that this book does not attempt, in any sense, to cover the entire field of Statistical Quality Control. It does describe certain procedures and methods which the Western Electric Company has found it desirable to emphasize in order to secure the wanted results from its quality control programs.

BONNIE B. SMALL
Chairman
Writing Committee

Table of Contents

Foreword v
Preface vii

Section I

Fundamental Principles

Part A. Introduction to Statistical Quality Control

A-1 Meaning of the Term "Statistical Quality Control" 3
A-2 Meaning of "Process" 3
A-3 Essential Techniques in Statistical Quality Control 4

Part B. Introduction to Control Charts

B-1 Statistical Phenomena in the World Around Us 5
B-2 Principal Kinds of Control Charts. 10
B-3 $\bar{X}$ and R Charts. 12
B-4 p-Charts and Other Attributes Charts 17
B-5 Charts for Individual Measurements with Control Limits Based on the Moving Range 21
B-6 Tests for Unnatural Patterns 23
B-7 Tests to Be Used When the Control Limits Are Not Symmetrical 28
B-8 Other Unnatural Patterns 28
B-9 Simple Interpretation of Control Charts 30

Part C. Essential Elements in a Quality Control Program

C-1 Process Capability Studies to Obtain Information and Solve Problems. 34
C-2 Process Control Charts to Secure Tangible Results in the Shop. 36
C-3 Statistical Sampling Plans to Reduce the Cost of Inspection. 38
C-4 Quality Control Meetings to Make Quality Control Work . 39

Section II

Engineering Applications

Part A. Process Capability Studies

A-1 The Scientific Foundation of a Process Capability Study . . 45
A-2 Obtaining the Data 47
A-3 Analyzing the Data 51
A-4 Making an Estimate of the Process Capability 56
A-5 Using the Information from a Process Capability Study . . 61
A-6 Translating a Process Capability Study into a Shop Control Chart 63
A-7 Simple Examples of Process Capability Studies 66
A-8 Performance Studies. 74

Part B. Designed Experiments

B-1 Place of Designed Experiments in a Process Capability Study 75
B-2 Experiment I (Comparison of Two Methods) 77
B-3 Experiment II (Error of Measurement) 84
B-4 Experiment III (Four Factor Experiment) 91
B-5 Explanation of the Four Factor Analysis (With Special Reference to the Control Chart Method). 101
B-6 Directions for Plotting. 107
B-7 Drawing Conclusions from Experimental Control Charts . . 111
B-8 Some Suggestions on Planning the Experiment 112

Part C. Specifications

C-1 Specifications in General 119
C-2 Relationship Between Process and Specification. 119
C-3 Specification Conflicts and What Can Be Done to Avoid Them 122
C-4 Statistical Addition of Tolerances 122
C-5 Clearance and Fits 126

Part D. Distributions

D-1 Characteristics of Frequency Distributions 129
D-2 Distributions Derived from Samples. 137
D-3 Methods of Plotting a Frequency Distribution 138
D-4 Practical Uses of Frequency Distributions 140

Part E. Correlation

E-1 Graphical Methods of Studying Correlation. 143
E-2 Regression Lines 144
E-3 Formal Correlation Analysis 146
E-4 Other Information on Correlation 148

Part F. Control Chart Patterns

F-1 Control Chart Theory 149
F-2 Interpretation of $\bar{X}$ Charts 152
F-3 Interpretation of R Charts 154
F-4 Joint Interpretation of $\bar{X}$ Charts and R Charts 156
F-5 Interpretation of p-Charts and Other Attributes Charts . . 157
F-6 Interpretation of a Chart for Individual Measurements . . 160
F-7 Analysis of Patterns. 161
F-8 Cycles 161
F-9 Freaks. 162
F-10 Gradual Change in Level. 164
F-11 "Grouping" or "Bunching". 165
F-12 Instability 166
F-13 Interaction. 167
F-14 Mixtures. 169
F-15 Natural Pattern. 170
F-16 Stable Forms of Mixture. 171
F-17 Stratification 172
F-18 Sudden Shift in Level 174

F-19 Systematic Variables 175
F-20 Tendency of One Chart to Follow Another 176
F-21 Trends. 177
F-22 Unstable Forms of Mixture. 179
F-23 Calculation of Tests for Unnatural Patterns 180

Section III

Shop Applications

Part A. Process Control Charts

A-1 Planning the Control Charts 187
A-2 Detailed Procedures in Setting Up the Charts. 190
A-3 Other Methods of Charting. 197
A-4 Making Changes in Shop Control Charts. 198

Part B. Introduction of Charts in the Shop

B-1 Explaining the Charts to the People. 201
B-2 Simple Examples of the Advantages of Control Charts. . . . 202
B-3 General Instruction for Process Control 205
B-4 Instructions for Process Checkers. 213

Part C. Action on Control Charts

C-1 Importance of Promptness in Acting on Shop Charts . . . 217
C-2 First Type of Action: To Be Taken by the Process Checker 217
C-3 Second Type of Action: To Be Taken by the Operator, Machine Setter, Layout Operator or Other Responsible Person. 217
C-4 Third Type of Action: To Be Taken by the Supervisor . . 218
C-5 Fourth Type of Action: To Be Taken by the Quality Control Team 219
C-6 Using Shop Charts to Experiment with the Process 220
C-7 Meaning of an "Economical State of Control" 220
C-8 Summary Control Charts 221

Part D. Quality Control Teams

D-1 Regular Meetings of the Team 223
D-2 Quality Control Coverage 224
D-3 Reports on Progress. 225
D-4 Cost Reduction. 226
D-5 Control Chart Audits 227
D-6 Routine Duties in Connection with Process Control Charts. 228
D-7 Manual for Statistical Clerks 229

Section IV

Inspection Procedures

Part A. Principles of Inspection

A-1 Place of Inspection in the Quality Control Program 233
A-2 Why Inspection Can Be Reduced But Never Completely Eliminated 234

A-3   Uses of Sorting and Sampling Inspection   234
A-4   Inspection Planning   236

Part B.   Acceptance Sampling

B-1   Elementary Concepts   237
B-2   Methods of Calculating the Probability of Acceptance . . .   239
B-3   Economic Importance of OC Curves   242
B-4   Classification of Sampling Plans According to AQL, LTPD and AOQL   246
B-5   Sampling Plans for Continuous Processes   255
B-6   Sampling Plans for Lot-by-Lot Inspection   259
B-7   Special Types of Sampling Plans   262
B-8   Proper Grouping of Inspection Items   263
B-9   How to Select a Quality Level for Sampling   263
B-10   Factors Determining the Choice of a Particular Plan . . .   265

Part C.   General Instruction for Inspection   267

Part D.   Inspection Levels   273

Acknowledgments   275
References   277
Index   279

Section I

Fundamental

Principles

PART A

Introduction to Statistical Quality Control

Statistical Quality Control is a scientific method of analyzing data and using the analysis to solve practical problems. It can be applied to anything that it is possible to express in the form of numbers. In a manufacturing plant it can be applied to

- Engineering problems
- Operating problems
- Inspection problems
- Management problems
- Accounting and clerical problems

or virtually any other field of activity. Few of us can think of anything, in connection with our own jobs, that is not associated in some way with numbers.

———— ✦ ————

A-1 MEANING OF THE TERM "STATISTICAL QUALITY CONTROL"

The word **"Statistical"** means "having to do with numbers," or more particularly with "drawing conclusions from numbers."

The word **"Quality"** means much more than the goodness or badness of a product. It refers to the *qualities* or *characteristics* of the thing or process being studied.

The word **"Control"** means "to keep something within boundaries," or "to make something behave the way we want it to behave."

Taken together, and applied to a manufacturing operation, the words **Statistical Quality Control** mean this:

STATISTICAL	With the help of numbers, or data,
QUALITY	We study the characteristics of our process
CONTROL	In order to make it behave the way we want it to behave.

The term "process," as used in the previous statement, is capable of assuming many different meanings.

A-2 MEANING OF "PROCESS"

A "process" is any set of conditions, or set of causes, which work together to produce a given result. In a manufacturing plant we usually think first of a series of fabricating and assembling operations which result, for example, in the production of cable, electron tubes, relays, switchboards and other apparatus or equipment.

However, since the word "process" means merely a *system of causes*, a process may be far simpler than the ones mentioned above, or it may be far more complex. In statistical quality control the "process" we choose to study may be:

- a single machine, or a single fixture or element of a machine.
- a single human being, or a single motion performed by a human being.
- a piece of test equipment.
- a method of measurement or gaging.
- a method of assembly.
- the act of typing (or performing any clerical operation).
- a group of many machines turning out different or similar pieces of product.
- a group of many human beings (for example, a pay group or a Shop).
- a combination of human beings, machines, materials, methods, pieces of equipment, etc. For example, the procedures required to manufacture

switches, rubber or wire.

- a method of processing, such as chemical treatment or plating.
- a mental activity, such as visual checking or making calculations.
- intangible human elements, such as attitudes, motives and skills.
- the whole mass of causes which result in a Guided Missile System (for example), including thousands of resistors, capacitors, tubes and other components furnished by hundreds or thousands of different suppliers.
- anything else which results in a series of numbers and is connected with unsolved problems.

In its narrowest sense the term "process" refers to the operation of a single cause. In its broadest sense it may refer to the operation of a very complicated "cause system." This is why it is possible to make "process capability studies" in connection with practically any type of Engineering, Operating, Inspection or Management problem; including such problems as overall merchandise losses, the overall cost of maintenance or plant-wide inspection ratios.

A-3 ESSENTIAL TECHNIQUES IN STATISTICAL QUALITY CONTROL

The following techniques are essential in the quality control programs to be described in this Handbook:

(1) Process Capability Studies (the basic use of control charts).

(2) Process Control Charts (the use of control charts in the shop).

(3) Statistical Sampling Inspection (which may or may not make use of control charts).

(4) Statistical Design of Experiment (a device for comparing variables and determining their significance. This also is frequently handled with control charts).

The principal concept presented in this Handbook is that of the control chart, which consists of a plotted series of observations or "samples." The unique feature of the control chart is its ability to form data into patterns which, when tested statistically, can lead to information about the process.

The Process Capability Study is used by engineers, Operating supervisors and management to obtain information about how a process behaves.

Process Control Charts are used in the shop to increase yields, cut down scrap and repair, and help the people to do better work.

Statistical Sampling Inspection is used by inspectors as a scientific basis for accepting or rejecting product.

Design of Experiment is used in research and development problems, to study the effect of many variables at once, to throw light on mysterious or puzzling causes and effects, and to explore the unknown.

These four techniques are described more fully in later parts of the Handbook.

PART B

Introduction to Control Charts

B-1 STATISTICAL PHENOMENA IN THE WORLD AROUND US

B-1.1 Fluctuating patterns

If data are collected which have a bearing on any problem, any series of events or any manufacturing situation, these data are always found to exhibit variation. Instead of being exactly the same from point to point or from time to time, the numbers vary. If plotted on a piece of graph paper, so the variations can be studied, the numbers always form a fluctuating, zig-zag pattern. Some typical examples of fluctuating patterns are shown in Figures 1–4.

In the first case an operator was assembling spoolheads onto a core. The supervisor kept a record of the percentage of loose spoolhead assemblies made by this operator day after day. He found that the percentages varied. The percentage of loose spoolheads was not the same every day.

Figure 2 is a record obtained from an automatic welding operation. This is an entirely different type of operation from Figure 1. It involves different materials, different facilities, a different operator, different problems. When the supervisor kept a record of the daily percentage of offcenter welds, he found that the percentages varied in much the same manner as Figure 1. The percentage of offcenter welds was not the same every day.

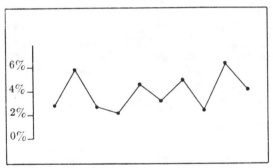

Fig. 1. Daily percentage of loose spoolheads.

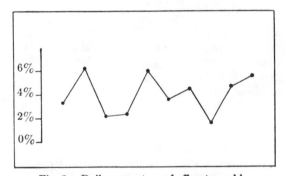

Fig. 2. Daily percentage of offcenter welds.

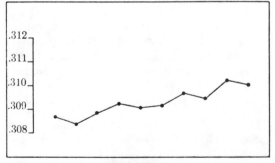

Fig. 3. Successive parts coming from a screw machine (diameter).

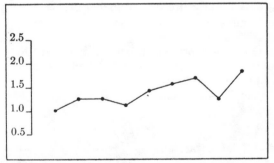

Fig. 4. Electrical measurement on a series of assemblies (noise level).

The same thing was found on plotting the dimensions of successive parts coming from a screw machine (Figure 3), and also the electrical characteristics of a series of assembled units (Figure 4). Any series of numbers from a process, if plotted in sequence, will form a fluctuating pattern. Even repeat measurements made on the same object will not be exactly the same, time after time or day after day.

Similar variation is found in accounting figures, production figures, records of attendance, temperatures, pressures, medical reports or any other set of numbers from an industrial process. We do not know of any type of manufacture in which variation is not present.

B-1.2 What causes the fluctuations in a fluctuating pattern?

Fluctuations in the data are caused by a large number of minute variations or differences: differences in materials, equipment, the surrounding atmospheric conditions, the physical and mental reactions of people. Most of these differences are extremely small. They cause the pattern to fluctuate in what is known as a "natural" or "normal" manner. Occasionally, however, there will be a large or unusual difference, much more important than all the other differences put together. For example, material is taken from a different batch; the machine setter makes a new setting; an inexperienced operator takes the place of an experienced operator. These large causes make the pattern fluctuate in an "unnatural" or "abnormal" manner.

Experience shows that there are definite detectable differences between the "natural" and "unnatural" patterns. It is possible to discover and study these differences by means of simple calculations based on well-known statistical laws.

Once we know that a pattern is unnatural, it is possible to go further and find the *cause* of the unnaturalness. This makes it possible to detect, identify and study the behavior of *causes*.

B-1.3 Distributions

Fluctuations are not the only statistical phenomena which are observable in nature.

It has long been known that if we take large numbers of observations on some physical quantity (such as the charge on an electron), or large numbers of measurements on an industrial product (such as the diameter of a wire or shaft), these measurements will tend to group themselves around some central value with a certain amount of variation or "scatter" on either side. The pattern or shape formed by the grouped measurements is called a "frequency distribution." We observe that if the causes which produce the observations or measurements remain essentially unchanged, the distribution tends to have certain distinguishable and stable characteristics. These characteristics become more definite as the number of observations or measurements increases. We conclude from this that, if the cause system is constant, the observed distribution tends to approach, as a statistical limit, some distribution function or "law."

This tendency to form a distribution is observed throughout nature. It is one of the most fundamental of all natural laws.

Experience tells us that the two sets of statistical phenomena—distributions and fluctuations—are not separate and unrelated. A distribution can be thought of as a *composite mass of fluctuations*, and the fluctuations can be thought of as *confined within the limits of a distribution*. It is therefore possible to make use of statistical limits, derived from distributions, to predict the behavior of a fluctuating pattern *when there are no abnormal causes*.

This can be stated formally as follows:

Whenever we have a series of events proceeding from a given system of causes, those events will not in general be identical with each other. Instead, they will fluctuate or vary in a manner described as "random." Nevertheless, if the cause system remains unchanged, the frequencies with which the events occur will tend to approach an objective probability, or set of probabilities, as the number of events increases indefinitely.

Translated into industrial terms, this can be stated as follows:

Whenever we have a series of observations or measurements, obtained from a given process, those measurements will not in general be identical with each other. Instead they will vary in such a way as to form a fluctuating pattern. Nevertheless, if nothing disturbs the process, these fluctuating measurements will be held within definite mathematical limits. In the aggregate, a large number of these measurements will tend to form a predictable distribution.

Translated into everyday language, the statements above mean this:

a. Everything varies.
b. Individual things are unpredictable.
c. Groups of things from a constant system of causes tend to be predictable.

Check your understanding of these fundamental concepts by studying the following simple examples:

Example 1

a. People live to different ages.
b. No one knows how long he himself will live.
c. Insurance companies can tell with great accuracy what percentage of people will live to be 60, 65, 70 etc.

Example 2

a. You cannot write the letter "a" twice in exactly the same way.
b. You have no way of knowing how your next "a" will differ from the last one.
c. Nevertheless there is something about your "a's" that makes them recognizably different from my "a's."

Example 3

a. All patterns fluctuate.
b. The individual points are unpredictable.
c. A group or series of points from a constant process will tend to follow a pattern that obeys a fixed law.

These concepts are carefully developed by Shewhart in Reference No. 37.

B-1.4 Statistical limits for fluctuating patterns

By making use of certain equations, derived from statistical laws, it is possible to calculate "limits" for any given pattern. If a pattern is natural, its fluctuations will fit within these limits. If a pattern is unnatural, its fluctuations will not fit these limits. The following are examples of the calculation of statistical limits.

(1) *Statistical limits for the chart on the spoolhead operation (Figure 1).*

To calculate limits for this chart, proceed as follows:

a. First take the percentage of loose spoolheads turned out by the operator, on the average, over a period of time. In this case it was 4%.

The average percentage is called $\bar{p}$ (pronounced p-bar). The "p" means percentage or proportion, and the bar above it means average.

b. Then take the average number of spoolheads assembled by this operator during the day. In the example used, this number was 400.

The number assembled is called n (meaning number).

c. The equation for the calculation of statistical limits is as follows:

$$\text{Limits of fluctuation} = \pm 3 \sqrt{\frac{\bar{p}(1 - \bar{p})}{n}}$$

$$= \pm 3 \sqrt{\frac{.04\,(.96)}{400}}$$

$$= \pm 3 \times .0098$$

$$= \pm .0294$$

The limits of fluctuation are therefore 2.94% on either side of the average, or 6.94% and 1.06%. The pattern for the spoolhead process should stay inside of these limits.

(2) *Statistical limits for the chart on the welding operation (Figure 2).*

To calculate limits for this chart, proceed as follows:

a. Use the same equation that was used in (1) above.

b. The average percentage of offcenter welds ($\bar{p}$) was again 4%.

7

c. The average number of welds made by the operator per day (n) was in this case 1000.

d. Limits of fluctuation $= \pm 3 \sqrt{\dfrac{\bar{p}(1-\bar{p})}{n}}$

$$= \pm 3 \sqrt{\frac{.04\,(.96)}{1000}}$$

$$= \pm 3 \times .0062$$

$$= \pm .0186$$

The limits of fluctuation are therefore 1.86% on either side of the average, or 5.86% and 2.14%. The pattern for the welding process should stay inside of these limits.

(3) *Statistical limits for the charts on (a) screw machine and (b) electrical characteristic.*

Since these involve a different type of data (individual measurements rather than percentages), it is necessary to use a different equation.

Limits of fluctuation around the average of the data $= \pm 2.66\,M\bar{R}$,

where the symbol "$M\bar{R}$" refers to the average difference between successive pairs of measurements. This is explained on page 21.

The limits of fluctuation for the screw machine chart turn out to be .3102 and .3086. The limits of fluctuation for the electrical chart are 1.95 and 0.75. The patterns for these two processes should stay inside of these limits.

In a similar way, limits can be calculated for any other type of data. Detailed instructions are given on pages 12–23.

When we add the statistical limits to a fluctuating pattern, the result is called a "control chart." The control chart is one of the most sensitive devices known for analyzing data and obtaining information.

B-1.5 Meaning of a control chart

The following are control charts for the four operations discussed above.

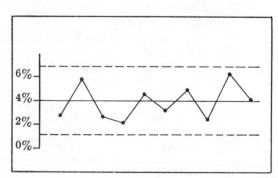

Fig. 5. Control chart for the percentage of loose spoolheads.

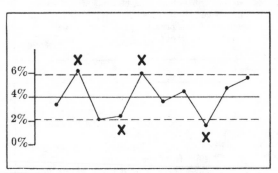

Fig. 6. Control chart for the percentage of offcenter welds.

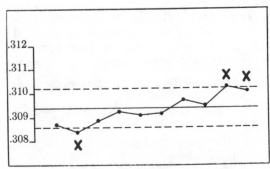

Fig. 7. Control chart for screw machine parts (diameter).

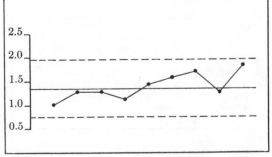

Fig. 8. Control chart for electrical assemblies (noise level).

The statistical limits are drawn in as dotted lines and are called "control limits." The control limits used in this Handbook, unless otherwise stated, are "3 sigma control limits." *

The control limits are used to determine whether the pattern is "natural" or "unnatural." The following procedure is used:

(1) Check the fluctuating pattern to see whether it is in conflict with the natural statistical limits. The pattern is in conflict if it (a) jumps outside the control limits or (b) forms unnatural clusters of points inside the control limits.

Tests for unnatural points or clusters of points are given on pages 23–28.

(2) Mark any unnatural points or clusters of points with "x's."

(3) If the pattern is not in conflict with the limits (that is, there are no x's), consider it a "natural" pattern. In general, the longer the series of points without evidence of unnaturalness, the stronger is the evidence that this is a natural pattern.

An occasional "x" (perhaps once in a hundred points) may be the result of chance alone, and is not considered to make the pattern unnatural.

(4) If the pattern is in conflict with the limits (that is, there are x's), consider the pattern "unnatural" and the process "out of control." The more numerous the x's, in general, the stronger is the evidence of lack of control.

When a pattern is natural, it means that there are no abnormal extraneous causes working in the process. When the pattern is unnatural, it means that outside disturbances are present and are affecting the process.

When a pattern is unnatural, those familiar with the process should investigate to find what the outside disturbances are.

On most control charts, we prefer to have a longer series of points than those shown in Figures 5–8. In the following discussion these charts should be considered as typical portions of a more complete control chart.

---

* "Sigma" (usually written σ) is a unit of measure which is used to describe the width or spread of a distribution or pattern. The fluctuations in a "natural" pattern tend to spread about ±3 sigma.

Interpretation of Figures 5–8

The chart for the spoolhead operation (Figure 5) is interpreted as follows:

(1) There are no x's.
(2) There is no evidence that the process is out of control.
(3) It is not being disturbed by any unusual, outside causes.

The chart for the welding operation (Figure 6) is interpreted as follows:

(1) Four out of the 10 points are marked with x's.
(2) There is strong evidence that the process is out of control.
(3) It is being disturbed by large and unnecessary outside causes.

The chart for the screw machine process (Figure 7) is interpreted as follows:

(1) Three out of the 10 points are marked with x's.
(2) There is strong evidence that the process is out of control.
(3) The pattern shows a continuous movement in one direction which, in the presence of x's, indicates a trend.

The chart for the electrical process (Figure 8) is interpreted as follows:

(1) There are no x's.
(2) There is no evidence that the process is out of control.
(3) The pattern appears to show an upward movement, but since there are no x's there is no reason to believe that this is a trend.

Note how this information depends on having a set of control limits. Without the control limits, Figures 1 and 2 look very much the same. With the control limits added, they look entirely different. The same is true of Figure 3 as compared with Figure 4.

This leads to one of the most fundamental principles in statistical quality control, which may be stated as follows:

To interpret data correctly, we must have (a) a pattern and (b) control limits. This is the same as saying: To interpret data correctly, put it on a control chart.

B-1.6 Experience as the basis for confidence in control charts

No one has to accept the evidence of a control chart on faith. It is always possible to make an investigation to see whether the chart is correct. The following is a record of the investigations actually made in connection with Figures 5–8.

(1) When the people who had the spoolhead operation made a careful check of all the elements in their process, including the materials, piece parts, tools, fixtures, gages and the activities and habits of the operators and machine setters, they were unable to find anything abnormal or out of order. This agreed with the indications of the control chart.

(2) When the people who had the welding operation made a careful check of all the elements in their process, including the materials, piece parts, tools etc., they discovered to their surprise the following two conditions:

   a. The method of regulating the voltage supply was not adequate for this job.

   b. Two of the machine setters were being careless in dressing the electrodes.

When these two conditions were corrected, the chart came into control. The statistical analysis made by the control chart had revealed the presence of "causes" which the people were not aware of.

(3) The people who had the screw machine process did not believe that the diameter of the parts could change, since the machine was locked at the beginning of the run and the run was too short to be affected by toolwear. However, when they carefully checked the condition of the machine, they discovered worn threads in the locking device. The machine was being "locked" but was not staying locked. When the locking device was repaired, the trend disappeared from the control chart.

(4) The engineers working on the electrical assemblies believed that the noise level of the product was increasing. They said that this was due to poor housekeeping in the shop. However, when large quantities of product were tested, made at the beginning and end of the period shown, it was found that the noise level was no higher at the end than at the beginning. This agreed with the indications of the control chart.

This has happened in shops and in laboratories many hundreds of times. Time after time, on chart after chart, investigation and experience have proved that the chart is correct. Anyone can verify this for himself by running a few control charts.

The following evidence is also of direct interest to management:

When large numbers of people in a plant begin to act regularly in accordance with control charts, doing what the charts tell them in the details of running their jobs, the plant almost invariably begins to show certain remarkable results:

- Costs are reduced.
- Quality and yields improve rapidly.
- There are major reductions in scrap, rework and the necessary amount of inspection.
- The engineers find their knowledge about the process increasing.
- Experiments are faster and more successful.
- Many design problems vanish.
- Difficult problems having to do with specifications and requirements are solved easily and economically.

All of this is evidence of the reliability of control charts.

B-2 PRINCIPAL KINDS OF CONTROL CHARTS

The control charts shown in Figures 5–8 were based either on percentages or on individual measurements. However, control limits can be applied with equal ease to any other form of data. Some kinds of data are much more sensitive than others in detecting the causes that tend to disturb a process.

The most common kinds of data, listed in order of sensitivity, are as follows:

(1) Ranges (difference between highest and lowest in a small group of measurements).

(2) Averages (especially of small groups).

(3) Percentages (as in the charts for the spoolhead and welding operations)—or counts, which are another form of percentages.

(4) Individual numbers, such as temperatures, pressures, records of earnings or absences, chemical analyses etc.

The two most sensitive kinds of data, ranges and averages, are plotted together to form an "$\bar{X}$ and R" chart. This is the most powerful of all control charts for diagnosing production troubles. Next in order come p-charts, which use percentages, and "charts with control limits based on the moving range," which make use of individual numbers.

There are also various substitutes for, or variations of, the p-chart, which use counts instead of percentages. These are known as np-charts, c-charts or u-charts.

$\bar{X}$ and R charts

These are also called "average and range" charts. The $\bar{X}$ is pronounced "X-bar" and means "average of a sample." The R stands for "range," or difference between highest and lowest in a sample. This chart is plotted as a pair of patterns, one for average and one for range. Directions for making an $\bar{X}$ and R chart are given on pages 12–15.

As indicated above, the $\bar{X}$ and R chart is the most sensitive control chart for tracing and identifying causes. The R pattern is read first, and from this it is possible to identify many causes directly. The $\bar{X}$ pattern is read in the light of the R chart, and this makes it possible to identify other causes. Finally, the $\bar{X}$ pattern and R pattern are read jointly, which gives still further information.

Among the patterns which may form on an $\bar{X}$ and R chart are the following:

- Cycles.
- Trends.
- Freaks.
- Mixtures.
- Grouping or "bunching" of measurements.
- Sudden shift in level.

- Gradual change in level.
- Instability (abnormally large fluctuations).
- Stratification (abnormally small fluctuations).
- Interactions (two or more variables acting together).
- Systematic variation.
- Tendency of one chart to follow another.

Each type of pattern can be associated with particular causes. The causes which affect the $\bar{X}$ chart are in general different from the causes which affect the R chart. This information, when combined with job knowledge, makes it possible to isolate the factors disturbing the process.

The patterns listed above are fully explained in Engineering Part F.

p-Charts

These are also called "percentage charts" or "attributes charts." The "p" means "proportion." It often represents the proportion of bad compared to total—that is, the "percent defective." Directions for making a p-chart are given on pages 17–20.

The p-chart is the second most sensitive chart for identifying causes. It is less powerful than the $\bar{X}$ and R chart because it has only one pattern, and thus it is not possible to identify causes so accurately. However, the p-chart forms the same kinds of pattern as $\bar{X}$ and R charts (cycles, trends, freaks, gradual change, sudden shift, etc.), and the patterns can be related to one's knowledge of the variables in the process.

The p-chart relies more heavily on job knowledge than the $\bar{X}$ and R chart. It is therefore used mainly in situations where the important causes are known.

Other attributes charts

For information about np-charts, c-charts and u-charts, see pages 20–21.

Charts for individual measurements with control limits based on the "moving range"

These charts are used for individual numbers which cannot easily be formed into samples. The "moving range" refers to the method of calculating the control limits, which depends on taking successive differences or ranges between the individual observations. Only the individual numbers are plotted, however, not the moving ranges.

This chart is less sensitive than either the $\bar{X}$ and R chart or p-chart, but it forms the same types of pattern and can be interpreted in much the same way. This chart is used wherever it is not practical to use $\bar{X}$ and R charts or p-charts.

Directions are given on pages 21–23.

B-3 $\bar{X}$ AND R CHARTS

B-3.1 Variables measurements

For $\bar{X}$ and R charts it is necessary to have measurements that are capable of showing actual degrees of variation. Measurements of this type are called *variables measurements*. Common examples of variables measurements are length in feet, diameter in inches, resistance in ohms, noise in decibels, weld strength in grams or pounds, etc. Many characteristics which are not ordinarily measured in the shop (cracks, appearance or workmanship, for example) can be put in a form which is roughly equivalent to variables measurements, if necessary. Methods of doing this are explained on pages 49–50.

B-3.2 Definitions and symbols for $\bar{X}$ and R charts

The following symbols are used in connection with $\bar{X}$ and R charts:

X = an individual reading or observation.

n = the number of observations in a group or set, often referred to as the sample size. "n" may be 2, 3, 4, 5 or more, but should not be greater than 10.

$\bar{X}$ (X bar) = the average of a group of X's. $\bar{X}$ is calulated by the formula

$$\bar{X} = \frac{X_1 + X_2 + X_3 \ldots X_n}{n}$$

$\bar{\bar{X}}$ (X double bar) = the average of a series of $\bar{X}$ values.

R (range) = the difference between the largest and smallest reading in a sample of n measurements.

$\bar{R}$ (R bar) = the average of a series of R values.

A_2 = a factor used in calculating the control limits for the $\bar{X}$ chart.

D_4 = a factor used in calculating the upper control limit for the R chart.

D_3 = a factor used in calculating the lower control limit for the R chart.

The factors A_2, D_4 and D_3 vary with the size of the sample. Select the appropriate factor from the table shown below.

Number of Observations in Sample	$\bar{X}$ Chart. Factors for Control Limits	R Chart. Factors for Control Limits	
(n)	(A_2)	(D_2)	(D_4)
2	1.88	0	3.27
3	1.02	0	2.57
4	.73	0	2.28
5	.58	0	2.11
6	.48	0	2.00
7	.42	.08	1.92
8	.37	.14	1.86
9	.34	.18	1.82
10	.31	.22	1.78

Fig. 9.   Table of factors for $\bar{X}$ and R charts.

B-3.3 Directions for making an $\bar{X}$ and R chart

Always make the R chart before the $\bar{X}$ chart. Proceed as follows.

R chart

(1) Decide on the sample size (n) to be used.

(2) Obtain a series of groups of measurements, each group containing "n" measurements. Have 20 or more groups, if possible, but not less than 10 groups.

(3) Compute R for each sample and take the average of the R's ($\bar{R}$). This is the centerline for the R chart. It is drawn as a solid horizontal line. See Figure 10.

(4) Multiply $\bar{R}$ by D_4 and D_3 to obtain upper and lower control limits for the R chart.

The control limits are drawn as dotted horizontal lines. See Figure 10.

(5) Obtain a piece of graph paper (or a standard control chart form) and set up an appropriate scale. Be careful not to make the R chart too wide. Set up the R chart at the bottom of the sheet as shown in Figure 10.

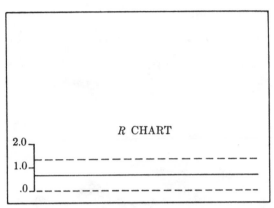

Fig. 10. Construction of the R chart.

(6) Plot on this chart the successive values of R and connect the points with straight lines.
(7) Mark x's on the chart, if necessary, in accordance with the rules given on pages 25–28.
(8) Interpret the chart as explained on page 30. For a fuller interpretation of the R chart see pages 154–156.

$\bar{X}$ chart

(1) Use exactly the same groups of measurements that were used for the R chart.
(2) Calculate $\bar{X}$ for each sample and take the average of the $\bar{X}$'s ($\bar{\bar{X}}$). This is the centerline for the $\bar{X}$ chart. It is drawn as a solid horizontal line. See Figure 11.
(3) Multiply $\bar{R}$ by A_2 to get the width of the control limits for the $\bar{X}$ chart. Add the $A_2\bar{R}$ value to (and subtract it from) $\bar{\bar{X}}$ to get the location of the control limits.

Upper control limit for $\bar{X}$ chart = $\bar{\bar{X}} + A_2\bar{R}$.

Lower control limit for $\bar{X}$ chart = $\bar{\bar{X}} - A_2\bar{R}$.

The control limits are shown as dotted horizontal lines. See Figure 11.

(4) Choose a scale for the $\bar{X}$ chart that is properly related to the scale already chosen for the R chart. The scale should be such that the distance between the control limits on the $\bar{X}$ chart is roughly similar to the distance between the control limits on the R chart. This relationship can be obtained as follows:
  a. For samples of 2, use the same spacing on the $\bar{X}$ chart as on the R chart.
  b. For samples of 5, let each division on the graph paper represent an increment of measurement half as large as on the R chart.
  c. For samples of 10, let each division on the graph paper represent an increment of measurement one-third as large as on the R chart.

This relationship between the scales corresponds roughly to $1/\sqrt{n}$. For other sample sizes, use the scale nearest to those given above.

(5) Set up an $\bar{X}$ chart in the upper portion of the sheet as shown in Figure 11.

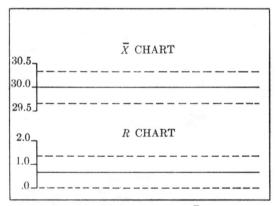

Fig. 11. Construction of the $\bar{X}$ chart.

(6) Plot on this chart the successive values of $\bar{X}$ and connect the points with straight lines.

(7) Mark x's on the chart, if necessary, in accordance with the rules given on pages 25–28.

(8) If drawing limits are specified for the characteristic being plotted, draw arrows in the left-hand margin along the $\bar{X}$ scale to represent the drawing limits. See

page 30. Notice how the arrows are drawn in Figure 45 on page 31.

(9) Interpret the chart as explained on pages 30–31. For a fuller interpretation of the $\bar{X}$ chart, see pages 152–154 and 156.

Directions for samples of 5

Since samples of 5 are used more commonly than any others, the instructions for this sample size are summarized for easy reference in Figure 12.

$\bar{X}$ and R chart for n = 5

Divide the data into groups of 5.

R Chart
For each group obtain R.
Centerline on R chart = $\bar{R}$.
Lower control limit = 0.
Upper control limit = 2.11 $\bar{R}$.

$\bar{X}$ Chart
For each group obtain $\bar{X}$.
Centerline on $\bar{X}$ chart = $\bar{\bar{X}}$.
Control limits = $\bar{\bar{X}} \pm .58\,\bar{R}$

Fig. 12. Instructions for $\bar{X}$ and R chart—samples of 5.

B-3.4 Example of calculations for an $\bar{X}$ and R chart

Obtain a set of data as shown in Figure 13.

(1) Centerline for R chart:

$$\bar{R} = \frac{\text{Total of } R\text{'s}}{\text{No. of Samples}} = \frac{31.8}{20} = 1.59$$

(2) Control limits for R chart:

$$D_4\bar{R} = 2.11 \text{ x } 1.59 = 3.35$$
$$D_3\bar{R} = 0 \text{ x } 1.59 = 0$$

(3) Centerline for $\bar{X}$ chart:

$$\bar{\bar{X}} = \frac{\text{Total of } \bar{X}\text{'s}}{\text{No. of Samples}} = \frac{213.20}{20} = 10.66$$

(4) Control limits for $\bar{X}$ chart:

$$\bar{\bar{X}} + A_2\bar{R} = 10.66 + (.58 \text{ x } 1.59)$$
$$= 10.66 + .92 = 11.58$$
$$\bar{\bar{X}} - A_2\bar{R} = 10.66 - .92 = 9.74$$

The completed chart is shown in Figure 14.

GAIN IN DB.

	3/31			4/1			4/4			4/5
	1	2	3	4	5	6	7	8	9	10
	11.1	9.6	9.7	10.1	12.4	10.1	11.0	11.2	10.6	8.3
	9.4	10.8	10.0	8.4	10.0	10.2	11.5	10.0	10.4	10.2
	11.2	10.1	10.0	10.2	10.7	10.2	11.8	10.9	10.5	9.8
	10.4	10.8	9.8	9.4	10.1	11.2	11.0	11.2	10.5	9.5
	10.1	11.0	10.4	11.0	11.3	10.1	11.3	11.0	10.9	9.8
	52.2	52.3	49.9	49.1	54.5	51.8	56.6	54.3	52.9	47.6
$\bar{X}$	10.44	10.46	9.98	9.82	10.90	10.36	11.32	10.86	10.58	9.52
R	1.8	1.4	.7	2.6	2.4	1.1	.8	1.2	.5	1.9
			4/6			4/7			4/8	
	11	12	13	14	15	16	17	18	19	20
	10.6	10.8	10.7	11.3	11.4	10.1	10.7	11.9	10.8	12.4
	9.9	10.2	10.7	11.4	11.2	10.1	12.8	11.9	12.1	11.1
	10.7	10.5	10.8	10.4	11.4	9.7	11.2	11.6	11.8	10.8
	10.2	8.4	8.6	10.6	10.1	9.8	11.2	12.4	9.4	11.0
	11.4	9.9	11.4	11.1	11.6	10.5	11.3	11.4	11.6	11.9
	52.8	49.8	52.2	54.8	55.7	50.2	57.2	59.2	55.7	57.2
$\bar{X}$	10.56	9.96	10.44	10.96	11.14	10.04	11.44	11.84	11.14	11.44
R	1.5	2.4	2.8	1.0	1.5	.8	2.1	1.0	2.7	1.6

Fig. 13. Typical data for an $\bar{X}$ and R chart.

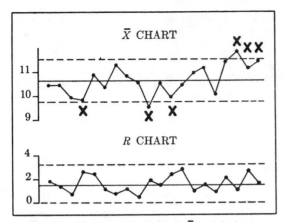

Fig. 14. Example of a finished $\bar{X}$ and R chart.

B-3.5 Example of the use of an $\bar{X}$ and R chart

A certain shop was having trouble in meeting a dimensional specification. The engineer decided to take a sample of the parts coming from the process and group them together in the form of a frequency distribution. The result of taking parts from a tote pan, measuring them and plotting the distribution is shown in Figure 15.

This distribution showed that parts were failing to meet the specification on both the high and low sides. No apparent solution was found, however, by treating the data in this manner. The engineer then made a second attempt to analyze the trouble as follows:

These parts were being produced by two machines, each of which was supposed to perform the same function. The engineer decided to measure parts from the individual machines.

The separate distributions are shown in Figure 16.

This also failed to give a solution to the problem. Both machines were in trouble and the distributions were very similar.

At this point the engineer decided to plot an $\bar{X}$ and R chart. This required grouping the data into samples of 5 for each machine and plotting the average and range of each group of measurements in the order in which they were produced. The result of this is shown in Figures 17 and 18 on page 16.

These charts showed immediately that there was a significant difference between the two machines. Machine No. 1 had a wide pattern on its R chart (Figure 17) and the pattern was not in control. This meant that the machine was not behaving consistently. There was something about it that needed maintenance or repair.

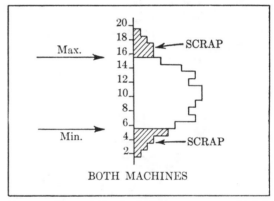

Fig. 15. Typical distribution from a process which is in trouble.

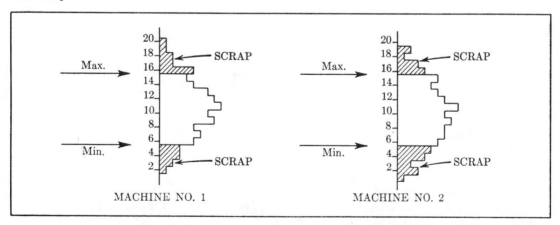

Fig. 16. Separate distributions from individual machines.

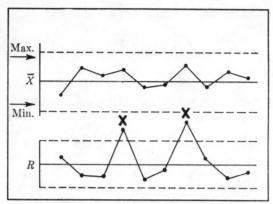

Fig. 17. $\bar{X}$ and R chart for Machine No. 1.

When the Maintenance Department checked Machine No. 1 they found a worn bearing. When this was replaced, the R chart became much narrower and the product was no longer in trouble.

The cause of the trouble on Machine No. 2 was entirely different. This machine was already in good repair, as shown by the controlled pattern on its R chart.

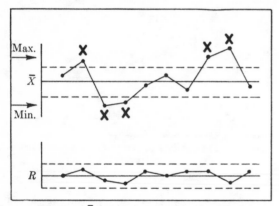

Fig. 18. $\bar{X}$ and R chart for Machine No. 2.

However, the center of the distribution on this machine was shifting back and forth, from the high side to the low side. This is shown by the out-of-control pattern on its $\bar{X}$ chart. This meant that the machine setter was either making poor settings or changing the setting too often.

When the machine setter was instructed to stop re-setting the machine on the basis of one or two measurements, and to use a control chart instead, the trouble disappeared also from Machine No. 2.

The $\bar{X}$ and R chart is able to separate causes of trouble on processes of all types, operator-controlled as well as machine-controlled.

B-3.6 Additional information about $\bar{X}$ and R charts

(1) By studying the $\bar{X}$ chart and the R chart together, it is possible to get indications of whether the distribution of product is symmetrical or skewed. See page 156.

(2) By studying the $\bar{X}$ chart and R chart together, it is possible to tell whether the process is capable of meeting a specification. This is explained briefly on pages 30–31. More detailed information is given on pages 56–61.

(3) Do not confuse the control limits on the $\bar{X}$ chart with the specified "blueprint" limits which are commonly found on a drawing. The control limits are natural process limits, determined by calculation from the nature of the process itself. The limits on a drawing are artificial, selected limits. They may or may not have any reasonable connection with the natural limits of the process. One of the objects of the control chart is to see how the natural limits compare with the limits shown on the drawing.

Also, the control limits on an $\bar{X}$ chart are limits for *averages*, while the limits on a drawing are usually limits for *individuals*. Limits for averages are always narrower than limits for individuals.

B-3.7 Useful adjuncts to the $\bar{X}$ and R chart

The data which have been used to plot an $\bar{X}$ and R chart may also be plotted in two other ways:

a. As a running record of individual measurements.

b. As a frequency distribution.

While neither of these should be used in *place* of an $\bar{X}$ and R chart, they are both very useful when plotted in *addition*. They give information which reinforces the $\bar{X}$ and R chart.

B-4 p-CHARTS AND OTHER ATTRIBUTES CHARTS

B-4.1 Attributes measurements

The *p*-chart does not require any actual measurements such as a measurement of length, width or resistance. It is only necessary to count the number of pieces that are oversize or warped, or have any other characteristic in which we are interested, and translate this count into a percentage. Measurements of this type which depend on counting are called *attributes measurements*. Common examples of attributes measurements are the number of cracked insulators in a lot, the number of poor soldered connections in a piece of wired equipment, the percent defective in the work of a certain operator, etc.

p-Charts are used in places where it is difficult or uneconomical to make a numerical measurement, or where it is desired to combine many types of defect into an overall percentage. However, if many characteristics are combined on a single chart, the *p*-chart becomes progressively more difficult to interpret.

B-4.2 Definitions and symbols for a p-chart

The following symbols are used in connection with *p*-charts:

n = number of units in a sample.

p = fraction defective in a sample.

$$= \frac{\text{number of defective units in a sample}}{\text{sample size }(n)}$$

$\bar{p}$ = average fraction defective in a series of samples

$$= \frac{\text{total number of defective units in all samples in the series}}{\text{total number checked in all samples in the series}}$$

B-4.3 Directions for making a p-chart

Proceed as follows:

(1) Obtain a series of samples of some appropriate size. Convenient sample sizes are 50 and 100. The "sample" may actually be the complete lot if the entire lot has been checked. Have 20 or more groups if possible, but not less than 10 groups.

(2) Count the number of defective units (warped, undersize, oversize, or whatever the characteristic may be in which you are interested). Calculate the value of *p* for each sample.

(3) Calculate $\bar{p}$ (the average fraction defective) as shown in B-4.2. This is the centerline for the *p*-chart. It is drawn as a solid horizontal line. See Figure 19.

(4) Calculate upper and lower control limits for the *p*-chart by using the following formulas.

Upper control limit for *p*-chart =

$$\bar{p} + 3\sqrt{\frac{\bar{p}(1-\bar{p})}{n}}$$

Lower control limit for *p*-chart =

$$\bar{p} - 3\sqrt{\frac{\bar{p}(1-\bar{p})}{n}}$$

The control limits are drawn as dotted horizontal lines. See Figure 19.

(5) Decide on an appropriate scale and set up a *p*-chart on graph paper or a standard control chart form. Be careful not to make the *p*-chart too wide. See Figures 19 and 21.

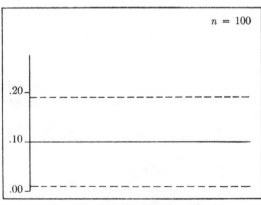

Fig. 19. Construction of a *p*-chart.

(6) Plot on this chart the successive values of p and connect the points with straight lines.

(7) Mark x's on the chart, if necessary, in accordance with the rules given on pages 25–28.

(8) Interpret the chart as explained on page 31. For a fuller interpretation of the p-chart, see pages 157–159.

Average value of n

If the samples to be used for a p-chart are not of the same size, it is sometimes permissible to use the *average sample size* for the series in calculating the control limits. The largest sample in the series should not be more than twice the average sample size, and the smallest sample in the series should not be less than half the average sample size.

If the individual samples vary more than this, either separate or combine samples to make them of suitable size, or calculate control limits separately for the samples which are too large or too small. See paragraph B-4.5.

p-Charts are most useful when this problem is avoided by keeping the sample size constant.

B-4.4 Example of calculations for a p-chart

Obtain a set of data as shown in Figure 20.

(1) Centerline for p-chart:

$$\bar{p} = \frac{\text{total number of defective units in all samples}}{\text{total number checked in all samples}}$$

$$= \frac{2103}{36060} = .0583, \text{ or } 5.83\%$$

(2) Average n for p-chart:

$$\text{average } n = \frac{\text{total number checked in all samples}}{\text{number of samples in the series}}$$

$$= \frac{36060}{25}$$

$$= 1442$$

(3) Upper control limit for p-chart:

$$= \bar{p} + 3 \sqrt{\frac{\bar{p}(1 - \bar{p})}{n}}$$

$$= .0583 + 3 \sqrt{\frac{.06 (.94)}{1442}}$$

$$= .0583 + .0186 = .0769$$

Lower control limit for p-chart

$$= .0583 - .0186 = .0397.$$

These may be converted to percentage by multiplying by 100. The completed chart is shown in Figure 21.

Separate control limits should properly be calculated for the samples dated 9/12 and 9/15.

B-4.5 Stairstep limits on a p-chart

The control limits in Figure 21 were calculated by using an average value of n. It is also possible to calculate control limits for each point on a p-chart individually, using the in-

Date	Number in Sample	Number Defective in Sample	% Defective in Sample
8/11	1524	70	4.59
8/12	1275	53	4.16
8/15	1821	132	7.25
8/16	1496	91	6.08
8/17	1213	32	2.64
8/18	1371	55	4.01
8/19	1248	69	5.53
8/20	1123	67	5.97
8/22	1517	159	10.48
8/23	1488	94	6.32
8/24	2052	105	5.12
8/25	1696	37	2.18
8/26	1427	58	4.06
8/29	1277	75	5.87
8/30	1613	73	4.53
9/2	1987	145	7.30
9/6	1360	41	3.01
9/7	1439	50	3.47
9/8	1723	118	6.85
9/9	2035	169	8.30
9/10	1314	88	6.70
9/12	215	24	11.16
9/13	1384	77	5.56
9/14	1995	185	9.27
9/15	467	36	7.71
Total	36060	2103	

Fig. 20. Typical data for a p-chart.

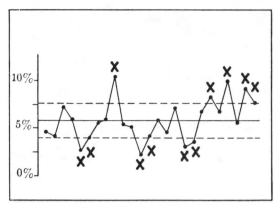

Fig. 21. Example of a finished *p*-chart.

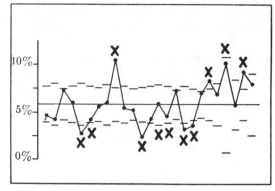

Fig. 22. Stairstep limits for the *p*-chart shown in Fig. 21.

dividual values of *n*. When this is done, the control limits may have an irregular "stairstep" effect as shown in Figure 22. Where the sample size is small, the control limits are wider. Where the sample size is large, the control limits are tighter. The pattern is marked with x's in the same way as if these were ordinary control limits.

"Stairstep" limits make a *p*-chart more difficult to interpret, and their use should be avoided. As mentioned above, limits of this kind are occasionally used for individual samples, where the sample is too small or too large to be covered by the "average value of *n*."

B-4.6 Example of the use of p-charts

In the manufacture of a relay, 24 palladium contacts are welded to the tips of 24 wire springs. One of the desired quality characteristics of the relay is the proper location of the contacts on the springs. The print tolerance allows for a maximum of .010″ offcenter. That is, the centerline of the contact must not be more than .010″ to the left or right of the centerline of the wire. The automatic welder designed for this operation has two welding heads. The first head welds the odd-numbered contacts and the second head welds the even-numbered contacts.

In the process of proving-in the welder, a *p*-chart was made for each head. After four days of operation the *p*-charts indicated two different levels, 10% defective on the first head and 22% defective on the second head. The second head also indicated an out-of-control condition.

An investigation was made on the feeding and guiding mechanism for each head. Replacement of the contact wire guides on both heads, and a tightened wire comb and locator on the second head, brought the percent defective down to a controlled average of 3% for both heads.

The process was allowed to continue at this level and the *p*-charts were continued on a 100% inspection basis. Occasional out-of-control points were noticed on each head due to loosening of the wire comb and locator. A redesign of the wire comb and locator to prevent its working loose and shifting led to a stabilized process at an average level of 0.5% defective. This level was acceptable to the assembly department.

The *p*-charts were continued, but put on a sampling basis. The charts acted as warning devices on the wearing or loosening of the guides and locators. Figure 23 shows the

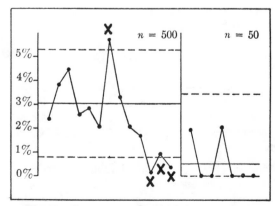

Fig. 23. Improvement resulting from a *p*-chart.

19

reduction in percent defective which was brought about by the effective use of p-charts.

B-4.7 Additional information about p-charts

(1) When the lower control limit for a p-chart is found to be less than zero, it should be shown as zero on the chart.

(2) In setting up the chart and plotting the samples, it is permissible to work with either decimals or percentages. On shop charts it is generally preferable to use percentages.

In calculating the control limits for a p-chart, however, always use the decimal value instead of the percentage. The limits may then be converted to percentages after the calculations are completed.

B-4.8 np-Charts

If the samples to be plotted on a p-chart are all of the same size, it is simpler to plot the *number of defectives* found in each sample instead of calculating the percentage. When this is done, the chart is called an np-chart instead of a p-chart.

Control limits for the np-chart are calculated as follows:

For each of a series of equal samples, count the number of defectives, np.

Centerline on chart = $n\bar{p}$

Control limits = $n\bar{p} \pm 3\sqrt{n\bar{p}(1-\bar{p})}$

Except for plotting the number defective instead of the percentage or fraction, this chart is in every way the equivalent of a p-chart. Plot the points, connect them, mark the x's and interpret the pattern in the same way as on a p-chart.

B-4.9 c-Charts

The c-chart is a special type of attributes control chart which uses the number of *defects* instead of the number of *defectives*. The distinction between "defect" and "defective" is as follows:

A defect is an individual failure to meet a single requirement.

A defective is a unit of product which contains one or more defects.

It is possible for a unit of product to contain many "defects" and still be counted as only one "defective."

In cases where a single unit of product is likely to contain many defects, a c-chart is generally more appropriate than a p-chart.

Nature of the c-chart: theoretical restrictions

The c-chart may be considered a special form of p-chart, in which

(a) the possibilities for defects are theoretically infinite, and

(b) the probability of getting a defect at any specific point is very small.

With a complicated product, the number of possibilities for defects increases very rapidly, until it approaches (for practical purposes) an "infinite" number of possibilities. Under these circumstances it is generally possible to use a c-chart.

c-Charts can be used only where the "area of opportunity for finding defects" is kept constant. That is, the samples must all consist of a certain fixed length, area, quantity, etc. If the first sample consists of 10,000 conductor-feet of wire, do not let the second sample consist of 20,000 conductor-feet, or the third sample of 8000. If the sample is to be a square yard of paper or other material, each successive sample must be of the same size.

The sample may, however, consist of a constant number of units considered as if they were one.

Typical places for using c-charts are the following:

- Number of loose soldered connections on a piece of wired equipment.
- Number of flaws in a square foot of rubber or cloth.
- Number of foreign particles inside of a sealed switch.
- Number of defects of all kinds on a crossbar frame.
- Number of points at which breakdown occurs per thousand feet of insulated wire.
- Number of reported failures in a radar system per month.

Directions for plotting

Control limits for the c-chart are calculated as follows:

For each of a series of equal samples, count the number of defects, c.

Centerline on chart $= \bar{c}$

Control limits $= \bar{c} \pm 3\sqrt{\bar{c}}$

c-Charts are plotted, marked and interpreted in the same way as p-charts. An example of a c-chart is given on pages 72–73.

B-4.10 u-Charts

The u-chart is a variation of the c-chart. The point plotted is the average number of defects per unit in a sample of n units. Each of the units in the sample must satisfy the requirements for a c-chart, but the number of units which are averaged need not be the same for all samples. This type of chart is sometimes used for aircraft, radar systems and other complicated assemblies.

Control limits for the u-chart are calculated as follows:

$$u = \frac{\text{number of defects}}{n \text{ (number of equal units)}}$$

Centerline on chart $= \bar{u}$

Control limits $= \bar{u} \pm 3\sqrt{\dfrac{\bar{u}}{n}}$

If the number of units is not the same from sample to sample, handle the varying sample sizes in the same manner as for a p-chart. u-Charts are plotted, marked and interpreted in the same way as p-charts or c-charts.

B-5 CHARTS FOR INDIVIDUAL MEASUREMENTS WITH CONTROL LIMITS BASED ON THE MOVING RANGE

B-5.1 Individual measurements

The principal kinds of data for which this chart should be used are the following:

a. Accounting figures of all kinds, including shipments, efficiencies, absences, losses, inspection ratios, maintenance costs, accident reports, records of medical tests, etc.

b. Production data such as temperatures, pressures, voltages, humidity, conductivity, furnace heat, gas composition, the results of chemical analysis, etc.

In all of these cases only one number is available to represent a given condition.

B-5.2 Definitions and symbols for charts with "moving range" limits

The only new symbol is MR which stands for the "moving range." This is the difference between successive pairs of numbers in a series of numbers: that is, the difference between the first and second numbers, then between the second and third, then between the third and fourth, etc.

Each of the individual numbers is used in calculating two of the moving ranges.

$M\bar{R}$ is the average of a series of moving ranges.

B-5.3 Directions for making a chart with "moving range" limits

To plot this type of chart, proceed as follows:

(1) Start with a series of individual numbers. Have 20 or more numbers if possible, but not less than 10 numbers.

(2) Take the difference between the first and second numbers, and record it; then the difference between the second and third numbers, etc. Continue in this way until you have taken the difference between the next-to-the-last and the last numbers. The number of differences or "ranges" should be one less than the number of individuals in the series.

The differences are calculated without regard to sign. That is, it does not matter whether they are plus or minus (gain or loss).

(3) Take the average of the original numbers in the series $(\bar{X})$. This is the centerline for the chart. It is drawn as a solid horizontal line. See Figure 25 (page 22).

(4) Take the average of the "ranges" obtained in step (2). Be sure to divide by

the number of ranges, which is one less than the number of original measurements. This average range is called $M\bar{R}$.

(5) Multiply $M\bar{R}$ by 2.66 (a constant factor) to get the width of the control limits for the moving range chart. Add this value to (and subtract it from) $\bar{X}$ to get the location of the control limits.

Control limits = $\bar{X} \pm 2.66\ M\bar{R}$

The control limits are shown as dotted horizontal lines. See Figure 25.

(6) Set up a chart on graph paper or a standard control chart form. Be careful not to make the chart too wide. See Figure 25.

(7) Plot on this chart the series of original numbers, and connect the points with straight lines. *Do not plot the moving ranges calculated in Step (2).*

(8) Mark x's on the chart, if necessary, in accordance with the rules given on pages 25–28.

(9) Interpret the chart as explained on page 31. For a fuller interpretation of this type of control chart, see pages 160–161.

B-5.4 Example of calculations for a chart with "moving range" limits

Obtain a set of data as shown in Figure 24.

(1) Centerline for chart:

$$\bar{X} = \frac{\text{total of individuals}}{\text{number of individuals}}$$

$$= \frac{460.4}{15} = 30.7$$

(2) Average moving range:

$$M\bar{R} = \frac{\text{total of moving ranges}}{\text{number of moving ranges}}$$

$$= \frac{53.6}{14} = 3.8$$

(3) Upper control limit

$= \bar{X} + 2.66\ (M\bar{R})$

$= 30.7 + (2.66 \times 3.8)$

$= 30.7 + 10.1$

$= 40.8$

Earnings of a Group of Workers		
	% Earned	Change from Preceding Month (Moving Range)
January (last year)	25.0	...
February	25.3	.3
March	33.8	8.5
April	36.4	2.6
May	32.2	4.2
June	30.8	1.4
July	30.0	.8
August	23.6	6.4
September	32.3	8.7
October	28.1	4.2
November	27.0	1.1
December	26.1	.9
January (this year)	29.1	3.0
February	40.1	11.0
March	40.6	.5
	460.4	53.6

Fig. 24. Typical data for a chart with "moving range" limits.

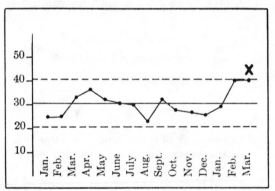

Fig. 25. Example of a finished chart with "moving range" limits.

(4) Lower control limit

$= \bar{X} - 2.66\ (M\bar{R})$

$= 30.7 - 10.1$

$= 20.6$

The completed chart is shown in Figure 25.

B-5.5 Typical uses for charts with "moving range" limits

The following will suggest other applications for this type of chart.

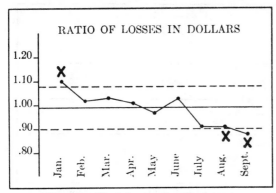

Fig. 26.   Chart for merchandise losses.

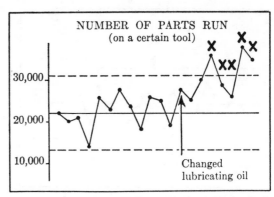

Fig. 27.   Chart for length of run after a tool is repaired.

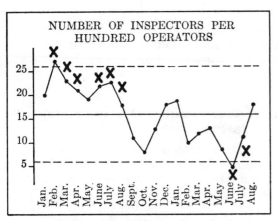

Fig. 28.   Chart for inspection ratios.

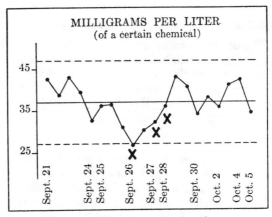

Fig. 29.   Chart for chemical analyses.

B-6 TESTS FOR UNNATURAL PATTERNS

The points plotted on a control chart form an irregular, up-and-down pattern which can be classified as "natural" or "unnatural." Ability to interpret the control chart depends on the ability to make this classification.

The following tests are taught in all Western Electric training classes on quality control. They involve (a) making a visual check on each point to see whether it is part of an unnatural pattern, and (b) marking the point with an "x" if it reacts to the visual check. The tests should be memorized and practiced until they can be applied automatically while glancing at a control chart pattern, and *all control charts should be marked immediately with x's in accordance with these tests as the charts are being plotted.*

Failure to mark the x's on a control chart* may make it difficult to interpret the chart correctly.

Theoretical basis for control chart tests

A control chart is essentially a picture of a sampling distribution.   That is, it consists of a series of sample values or "statistics" which, if they were gathered together instead of being plotted in sequence, would form a distribution. An example of this is shown in Figure 30.

If the plotted points were gathered together at one end of the chart, they would form a distribution as shown in Figure 31.

There is a large amount of theoretical and practical knowledge having to do with sampling distributions.   From this we obtain the following characteristics of natural and unnatural patterns.

* See footnote on bottom of page 25.

23

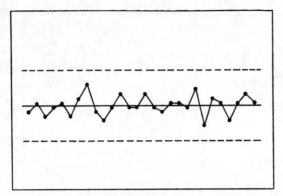

Fig. 30. Typical pattern on a control chart.

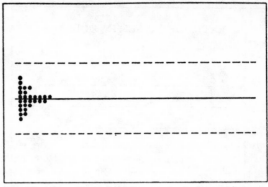

Fig. 31. Grouping of points on a typical control chart.

B-6.1 Characteristics of a natural pattern

The primary characteristic of a natural pattern is that the points fluctuate at random, and obey the laws of chance. This means that they follow no particular recognizable "system" or order. In addition, the following characteristics are found in natural patterns:

Since most of the values in a sampling distribution tend to cluster about its center, it is natural for most of the points on a control chart to be somewhere near the centerline. Since most sampling distributions tend to be reasonably symmetrical, it is natural for the number of points on one side of the control chart centerline to be about equal to the number on the other side. Since most sampling distributions have "tails" extending as far as ± 3 sigma, it is natural for an occasional point on a control chart to approach or reach the 3 sigma control limits.

These characteristics of a natural pattern can be summarized as follows:

(1) Most of the points are near the solid centerline.

(2) A few of the points spread out and approach the control limits.

(3) None of the points (or at least only a very rare and occasional point) exceeds the control limits.

A natural pattern has all three of these characteristics simultaneously. The pattern will look unnatural if any one of the three is missing.

B-6.2 Characteristics of an unnatural pattern

Unnatural patterns tend to fluctuate too widely, or else they fail to balance themselves around the centerline. A pattern may also be unnatural because it does not fluctuate widely enough. Unnatural patterns always involve the absence of one or more of the characteristics of a natural pattern. For example:

(1) Absence of points near the centerline produces an unnatural pattern known as "Mixture."

(2) Absence of points near the control limits

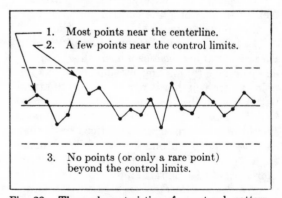

1. Most points near the centerline.
2. A few points near the control limits.
3. No points (or only a rare point) beyond the control limits.

Fig. 32. Three characteristics of a natural pattern.

produces an unnatural pattern known as "Stratification."

(3) Presence of points outside of the control limits produces an unnatural pattern known as "Instability."

Many types of unnaturalness can be recognized informally by glancing at the control chart. When formal tests are available, however, they tend to put the interpretation of patterns on a scientific basis. The tests given below should be applied to all control charts so that everyone will be able to interpret the charts in the same way.

The tests for unnatural patterns are obtained from probability calculations which tell us the "natural" proportion of points that will fall near the centerline, near the control limits, etc. The method of calculating these tests is explained on pages 180–183.

B-6.3 Tests for instability

The most important of the tests for unnatural patterns are the tests for "instability." These are tests to determine whether the cause system is changing.* In applying these tests consider only one-half of the control band at a time; that is, consider only the area between the centerline and one of the control limits. Divide this area mentally into three equal zones.

Since the control limits are 3 sigma limits, each of the zones is one sigma in width. For this reason the zones are sometimes referred to as the "one sigma zone," the "two sigma zone," etc. See Figure 33.

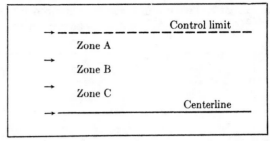

Fig. 33. Method of applying the tests for unnatural patterns.

The pattern is unnatural if any of the following combinations are formed in the various zones:

Test 1. A single point falls outside of the 3 sigma limit (beyond Zone A). See Figure 34.

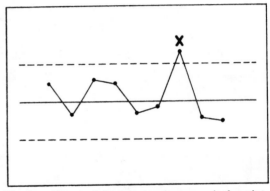

Fig. 34. First test for unnaturalness: a single point outside of 3 sigma.

Mark the unnatural point with an "x."

---

* The reader may be interested in the following brief description of the tests used in this book.

The standard control chart test devised by Shewhart (and called by him Criterion I) makes use of 3 sigma control limits as a criterion for indications of lack of control. This criterion is intended to strike an economic balance between the net consequences of two types of error:

(1) Error of the first kind: Looking for assignable causes when no such causes exist; that is, having a point fall outside of control limits when, in fact, there has been no change in the process.

(2) Error of the second kind: Not looking for assignable causes when such causes do exist; that is, having a point fall within the control limits when, in fact, there has been a change in the process.

In extensive process-control programs such as those developed at Western, it is generally advantageous to use, in addition, one or more tests based on sequences or runs. At Western Electric three such tests are used in addition to Criterion I.

If assignable causes are present (as they usually are in a process capability study), the multiple tests will detect those causes sooner than will Criterion I alone. If assignable causes are not present (as may be the case in some shop situations), the multiple tests will produce an "x" on the chart more often than will Criterion I alone. The action required to be taken in the shop when an "x" occurs is covered in engineering layouts, which take account of the probabilities associated with the multiple tests. A brief discussion of the multiple probabilities is given on pages 180–183.

Test 2. Two out of three successive points fall in Zone A or beyond.
(Note: The odd point may be anywhere. Only the two points count.) See Figure 35.

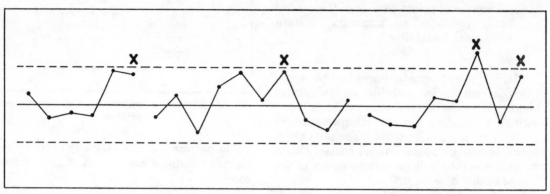

Fig. 35. Second test for unnaturalness: Two out of three successive points outside of 2 sigma.

Mark only the second of the two points with an "x," since the second point is necessary to produce a reaction to the test. In the last example above, the point which is third from the end is marked because it reacted to Test 1, and not because it was part of the test for "2 out of 3."

Test 3. Four out of five successive points fall in Zone B or beyond.
(Note: The odd point may be anywhere. Only the four points count.) See Figure 36.

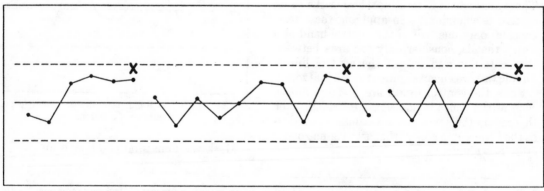

Fig. 36. Third test for unnaturalness: Four out of five successive points outside of 1 sigma.

Mark only the last of the four points with an "x," since there is no reaction to the test until the fourth point.

Test 4. Eight successive points fall in Zone C or beyond.
(This is sometimes expressed as "eight points in a row on one side of the centerline.") See Figure 37.

Mark only the eighth point with an "x," since all eight points are necessary to produce a reaction to the test.

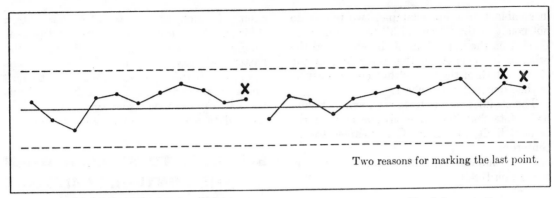

Two reasons for marking the last point.

Fig. 37. Fourth test for unnaturalness: Eight successive points on one side of the centerline.

In applying the tests, start with any point you choose (generally the last plotted point) and count backward as many points as are required to make the test. In the second example in Figure 37, the first "x" was arrived at by starting with the twelfth point and counting back to the fifth.

It is possible for the same point to react to more than one test. For example, in the last portion of Figure 37, the final point reacts to the test for "8 in a row" and also to the test for "4 out of 5." In this case there are two reasons for marking the point with an "x." Do not, however, show more than one "x" for the point.

Marking the x's

In marking x's, always put the "x" a uniform distance from the point being marked (preferably about $1/8$ inch). Put it directly above the point if the point is in the upper half of the control chart, and directly below the point if the point is in the lower half of the control chart. That is, put the "x" on the side that is *away from the centerline.*

Interpretation of the x's

The greater the instability in the system of causes, the more points will tend to react to these tests and be marked with x's. After the pattern is marked, it is possible to judge the amount of instability by the number of x's.

In looking for the *causes* which are producing the instability, remember that the causes may have affected more points than the ones actually marked. If a point has been marked for being the eighth on one side of the centerline, the cause has probably been in the picture for the whole run of eight points, and quite possibly before.

Applying the tests to the opposite half of the chart

The same tests for instability apply to both halves of the control chart. However, they are applied separately to the two halves, not

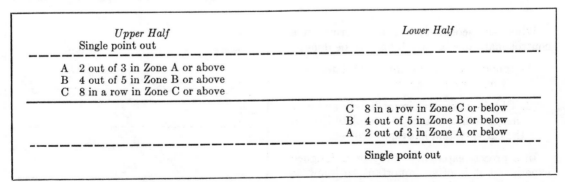

Upper Half		Lower Half
Single point out		
A 2 out of 3 in Zone A or above		
B 4 out of 5 in Zone B or above		
C 8 in a row in Zone C or above		
		C 8 in a row in Zone C or below
		B 4 out of 5 in Zone B or below
		A 2 out of 3 in Zone A or below
		Single point out

Fig. 38. Summary of tests for unnatural patterns.

27

in combination. For example, two points do not count in the "2 out of 3" test if one is in Zone A on the upper half of the chart and the other is in Zone A on the lower half of the chart. Both of the points that count must be in the same half of the chart.

The complete set of tests is shown in Figure 38. Note that Zone A is always next to the control limit, and Zone C is nearest to the centerline.

Other unnatural patterns are discussed in paragraph B-8.

B-6.4 Inconclusive patterns

When a pattern has not yet produced any evidence of unnaturalness, but it appears that one or two more points might complete a certain pattern and produce such evidence, the pattern is sometimes said to be "inconclusive." The following is an inconclusive pattern, because one more point (if it happened to fall in Zone B or beyond) would react and be given an "x".

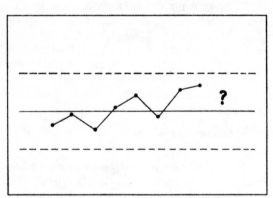

Fig. 39. Inconclusive pattern. Three out of four points in Zone B: one more point could react.

When an inconclusive pattern forms on a control chart, one of two things can be done:

(1) Ignore the pattern until such later time as it may produce an "x."

(2) Obtain more data immediately and give the pattern a chance to complete itself if the cause system has really shifted.

In a process capability study or a designed experiment it is often important to know as soon as possible whether the pattern is going to

react. In such cases we try at once to obtain sufficient data to complete or refute the test. In Figure 39, if the next point completes the pattern we say that the cause system has changed. If the next point breaks the pattern we say there is no evidence of a change. Thus the pattern itself can sometimes tell us how much data we need to reach a conclusion.

B-7 TESTS TO BE USED WHEN THE CONTROL LIMITS ARE NOT SYMMETRICAL

The above tests apply when the two control limits on the chart are at reasonably similar distances above and below the centerline. On an $\bar{X}$ chart the control limits are always symmetrical, but on an R chart or p-chart the control limits are sometimes unsymmetrical. Unsymmetrical limits may require a slight change in the application of the tests. For information on this see pages 182–183.

B-8 OTHER UNNATURAL PATTERNS

The following patterns should be watched for in addition to patterns of instability. The ability to recognize these patterns can greatly increase the usefulness of the control chart, by permitting a fuller interpretation of its meaning. These patterns are different from the patterns of instability in that *both halves of the control chart are considered together in looking for the patterns shown below.*

These patterns are marked with *circled x's*

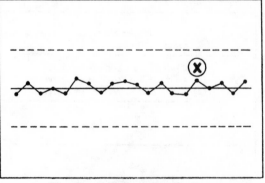

Fig. 40. Pattern of stratification.

to distinguish them from the patterns of instability.

(1) Stratification

If the up-and-down variations are very small in comparison with the width of the control limits, the control chart indicates stratification in the samples. This means that the sampling is being done systematically in such a way that two or more different distributions are represented. See pages 172–174.

Consider that stratification exists when 15 or more consecutive points fall in Zone C, either above or below the centerline.

(2) Mixture

If the pattern shows a tendency to avoid the centerline, with too many points near the control limits, this is an indication of mixture. See pages 169–170, 171, and 179–180.

Consider that mixture exists when the chart shows 8 consecutive points on both sides of the centerline with none of the points falling in Zone C.

(3) Systematic variable

The presence of a systematic variable in the process is indicated if a long series of points are high, low, high, low without any interruption in this regular sequence. See pages 175–176.

(4) Tendency of one chart to follow another

Two variables are likely to be related to each other if a long series of points on their respective patterns move up and down in unison. See pages 176–177.

(5) Trends

Trends may be indicated by:

  (a) x's on one side of the chart followed by x's on the other.
  (b) a series of consecutive points without a change in direction. See Figure 44 and pages 177–179.

For other information on unnatural patterns, see Part F in the Engineering Section (pages 149–183).

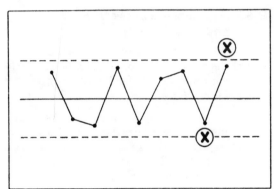

Fig. 41. Pattern of mixture.

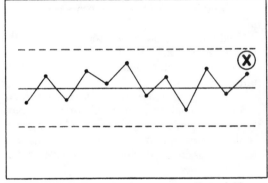

Fig. 42. Pattern showing a systematic variable.

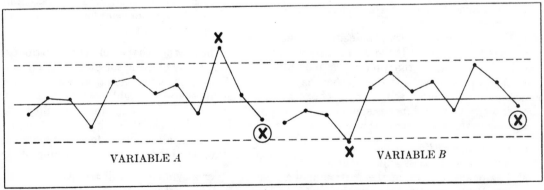

VARIABLE *A*   VARIABLE *B*

Fig. 43. One control chart follows another.

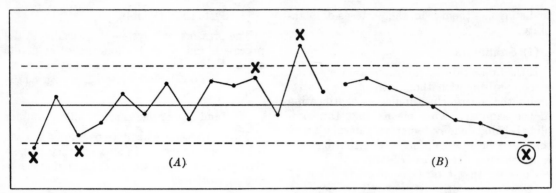

Fig. 44. Trends.

B-9 SIMPLE INTERPRETATION OF CONTROL CHARTS

B-9.1 Meaning of the R chart

Keep in mind that the R chart shows *uniformity* or *consistency*.

If the R chart is narrow, the product is uniform. If the R chart is wide, the product is not uniform. If the R chart is out of control, something is operating on the process in a non-uniform manner.

Machines in good repair tend to make the product more uniform. Carefully trained operators also tend to make the product more uniform.

In looking for causes when an R chart is out of control, look for poor repair or poor maintenance if this is a machine-controlled process. Look for new operators or something disturbing the operators if this is an operator-controlled process.

B-9.2 Meaning of the $\bar{X}$ chart

Keep in mind that the $\bar{X}$ chart shows where the process is *centered*.

If the $\bar{X}$ chart is natural, the center of the process is not shifting. If the $\bar{X}$ chart shows a trend, the center of the process is moving gradually up or down. If the $\bar{X}$ chart is erratic and out of control, something is changing the center rapidly and inconsistently.

Processes are ordinarily centered by:

a. A machine setting.
b. Some other process adjustment.
c. The characteristics of the particular material or piece parts being used.

d. A bias or change in technique on the part of an operator or inspector.

Check these possible causes when the $\bar{X}$ chart is out of control.

$\bar{X}$ charts can also be affected by out-of-control conditions on the R chart. If the $\bar{X}$ chart and R chart are both out of control, look first for the causes affecting the R chart.

B-9.3 Relationship between $\bar{X}$ chart and specification

To find the relationship between the process and the specification proceed as follows. *Both the $\bar{X}$ chart and the R chart must be in control before this check is made.*

(1) In the left-hand margin of the chart, along the $\bar{X}$ scale, draw one or more arrows to represent the specification limits. See Figure 45. The arrows may represent the tolerances specified on a drawing, a proposed specification, or merely some standard we wish to hold for economic reasons. Label each arrow "Maximum" or "Minimum," depending on whether it is an upper or lower limit.

(2) Check the shape of the distribution roughly by plotting the data in a frequency distribution as explained on pages 138–139. If the shape is roughly symmetrical, make the calculation explained in Step (3). If the shape is noticeably skewed, with a long thin tail on one side and a sharp cutoff on the other, proceed as in Step (4).

(3) For a symmetrical distribution, note the distance between the centerline on the $\bar{X}$

chart and one of the control limits. Multiply this distance by $\sqrt{n}$ and note whether it falls outside of the specification. If it does, some of the product from which these samples were taken is probably out of limits.

(4) For unsymmetrical distributions make a similar calculation, but allow more on the long side and less on the short side.

In the case of samples of 5, it is convenient to memorize the following:

a. If the distribution is symmetrical, the space between the control limit and the arrow should not be less than the space between the control limit and the centerline.

b. If the arrow is opposite the control limit, from 5 to 10% of the product is probably out of limits.

c. If the arrow is opposite the centerline, about 50% of the product is probably out of limits.

It is sometimes helpful to sketch the distribution of individuals on the $\bar{X}$ chart as shown in Figure 45. This provides a quick visual means of judging whether there is conflict between the process and the specification.

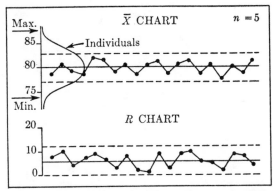

Fig. 45. Showing the probable spread of individuals on an $\bar{X}$ and R chart.

B-9.4 Meaning of a p-chart (or other attributes chart)

Keep in mind that a p-chart shows *proportion:* the proportion of product classified as defective if it is a "percent defective" control chart, the proportion classified as good if it is a "yield" control chart, etc. When the pattern changes on a p-chart, it means there is a change in proportion.

On a percent defective control chart, a change in level may mean:

(a) The percentage of bad product is increasing or decreasing, or

(b) We are not calling the same things defective as before.

Check both of these possibilities in interpreting the p-chart.

If the p-chart is erratic, look for causes which come and go spasmodically. Poorly trained operators and poorly controlled piece parts are two of the most common causes. An erratic p-chart is frequently a sign of need for further process controls.

B-9.5 Meaning of a chart of individual measurements

On a chart of individuals, look first for trends. Trends will appear in the same way, and mean the same thing, as on an $\bar{X}$ chart.

Look second to see whether the fluctuations are becoming narrower or wider. The fluctuations show uniformity or consistency, in much the same manner as an R chart.

Look third to see whether the pattern stays far away from one of the control limits. This may indicate that the distribution is "blocked" on that side, or has a short tail on that side and a long tail on the other.

Look fourth for any obvious peculiarities in the pattern, such as cycles or "bunching." Your knowledge of the process must tell you the probable causes for such peculiarities.

B-9.6 Conclusion

It is possible to go as deeply as we wish into the interpretation of control charts. Some of the less obvious meanings of the charts are explained in Engineering Parts A and F. However, the most important meanings are very simple, and anyone can learn to make these interpretations after seeing only a few charts. Engineers and supervisors who understand the simple principles outlined in this section will be able to make effective use of the charts in a wide variety of problems.

PART C
Essential Elements in a Quality Control Program

Introduction

It is fairly common to find control charts used to solve individual, isolated problems: for example, to determine the capability of a particular machine; to encourage the operators in a given area to be more careful; to solve a particular difficulty having to do with engineering specifications, etc. Such isolated uses of control charts are spoken of as *quality control applications*, but they do not constitute a *quality control program*. A "program" implies the regular, systematic and continuing application of the charts (and of certain other closely related techniques) to the problems in a given area, as the problems arise. The program usually starts with Shop and Engineering problems and is later extended to fields outside of direct engineering and manufacturing— for example, the field of *inspection* or of *scientific management*. A quality control program requires (a) an understanding of the statistical techniques, (b) a plan of development and (c) a series of systematic steps in carrying out this plan. While the details of planning may vary from location to location, the schedule of development at Western Electric normally includes the following:

(1) Management selects a certain area (a Shop, a type of product, a group of operations, etc.) as the place to begin work.

(2) A training program is conducted to acquaint all engineers and supervisors, and all members of management, with the fundamentals of control charts.

(3) Management provides one or more quality control engineers, trained not only in using the charts themselves but also in helping other people to use them effectively.

(4) Management sets up one or more "Quality Control Teams," consisting of a product engineer, an Operating supervisor and a quality control engineer. The Team is made responsible for all quality control applications in its area.

(5) Management states a goal toward which the Team will direct its efforts. The goal may be (a) cost reduction, (b) improved quality, (c) reduction of scrap, rework, repair time, etc., (d) elimination of "bottlenecks" and other interruptions in the shop, (e) increased shop efficiency, (f) reduced inspection, (g) better information about processing variables, (h) more stable production processes. The Team is expected to report its progress at regular intervals.

(6) Management guides the program through its successive stages to make sure it is developing properly.

Normal stages of growth

The program normally develops through several phases, as follows. The time of development varies from location to location, but each phase may require as much as one to three years. The time can often be shortened by good preliminary planning.

Phase I.   Initial Development.
This includes (a) training, (b) setting up teams, (c) overcoming the initial resistance to control charts, (d) developing the necessary cooperation between Operating and Engineering.

Phase II. Shop Coverage.
This includes (a) making the initial capability studies or performance studies and (b) discovering the proper number and type of charts for use in the shop. During this phase management expects to obtain results in the form of (a) reduced merchandise losses, (b) reduced inspection and (c) greater stability of shop processes.

Phase III. Engineering.
This includes (a) renewed emphasis on process capability studies, (b) use of designed experiments, (c) direct attack on fundamental engineering problems. During this period applications may also be started in clerical operations, wage incentives and all areas of scientific management.

Phase IV. Research.
The emphasis centers on process capability studies and their use in exploring unknown methods and processes, developing new and improved techniques, eliminating difficult or expensive operations, making improvements in machine, tool and product design. The management program may be extended to include surveys, audits and various forms of research.

Management should note that, throughout this program, the primary emphasis is on Process Capability Studies. These involve the basic use of control charts to detect assignable causes and solve problems. All other parts of the program are based on, and carefully integrated with, the Process Capability Studies.
The Process Capability Studies are reinforced or supplemented, where necessary, by other techniques such as Designed Experiments, Shop Charts and scientific plans for Inspection. The following pages describe these parts of the program in a general way, and show how they can be integrated to make a complete workable system.

———————— ✦ ————————

C-1 PROCESS CAPABILITY STUDIES TO OBTAIN INFORMATION AND SOLVE PROBLEMS

C-1.1 Definition of the term "process capability study"

In this book the term "process capability study" means the systematic study of a process by means of statistical control charts in order to discover whether it is behaving naturally or unnaturally; plus investigation of any unnatural behavior to determine its cause; plus action to eliminate any of the unnatural behavior which it is desirable to eliminate for economic or quality reasons. The natural behavior of the process after unnatural disturbances are eliminated is called the "process capability."

The information developed from the process capability study is used in two areas as follows:

(1) The immediate information results in the solution of many Engineering problems. It is used for (a) setting up shop processes, (b) investigating shop troubles, (c) establishing or checking on specifications, (d) obtaining new knowledge on cause and effect relationships or similar engineering questions, and (e) determining normal losses, normal wage incentive frequencies and other normal standards of all kinds. For a detailed list of the problems which can be solved through process capability studies, see pages 46–47.

Many of the solutions to these problems result in formal cost reduction. Consequently, one of the objects of a process capability study is to discover opportunities for, and aid in the realization of, cost reduction savings.

(2) If the initial capability of the process is not good enough to solve the problems listed above, the information on the control charts can be used to set up a new process having a different and better

capability. This procedure is continued until the problems are solved, or until the engineer is satisfied that they can not be solved economically.

For a description of the scientific steps in making a process capability study, see page 47. Note particularly the provision for repeating the cycle of steps until a solution is found.

C-1.2 Theoretical basis of a process capability study

The theory of the process capability study is covered in detail in Engineering Part A. The following is a brief graphical summary of the theoretical basis.

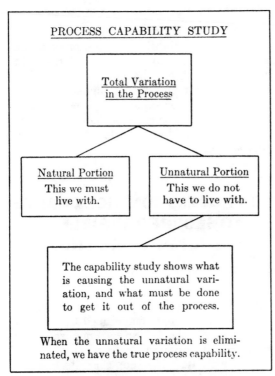

PROCESS CAPABILITY STUDY

Total Variation in the Process

Natural Portion
This we must live with.

Unnatural Portion
This we do not have to live with.

The capability study shows what is causing the unnatural variation, and what must be done to get it out of the process.

When the unnatural variation is eliminated, we have the true process capability.

Fig. 46. Theoretical basis of a process capability study.

The essential points for management to keep in mind in connection with these studies are the following:

(1) In most processes, a capability study shows a large amount of initial variation. Some of the variation is natural: it results from the normal variations in people, materials, methods, tools, machines and other process elements. Some of the variation, however, is unnatural: it is due to things that can be changed or corrected. The thing that can be changed or corrected may be a *shop-type variable* (operators not fully trained, machines or fixtures not properly maintained, poor control of plating or heat-treating operations); or it may be an unsuspected *relationship* or *correlation*.

(2) If capability studies have not been made on the process previously, the unnatural variation is likely to be by far the greater part of the total. It may also be the part that gets the shop into trouble, makes engineering experiments inconclusive and causes high manufacturing and inspection costs.

The process capability study will work to detect, and subsequently to reduce or eliminate, the unnatural variation. In the meantime, however, the unnatural variation, in itself, is a rich source of information for both Engineering and the Shop. *Unnatural variations will produce significant patterns on a control chart, and these in turn make it possible to detect and study the significant "cause and effect" relationships.* It is possible for the shop and engineers to take deliberate advantage of unnatural patterns on a control chart in order to obtain (a) quality improvement, (b) cost reduction or (c) new knowledge about the process.

Engineering Part A explains how the *elimination* of unnatural variation can result in

(1) proper standards.
(2) realistic specifications.
(3) good predictions, forecasts and estimates.
(4) a reliable measure of machine capability, operator capability, and the capabilities of tools, materials, methods, designs, etc.

It also explains how *taking advantage* of unnatural variation can result in

(1) an improved process.
(2) lower costs of manufacture.
(3) less inspection.
(4) information about processing variables.
(5) the solution of many perplexing engineering problems.

All these results depend on being able to distinguish between natural and unnatural variation. Process capability studies are a method of detecting, studying and doing something about unnatural variation.

C-1.3 Statistical procedure in the process capability study

The following is a brief summary of the procedures used in making a process capability study.

(1) The person who makes the study is ordinarily a supervisor or engineer. Many process capability studies are made jointly by the members of a Quality Control Team.

(2) The person making the study obtains data from the process and plots it on control charts. The charts show immediately whether the process is operating in a normal fashion.

(3) If the process is not operating normally, the patterns tend to fall into one of a dozen recognizable types, which can then be associated with the causes working in the process. For a detailed discussion of the various types of pattern, see pages 161–180.

(4) In case the disturbing causes are not immediately apparent on plotting the first charts, there are definite techniques to follow in tracing the disturbances to their source. First the study is broken down according to "production paths." That is, the data are split according to operators, machines, shifts, suppliers or whatever is believed to be a controlling element.

(5) If this does not yield the answer, the study is broken down more precisely by using a statistically designed experiment. This makes it possible to study many variables at once, including any interactions between them. It is also possible to determine which variables should be included in a new process, or one under development, and predict its general capability before the process is even set up.

(6) As rapidly as the unnatural disturbances are identified they are

a. eliminated,
b. reduced to an economical level, or
c. deliberately used to advantage as a regular part of the process.

(7) The detection of unnatural disturbances is continued until (a) the process is reduced to its true capability, as shown by long-continued natural patterns on a control chart; or (b) the process reaches an economical point beyond which it is evident that no further large gains will be realized. At this point the demonstrated behavior of the process, as shown by the control charts, is taken to be the "process capability."

C-1.4 Economic significance of the process capability study

Once the capabilities of the process are known, it becomes possible to set up the right shop controls, obtain changes in uneconomical or unnecessary requirements, minimize inspection and set proper standards. Lower inspection costs and lower costs of manufacture are two of the natural by-products of process capability studies.

C-2 PROCESS CONTROL CHARTS TO SECURE TANGIBLE RESULTS IN THE SHOP

C-2.1 Definition of the term "process control chart"

In this book the term "process control chart" means a control chart maintained by, and for the benefit of, the Operating organization in the shop. It is preferably based on a process capability study. The shop chart itself serves as a continuing capability study. It is used (a) to prevent defects, (b) to detect shop troubles at the source and (c) to achieve a stable, smoothly-running process that will combine high quality with minimum cost. For a detailed discussion of the purposes and planning of process control charts, see the Shop Section, Part A. Process control charts, like process capability studies, result in cost reduction if they are properly planned.

C-2.2 Theoretical basis of the process control chart

The theory of process control charts can be explained in three steps, as follows:

(1) The object of charts in the shop is to keep distributions where we want them. The intention is to keep the distributions moving down the most economical path day after day, as shown in Figure 47.

(2) In the absence of shop control charts, un-

wanted variables creep in and disturb the distributions as shown in Figure 48.

The results of the unwanted variables are quality troubles, poor efficiency, trouble in meeting schedules, excessive rework or scrap, and excessive amounts of product rejected by Inspection.

(3) Process control charts prevent these troubles in the manner shown in Figure 49. The key numbers indicate the information given by the chart and show how the shop is able to make use of this information.

Process control charts are designed to pick up unwanted variables one by one as they enter

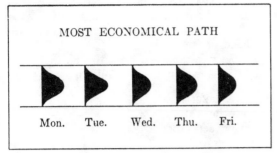

MOST ECONOMICAL PATH

Mon. Tue. Wed. Thu. Fri.

Fig. 47. Desired behavior of a series of distributions in the shop.

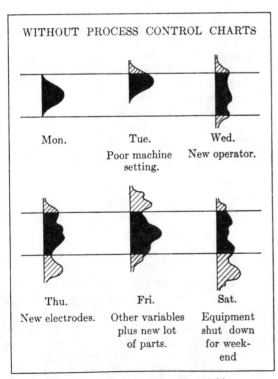

WITHOUT PROCESS CONTROL CHARTS

Mon.

Tue.
Poor machine setting.

Wed.
New operator.

Thu.
New electrodes.

Fri.
Other variables plus new lot of parts.

Sat.
Equipment shut down for week-end

Fig. 48. Effect of unwanted variables in a process.

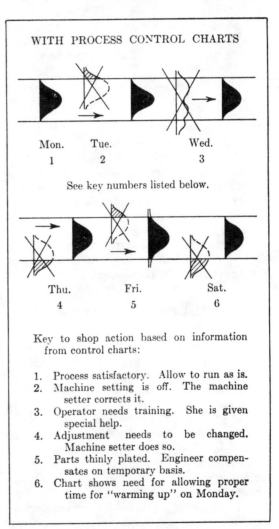

WITH PROCESS CONTROL CHARTS

Mon.   Tue.   Wed.
1   2   3

See key numbers listed below.

Thu.   Fri.   Sat.
4   5   6

Key to shop action based on information from control charts:

1. Process satisfactory. Allow to run as is.
2. Machine setting is off. The machine setter corrects it.
3. Operator needs training. She is given special help.
4. Adjustment needs to be changed. Machine setter does so.
5. Parts thinly plated. Engineer compensates on temporary basis.
6. Chart shows need for allowing proper time for "warming up" on Monday.

Fig. 49. How shop control charts act to prevent or eliminate unwanted variables.

the process—while their effects are still so simple that the shop can do something about them. In addition, many undesirable variables never enter the process at all, because they are prevented or forestalled by the control charts.

C-2.3 Importance of process control charts in the quality control program

The importance of process control charts can hardly be overemphasized. Without them the most brilliant analyses of capability studies and designed experiments may fail to be translated into increased production, better production and lowered costs. Furthermore, unless the important shop-type variables are kept in reasonably good control, it may not even be possible to plan and conduct successful engineering experiments.

On new processes, where there are many engineering unknowns, process control charts should be considered indispensable. On older products, where there is a great deal of knowledge and experience on the part of engineers and the shop, process control charts are usually necessary to put this knowledge to the most effective use. In any case, process control charts are likely to be needed to make the results of engineering studies effective and permanent.

The statistical procedures used in process control charts are discussed in detail in the Shop Section of the Handbook.

C-2.4 Correct number of process control charts

Process control charts are of two principal kinds: those intended to control the quality of work going to the next operation, and those intended to minimize losses or "dropouts" at the original operation. It may be necessary to have both kinds of chart on a single operation.

The total number of charts that will be needed in a shop varies with the nature of the operations and the number of unknowns. A complicated product does not necessarily require a large number of charts.

The number of charts tends to be small where only the operator's technique is involved, and tends to be larger where the variables include both operators and machines. The correct number of charts is determined for each job by a Quality Control Team as explained on page 189.

C-2.5 Cost of process control charts

A primary objective of each process control chart is to save money. If a particular chart is not saving considerably more than it costs, the chart should be eliminated. One of the functions of the Quality Control Team, as described on page 41, is to review all process control charts continuously and balance the savings against the cost. Charts found to be unnecessary, or not paying their way, are modified or removed.

Properly established control charts in the shop will save money in the following ways:

Fewer defectives.
Fewer operators.
Fewer inspectors.
Less scrap.
Less trouble at the next operation.
Less product rejected by Inspection.
Increased capacity.
Increased shop efficiency.
Fewer facilities needed for making, testing and handling the product.
Savings in time on the part of operators, supervisors and engineers.
Improvements in specifications.
Improvements in design.
Fewer interruptions to production.
Less downtime on machines.
Fewer complaints.
Less difficulty in meeting schedules.

Many formal cost reduction cases have been taken out on the savings resulting from the use of process control charts.

C-3 STATISTICAL SAMPLING PLANS TO REDUCE THE COST OF INSPECTION

Statistical sampling plans are an extension of the quality control methods into the field of inspection. Relatively small samples, and the probabilities associated with certain sampling distributions, are used to provide a scientific basis for acceptance or rejection of product.

The small size of the samples represents a saving as compared with 100% inspection. At the same time, the mechanics of rejection are set up in such a way as to encourage the making of good product and discourage the submission of poor product. Consequently, the use of statistical sampling plans is a proper adjunct to a quality control program.

Most statistical sampling plans are set up in such a way that the inspector uses his sample merely to accept or reject. Comparatively little use is made of the information available in samples (involving trends, patterns, etc.) which is used so extensively in process control. Sampling plans are generally chosen on the basis of a curve known as an "Operating Characteristic" curve which shows the proportion of product that will be accepted or rejected if the product submitted to Inspection is of a certain quality.

By the use of various sample sizes (n) and acceptance numbers (c), sampling plans can be made to reject larger or smaller percentages of product of a given quality. In addition, many sampling plans provide for doing something to improve the rejected product—for example, rework it or sort it. It is then possible to quote a maximum limit of defectiveness (called Average Outgoing Quality Limit, or AOQL) which can exist in the long run in the product leaving Inspection if the provisions of the sampling plan are faithfully followed.

C-3.1 Information to be obtained from inspection samples

In addition to their primary use for accepting or rejecting, inspection samples can be used to furnish certain kinds of information. For example, they can be used to calculate "process averages." The process average is the average percent defective in the product submitted to Inspection by the Operating department or by an outside supplier.

In the case of suppliers the process average can be used to rate the supplier as satisfactory or unsatisfactory. It can also be used to minimize the amount of inspection we must do, since product from a supplier having a good quality record can be accepted safely with less inspection.

While the methods outlined above represent the most common use of sampling plans, oc-casionally inspection is put on a regular control chart basis, and the inspector makes use of the information contained in levels, trends and patterns in deciding the disposition of the product. In other cases a chart is not actually plotted, but the inspector's action is influenced by the number of lots rejected in the recent series of lots submitted. This is an indirect use of pattern information.

C-3.2 Mistakes to be avoided in connection with sampling inspection

The most frequent mistake made in connection with sampling inspection is to attempt to use it as a substitute for Operating process control. No form of inspection, and no use or plotting of inspection findings, can be a substitute for the actual controlling of processes by Operating and Engineering. Sampling inspection is a very useful technique but it should never be regarded as the principal element in a quality control program.

Another common mistake is attempting to modify the provisions of a statistical sampling plan without taking account of its statistical nature. In order to obtain the protection and other benefits promised by a statistical plan, all provisions having to do with the method of selecting samples, the sample size, the acceptance number and the sorting or other disposition of rejected product must be strictly and faithfully carried out.

C-4 QUALITY CONTROL MEETINGS TO MAKE QUALITY CONTROL WORK

Practically all the action required by quality control is joint action, involving at least Operating and Engineering. More often than not, especially in the early stages, it requires direct help from a quality control engineer also. The three people who are jointly responsible for putting quality control into the job and seeing that it works are:

(a) The product engineer.
(b) The Operating supervisor.
(c) The quality control engineer.

These three people are often spoken of as a "Quality Control Team."

The quality control team is a technique borrowed from the field known as "operations research." The product engineer supplies the technical know-how, information on costs and facilities, and the ability to change layouts, place orders, contact design engineers and suppliers, etc. The Operating supervisor contributes his practical shop knowledge and experience, his ability to make decisions about the job and his knowledge of dealing with people. The quality control engineer contributes statistical advice and experience which is helpful to the supervisor and the product engineer. Other specialists, such as design engineers, metallurgists, or inspectors, may be called in to assist the team as needed.

Any of these people, working alone, would find it a long hard pull to put quality control in and get it working. Together they can do wonders in a short space of time. The importance of teamwork on the part of these particular people is so great that everything possible should be done to encourage it.

C-4.1 The Quality Control Team: its structure and operation

Experience shows that if no formal provision for teamwork is made, the consultations between Operating and Engineering tend to become desultory or spasmodic, action is often limited to emergencies, and the quality control program does not develop rapidly and soundly into a permanent integral part of the plant's operations. On the other hand, where the teams meet regularly on a schedule and go over the control charts, there is no recorded case where they have failed to obtain effective results.

Consequently, for the most rapid development of the program, a Quality Control Team should be set up for each product or product line, or for each general area or type of operation. Figure 50 shows how the Team is organized and how it functions.

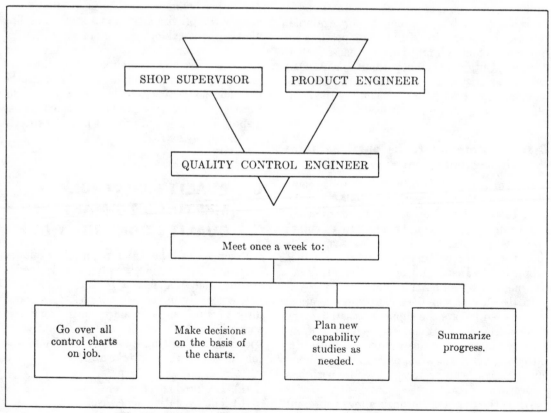

Fig. 50. Formation and functioning of a Quality Control Team.

The following are among the proper duties and responsibilities of a Quality Control Team:

(1) Planning and conducting process capability studies (or designed experiments) which cannot be conducted single-handed by the product engineer.

(2) Planning the process control charts in the shop and determining the proper type and number of charts.

(3) Installing the control charts, training the process checker and providing suitable forms and routines for the shop to use.

(4) Maintaining a continuous check on all the Operating process controls, to make sure that they are being used effectively and are resulting in maximum savings. This may include taking off charts that are not needed any longer, substituting one chart that will do the work of two, lengthening the checking intervals on charts as the processes are brought under control, or adding new charts as needed. It also includes regular and frequent audits of all control charts on the job to make sure that the charts are understood and that they are properly plotted, marked and used.

(5) Taking action as indicated by the charts to bring the job into a state of economical control.

(6) Measuring and reporting quality control progress.

The results obtained from a quality control program in the shop depend directly on the work of the Quality Control Team. Further information is given in Part D of the Shop Section (pages 223–229).

C-4.2 Management guidance

For the Quality Control Teams to function properly, they should be aware of the active interest and support of management at all levels. Management should assist in the formation of the Teams, drop in on their meetings occasionally, follow the reports on progress and recognize accomplishments.

It may also be necessary for management to make sure that the program moves smoothly from one phase to another, and at the proper time. For example, as soon as shop coverage (Phase II) is reasonably complete, management should see that the emphasis is shifted onto direct problems in Engineering.

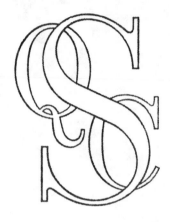

Section II

Engineering

Applications

PART A
Process Capability Studies

This part of the Handbook covers the theory and mechanics of the Process Capability Study. It starts with the selection of a problem to work on. The problem is translated into statistical terms. The problem is then solved statistically by following a definite set of procedures. Finally, the solution is translated back into the original terms.

The Process Capability Study is a basic technique for analyzing data. It can be used for any type of data obtained from a production process. It can be made by an engineer, a supervisor or anyone else having responsibility for the job. Primarily, however, the Process Capability Study is a research technique and, as such, it is particularly important in all fields of Engineering.

Process Capability Studies are also the foundation of all shop applications of quality control, and many studies are made jointly by Quality Control Teams.

An example of a Process Capability Study is given on pages 66–72.

A-1 THE SCIENTIFIC FOUNDATION OF A PROCESS CAPABILITY STUDY

A-1.1 Definitions and terms

Process

The term "process" refers to any system of causes; any combination of conditions which work together to produce a given result. While it often refers to the combination of men, materials, machines and methods used to manufacture a given product, it is also capable of taking on other meanings as explained on pages 3–4. The process to be studied may be as simple as the motion of a hand about the wrist. It may be as complex as the complete set of operations in the plant.

Process capability

The term "process capability" refers to the normal behavior of a process when operating in a state of statistical control; the predictable series of effects produced by a process when allowed to operate without interference from outside causes. In manufacturing terminology, process capability refers to the inherent ability of the process to turn out similar parts; the best distribution that can be maintained in statistical control for a sustained period of time under a given set of conditions.

Process capability may be expressed as per cent defective or as a distribution. In the latter case it refers to a single distribution with an irreducible spread (where "irreducible" means not reducible economically).

The "capability" of a process is not the same thing as its "performance," since performance may include all sorts of unnecessary variables and undesirable disturbances in the cause system. Capability means the natural or undisturbed performance after extraneous influences are eliminated. This is determined by plotting data on a control chart.

Process capability study

A "process capability study" is a scientific systematic procedure for determining the capability of a process by means of control charts, and if necessary changing the process to obtain a better capability. This procedure is continued as long as may be necessary until the problem which prompted the study is solved. A process capability study is sometimes described as "an industrial investigation whereby demonstrably true answers are found for one limited question after another until enough answers are found to make further questions unnecessary." In any case the term "process capability study" implies the solution of problems.

A-1.2 Scope of this technique

The field of application for process capability studies is very wide. They can be applied to almost any problem in Management, Engineering, Manufacturing or Inspection. The problems in these areas can ordinarily be reduced to those involving quality, cost, the need for new knowledge or information, the establishment of standards or estimates, new development and research.

The following is a list of typical problems which can be solved through the proper application of process capability studies. The list is included here to indicate the broad scope of this technique. The items on this list are not intended to be mutually exclusive, but rather to show the many different forms in which basically similar problems may present themselves. All of these problems are related essentially to the nature and behavior of a *distribution*. They can be solved through process capability studies because these studies provide a method for analyzing and changing distributions.

(1) Quality

- Too many defects leaving Operating.
- Too many defects leaving Inspection.
- Product unstable or drifting.
- Wrong distribution (in case of distribution requirements).
- Bad piece parts or material coming into the assembly line.

(2) Cost

- Too much inspection.
- Too much adjusting.
- Too much repair or rework.
- Too much scrap.
- Excessive merchandise losses.
- Trouble in meeting schedules.
- Low yield.

(3) Information

The need to:
- Trace the causes of trouble.
- Find why things happen.
- Discover correlations.
- Find how the early characteristics affect the end product.
- Find which dimensions are important.
- Obtain new knowledge about materials, methods, testing equipment, type of product.
- Get reliable information from pilot runs.
- Find the capability of new tools, methods, machines.
- Compare designs, tools, assembly methods.
- Study the effect of engineering changes.
- Study the effect of going over to a new design.
- Obtain continuity on intermittent operations.
- Make sense out of engineering data.
- Interpret the results of engineering experiments.
- Find the degree of training of operators.
- Test for significant differences.
- Detect trends.
- Determine whether conditions are constant.
- Check on error of measurement.
- Find assignable causes.
- Keep from being deceived by statistical fluctuations.

(4) Standards

- Estimates to be used for engineering purposes:
  Wage incentives.
  Standard costs.
  Normal amount of inspection.
  Normal losses.
  Normal yields.
  Normal capacity.
  Normal amount of sorting
     by Operating.
  Overall capability.
  Machine capability.
  Natural tolerances.
- Specifications of all kinds.
- Reliability of test sets, gages, and other standards.
- Maintenance schedules.
- Engineering responsibility vs. shop responsibility, etc.

(5) New development

- New products.
- New methods.
- Cost reduction.
- Automation.
- Machine and tool design.
- Purchase of new types of machines, test sets, etc.
- Elimination of difficult or expensive operations.

A-1.3 The scientific steps in experiment

A process capability study follows the method of scientific research. This method may be said to consist of four steps, as follows:

(1) Experiment.
(2) Hypothesis.
(3) Test of hypothesis.
(4) Further experiment.

The *experiment* consists of collecting observations from the process at several different points in time.

The *hypothesis* is that the observations, if they came from a stable process, should exhibit only natural fluctuations.

The *hypothesis is tested* by making a control chart and testing its pattern for naturalness. If the pattern is unnatural some "assignable cause" was interfering with the normal process. The cause is identified by proper study of the pattern, and its effect on the problem is traced.

Finally, depending on what the patterns show, it may be necessary to change the process, collect more data, revise the specification, or in some other way perform a *further experiment*.

Figure 51 shows the four steps in a process capability study expressed in slightly different terms.

Repetition of these four steps

If the person making the study finds a complete solution at the end of Step 4, he concludes the study there. Frequently, however, he finds that the initial study is merely one step in arriving at a solution. In that case Step 4 becomes the first step in a second study.

An example of this is given on pages 66–72.

A-2 OBTAINING THE DATA

Some processes can be studied by obtaining data on the process directly: for example, variation in a test set, or changes in the heat treating temperature in an oven. Others can be studied by observing the effect of the process on the product: for example, the diameter of a piece part or the presence of defects in an assembly. In either case we begin a process capability study by obtaining a series of measurements or by accumulating percent defective data.

In any case where there is a choice between variables and attributes measurements, it is worth going to considerable trouble to devise some method of obtaining actual readings. This will make it possible to take advantage of the great sensitivity of the $\bar{X}$ and R chart. In some cases where it is not possible to obtain true variables measurements, it may be possible to get "semi-variables" measurements as explained in paragraph A-2.5.

A-2.1 Where and how to use variables control charts

An $\bar{X}$ and R chart requires less data for the same amount of information than any other control chart. This is the type of chart to use when it is difficult or expensive to take measurements, where the test is destructive, or where it is desired to get the maximum amount of in-

Scientific Experimentation	Process Capability Study
1. Experiment.	1. Collect data from the process.
2. Hypothesis.	2. Plot statistical patterns.
3. Test of hypothesis.	3. Interpret the patterns.
4. Further experiment.	4. Do what the patterns tell you until you reach the process capability.

Fig. 51. The four steps in a process capability study.

formation with the least amount of effort. In addition, $\bar{X}$ and R charts have two advantages which are not possessed by any others:

(1) *Different kinds of trouble show up in different ways on these charts.*

For example, a wrong machine setting shows up on the $\bar{X}$ chart, while a machine in need of repair shows up on the R chart. In a similar way, various causes of trouble can be distinguished in the case of assembly operations, chemical processing, and so on. The $\bar{X}$ and R chart is the best one to use for getting answers to questions like these: Why aren't we getting consistent results? What could be causing so much trouble at 450 cycles? What can be done to improve this process and make it behave better? In general, the newer the job or the more there is to learn about a given type of product, the more it will be necessary to use $\bar{X}$ and R charts.

(2) *$\bar{X}$ and R charts make it possible to study the process without regard to the specification.*

This is not true of a p-chart. A p-chart starts with the specification and simply records failures to meet it.

$\bar{X}$ and R charts start with the process itself and give an independent picture of what the process can do. Afterward the process may be compared with the specification or not, depending on the problem. For this reason, $\bar{X}$ and R charts can be used to *obtain changes in specifications* and bring about the establishment of more realistic limits. The more cases we have where it is suspected that the specifications may need to be changed, the more it will be necessary to use $\bar{X}$ and R charts.

$\bar{X}$ and R charts are at their best when used at early operations, close to the causes that may affect later results. Use $\bar{X}$ and R charts on individual characteristics, operators, machines, machine setters, shifts, sources of voltage supply, etc. These charts are much less effective when used at the end of the line on final tests.

A-2.2 Where and how to use attributes control charts

A p-chart requires larger samples than an $\bar{X}$

and R chart. It is less versatile and less sensitive than an $\bar{X}$ and R chart for the following reasons:

- The p-chart cannot tell whether trouble is caused by lack of control of the average value of a characteristic; or by the fact that it is located too close to a specification; or by an uncontrolled process spread; or by a spread that is controlled but is too wide for the specification.
- The p-chart cannot warn of shifts or trends in the process unless those trends have proceeded so far that they have actually resulted in defectives.

On the other hand, a p-chart often has the advantage of using records which are already available in the shop. It is generally necessary to obtain special data for an $\bar{X}$ and R chart.

One common use for p-charts is to study an entire assembly process by means of an overall chart. The p-chart can be made to cover all defects and all characteristics, combined in a single percentage. This kind of chart can be a valuable capability study in itself, and will also provide a good measure of the effectiveness of changes, corrections or improvements which have been made as a result of other studies.

When used alone, however, p-charts on the overall process are often difficult to interpret. The causes for unnatural patterns may be so deeply hidden that it is not possible to find them in the overall data. One of the standard ways of interpreting p-charts is to break them down into individual sources or individual defects. If interpretation is still difficult, use an $\bar{X}$ and R chart.

p-Charts may be used for:

(1) Characteristics on which it is difficult or impractical to obtain variables measurements.

(2) Studies of defects produced by machines or operators which are directly under the machine setter's or operator's control.

(3) Direct studies of the amount of dropouts, shrinkage or scrap at specific operations.

Collect p-chart data, where possible, on the

work of individual operators or individual machines.

In this Handbook, unless otherwise stated, whatever is said about p-charts should be taken to apply also to np-charts, c-charts and u-charts.

A-2.3 Precautions in obtaining the measurements

In making a process capability study it is necessary to plan carefully for the proper collection of data. The following rules are based on the experience of many engineers.

(1) Take the data, if possible, in the same time-sequence in which the product is made.

(2) Arrange to take data on the product as made rather than after a screening or adjusting operation (unless the object of study is to be the screening or adjusting.) In the latter case you may wish to take data both before and after the screening or adjusting.

(3) Decide in advance on the proper technique for making the measurements.

(4) Decide how many measurements should be taken on each part and exactly where the measurements should be made.

(5) See that the proper identification is recorded in addition to the actual measurements. For example, time of day, number of machine, name of operator, number of test set, number of gage, etc. See paragraph A-2.9.

(6) Instruct the person taking the measurements to make a note of all known changes in the process during the period of study.

(7) If the data are to be taken on product and there is more than one source of product (for example, more than one machine, operator or test set) decide whether to cover all of these sources or only one or two.

(8) If the data are to be taken on processing conditions and there is more than one set of conditions, decide whether to cover all or only one or two.

A-2.4 Error of measurement

It is not possible to obtain the full advantages of the process capability technique unless the measurements are reliable to start with. This means that the measurements must be taken accurately, and at a point that is meaningful in its bearing on the problem being studied. It is very common in capability studies to find patterns that are seriously out of control when the first readings are plotted. Often this turns out to be largely the error or instability of the measurements rather than the actual condition of the product.

Remember that every observation on a piece of product is a composite of two different elements. One is the actual value of the characteristic; the other is the measurement of it. If the measurement is contributing more variability than the pieces of product, it will be difficult to detect some of the cause and effect relationships which may be important in solving the problem.

In making a capability study either obtain the measurements yourself or make sure that they are taken by someone who is properly instructed and in whom you have confidence. If there is doubt as to the adequacy of the method of measurement, it may be necessary to make a study of the measuring method itself before attempting to study the variations in the product.

It is possible to check (a) the accuracy of the measurements as compared to a fixed standard, and (b) their precision or reproducibility. For information on this see pages 84–91.

A-2.5 Semi-variables measurements

In cases where it would be desirable to have variables measurements but the characteristic is one which is ordinarily checked by attributes only, it is often possible to obtain "semi-variables" measurements by setting up a scale which is capable of showing degree, and ranking the units in accordance with this scale. For example, in a problem involving burrs it might be possible to use the following:

Size of Burr	Artificial Number
No burr	0
Small burr	1
Medium burr	2
Large burr	3
Very large burr	4

The numbers 0, 1, 2, 3 and 4 can be used to make $\bar{X}$ and R charts like any ordinary measurements.

Before attempting to assign numbers to the units, establish standards to make your judgment as consistent as possible. The "error of measurement" in semi-variables data can be reduced by obtaining separate observations or rankings from a number of independent observers. The error of measurement can be evaluated in the same way as any other error of measurement.

A-2.6 "Work sampling" measurements

It is possible to make process capability studies on such problems as the required frequency of machine settings or housekeeping activities in the shop, the ways in which a group of clerical workers or engineers spend their time, whether the shop is properly performing the specified chemical, washing, degreasing or heat treating operations, and similar situations where we do not ordinarily think of taking numerical measurements. To do this we make use of a special data-collecting technique which is known as "work sampling." This technique consists of the following:

(1) Prepare a check list of all the activities which it is desired to study. The list may include (a) desirable activities which we wish to encourage or on which we wish to set standards, and (b) undesirable activities which we wish to study for the purpose of reducing them or eliminating them from the process. It may also include activities which are essential but non-productive, such as waiting for work or changing the water in a wash tank. The key to the success of "work sampling" studies is the preparation of the check list.

(2) Have an observer go around at random intervals and record instantaneous observations of the activity being performed at that moment. The activity is recorded by making a tally mark on the check list. Randomness can be assured by having the observer draw a card from a shuffled deck of cards to determine the time at which he should make the observation, and a second card to determine the area or person to be observed. The number and frequency of the observations which must be taken depends on the nature of the process and the purpose of the process capability study.

The data obtained in this manner consist of a number of tally marks which constitute a "sample." The "sample size" is the total number of observations. Attributes data for p-charts or other purposes are obtained by taking the percentage of observations recorded for a given activity or group of activities as compared with the total number of observations in the sample.

Work sampling measurements can be used for process capability studies, shop control charts, or estimates based on samples. For further information on this method of obtaining data see References No. 1 and 22.

A-2.7 Amount of data required for a process capability study

$\bar{X}$ and R charts

The process capability study should cover at least three different periods in time. A suitable amount of data to start with would be as follows:

First period	50 measurements
Second period	25 measurements
Third period	25 measurements

This is a total of 100 measurements on the process.

p-Charts

Again we want the study to cover three or more periods in time. A suitable amount of data would consist of 20 to 25 samples for each one of these periods. Each sample should represent about 50 or 100 units checked.

Charts for individual measurements with control limits based on the moving range

In this type of study we are ordinarily limited to very little data. It is permissible to use as few as 10 consecutive numbers, provided these numbers cover a representative period of time. For example, if the chart is to cover merchandise losses or other accounting figures, the study might cover a period of approximately one year.

Special cases

While the rules given above are safe rules to follow, do not hesitate to use larger or smaller amounts of data if this is necessary or convenient. If more data are readily available, by all means use them. On the other hand, if very little data can be taken, it is still possible to obtain answers to many problems by using these data in a capability study.

A-2.8 Selection of samples

Samples should be selected so as to minimize all sources of variation other than the factor being studied. This can usually be accomplished by having each sub-group consist of consecutive units as produced. See page 151 for further information on suitable methods of selecting samples.

A-2.9 Identification of data

When collecting measurements, carefully identify the different periods in time. Also identify any other known changes in the source of data, or any surrounding conditions or elements in the process which might be able to affect the results. For example: Up to a certain point the data came from one location but after that the job was moved to another; at a certain point the design was changed; there was a new supervisor; the job was put on sampling inspection; the engineer decided to use a different furnace.

The more ways in which the data are identified, the more it will be possible to learn from the process capability study. This is one of the first principles in control chart analysis and is the source of much of its power. This applies not only to process capability studies but also to designed experiments.

A-2.10 Point at which the data should be collected

Data may be collected at any point where the problem is thought to exist. However, many troubles which first become apparent in the end product have roots which go back to the early operations. It is often possible to save time by studying the early operations in the first place.

A-3 ANALYZING THE DATA

A-3.1 Scales for plotting

Scales should be chosen in such a way as to get a readable width for the control limits. The control limits should preferably be not less than 1 inch and not more than 2 inches apart. For $\bar{X}$ and R charts, try to keep the width of the control band (that is, the distance between the centerline and either control limit) approximately equal for both $\bar{X}$ and R. For p-charts which are to be compared, use the same scale on all charts.

A-3.2 Calculating limits

When the data included in a capability study cover more than one set of conditions, some question may arise as to whether the centerline and control limits should be calculated from all the data or from one portion of it only. It is an important principle in capability studies that in any case where there are adequate amounts of data it does not matter which portion of it is used for calculations. A different selection of data may result in different control limits but should not result in different conclusions. This can be seen in Figure 52 on page 52. The data plotted here might represent an $\bar{X}$ chart, a p-chart or a chart for individual measurements.

In this example the pattern without control limits is shown in Figure 52(a). If control limits are calculated from the May data only, the chart will look like Figure 52(b). This chart shows that May and June are different, May being higher. If the control limits are based on the month of June only, the chart will look like Figure 52(c). This is a different centerline and set of control limits but it tells the same story: May is higher than June. If the control limits are based on May and June combined, this results in a third set of limits but the story is still the same. This will be true, in general, as long as there are adequate amounts of data on which to base the calculations.

When the data are limited, as in a designed experiment, it is best to use all the data in calculating the control limits. The data are considered to be "limited" if there are less than 20 points when the chart is plotted. The smaller

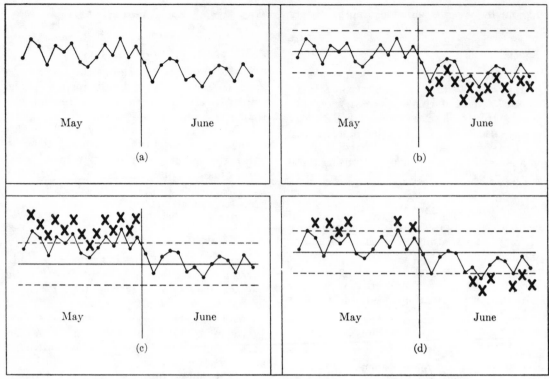

Fig. 52. Different levels of performance in May as compared with June.

the number of measurements, the less certain we are about the accurate location of the limits.

Addition of further data

The rules given above cover the initial calculation of control limits for a capability study. When more data are to be added, extend the original control limits across the page and plot the additional data against the original limits.

If you find on checking the patterns that the additional data are significantly different from the original data, it is proper to calculate new control limits, if desired, for the additional data. The new limits will make it possible to test the later set of data to see whether it shows control with respect to its own limits.

Do not, however, calculate new limits for additional data unless you have previously found a significant difference. Do not consider there is a significant difference unless there is reason to mark x's on the chart. If new limits are calculated without statistical evidence that the sets of data were different, this may easily lead to false conclusions. Separate control limits may make a set of data appear different when

in fact it has come from the same system of causes.

A-3.3 What to do about freaks

Engineers frequently wonder whether they ought to throw away portions of the data that appear to be "wild" or to have been caused by a "freak." In general, it is never wise to throw away any data in the calculations or plotting unless there is definite knowledge that something has affected that one group of readings and no others. Ordinarily it is difficult to obtain such positive knowledge. If supposed "freaks" are eliminated in the calculations or plotting, this may destroy the very information which might lead to solving the problem.

One exception to the above rule is a case encountered occasionally where the "wild" readings are very numerous. This is sometimes found in the early studies on new products or designs under development. When wild readings are numerous they should not properly be considered as freaks, but rather as a separate distribution resulting from a different system of causes. Such freaks should be separated from the rest of the data in order to make the patterns interpretable. They should not, however, be eliminated from the study. They should only be plotted on a separate chart.

It need hardly be pointed out that in any case where it is necessary to separate the freaks in this manner, one of the immediate objects of the capability study should be to identify the extraneous system of causes so that the freaks can be eliminated. See pages 162–164 for further help in dealing with freaks.

Repeated "freaks"

If freaks tend to occur in a capability study repeatedly, the repetition means that they are not freaks but rather the result of some cause operating regularly in the process. The principal rule in dealing with such freaks is: Don't underestimate their importance and don't eliminate them from the data.

A-3.4 Plotting the control charts

In all cases, follow the standard methods of plotting control charts when making a process capability study. If necessary review the material on pages 12–23.

Do not overlook the fact that the data can be plotted in more than one way. Plotting a chart of individual measurements or a grouped frequency distribution may help in interpreting an $\bar{X}$ and R chart. Changing the scale at the bottom of the chart (for example, to show operations rather than time) may help in interpreting a p-chart or c-chart.

A-3.5 Studying the patterns

Preliminary analysis of a process capability study consists of two steps as follows:

(1) Carefully record, on the chart, all known pertinent facts about the data as provided in paragraphs A-2.3 and A-2.9. These may be needed later for separating the data according to source. Also make notes on any surrounding conditions or elements which might be capable of affecting the results. Repair of a fixture, re-calibration of a test set, or the fact that maintenance work was performed may be vital information in securing a correct interpretation.

(2) Go over the patterns carefully and mark x's where they belong. If instability or other changes are indicated, determine the type of change. (For example: cycle, trend, gradual shift, sudden shift, erratic fluctuation, freak, interaction.) Mark the type of pattern on the chart near the corresponding x's. Note also any background information you may have which is related to the type of pattern. For example: "Trend—probably tool wear."

Be sure to include a check for stratification, stable mixture, systematic variables, tendency for one chart to be correlated with another. Note on the chart any background information related to these patterns. For example: "Stratification—may be due to samples being associated with bifurcated springs."

If the pattern is natural, make the calculations indicated in paragraph A-3.6. If the pattern is not natural, follow the directions in paragraph A-3.7.

Regardless of whether the patterns are natural or unnatural, a properly conducted process capability study should give valuable information. The chart will be used in different ways, however, depending on the naturalness or unnaturalness of the pattern.

A-3.6 Drawing conclusions from a natural pattern

The primary significance of a natural pattern is that it indicates a process which is in statistical control. Such a process is stable and undisturbed by extraneous causes. It tends to repeat itself day after day and is consequently predictable. It is possible to determine the underlying characteristics of such a process by making calculations based on the pattern on the control chart.

Among the calculations which may be based on a natural pattern are the following. Do not attempt to make any of these calculations unless the control chart is in control:

(1) Estimate the center of the process distribution as $\bar{\bar{X}}$.

(2) Estimate the shape of the process distribution by making a frequency plot of the process capability data.

(3) Estimate the spread of the process distribution by making the calculations shown on page 56.

(4) Compare the process distribution with the specification or other standards as shown on pages 119–122.

(5) Estimate the percentages outside of limits, if desired, by making the calculations shown on pages 58–59.

(6) Use the centerlines on the $\bar{X}$ chart and R chart, if desired, to calculate the effect of overlapping tolerances.

(7) Use the centerlines if desired to set up economic limits for shop control charts.

(8) Use the centerlines if desired to establish standards for budgets, forecasts, wage incentive allowances, etc.

In the case of a p-chart, estimate the capability as explained on page 59, and use the centerline as indicated in (7) and (8) above.

Note particularly that a natural pattern is essential when we wish to.

- Determine capability.
- Compare with standards.
- Generalize.
- Predict.

In the absence of a natural pattern we can obtain other information, but we cannot do the four things listed above.

For further information on the meaning of a natural pattern see pages 170–171.

A-3.7 Drawing conclusions from an unnatural pattern

An unnatural pattern indicates a process which is disturbed or out of control. Such a process may be erratic and unpredictable. It may or may not tend to repeat. We cannot determine the underlying characteristics of such a process by making calculations from the out-of-control data. We cannot use the out-of-control data to generalize or predict. We can, however, obtain other useful information in the manner shown below.

(1) In a process capability study the primary significance of an unnatural pattern is *the fact that important causes, capable of exerting a large effect on the process, are present in such a form that they are susceptible to analysis and study.* While natural patterns are used mainly for setting standards and making estimates, *un-*

natural patterns are used mainly for gaining new knowledge about the process.

(2) Unnatural patterns provide information about processing variables, process changes, cause and effect relationships, cost reduction possibilities, and potentialities for improvement. The information contained in an unnatural pattern may be far more important, for engineering purposes, than the information contained in a natural pattern.

Method of analysis

Unnatural patterns may be divided into two general types:

(a) Relatively simple.
(b) Relatively complex.

Among the relatively simple types are the following:

Cycles.
Trends.
Sudden or gradual changes in level.
Certain types of systematic variation.

Among the relatively complex patterns are the following:

Mixtures of all kinds, including both stable and unstable mixtures.
Freaks.
Grouping or bunching.
Stratification.
Tendency of one chart to follow another.
Interaction.
Instability.

The simple unnatural patterns can ordinarily be interpreted by the application of technical knowledge or shop experience. The relatively complex patterns must usually be reduced to one of the simple forms before they can be interpreted.

A-3.8 Simplification of complex patterns

General

The basic approach, in simplifying complex patterns, is to separate the data according to various sources. In many studies there is an obvious basis for performing this separation. For example, there may be several machines, shifts, operators, tools, chucks, sources of supply, fixtures, heads, methods of assembly, positions at different spots in an oven. In such cases it is easy to separate the data and plot a separate chart for each source. See Method A below.

In other cases the method of separating the data is not so simple. For example, a machine may behave like more than one machine if it is in a poor state of repair. A fixture may behave like more than one fixture if it is poorly anchored or has excessive play. In the same way, an operator who is careless or inadequately trained may behave like more than one operator. Piece parts which are not uniform, or which come from a mixed lot sent in by a supplier, may behave like two kinds of piece parts. In such cases it requires more ingenuity to separate the data. See Method B below.

The following methods of separating data are used in engineering studies:

Method A. Simple breakdown.
Method B. Elimination of variables.
Method C. Rearrangements of data.
Method D. Designed experiments.

All of these methods have the same basic objective. They attempt to separate the data into significant categories in such a way that the patterns will become simple enough to interpret.

Method A: Simple breakdown

This method is used where some of the possible sources of complexity are known or at least suspected. The engineer proceeds as follows:

(1) Separate the data according to known sources, major components, etc. Plot separate charts for each source. The source or component whose pattern is least stable, or whose pattern is most similar to the original complex pattern, is the one most likely to contain the important causes. Disregard the rest of the data and concentrate on this portion.

(2) Take the data for this least stable portion and break it down further. Plot separate patterns for each of the new sources or subcomponents. Again, the source or component with the most significant pattern is the one most likely to contain the important causes.

(3) With each separation, the patterns become simpler or stand out more prominently. Continue this process until the patterns become natural or until they consist of (a) simple shifts in level or (b) simple trends. At this point it is possible to make calculations as shown in paragraph A-3.10.

Suggestions on possible sources or "production paths" will be found on pages 166–167, 168, 180 and 219. It will also be helpful to study the material on control chart theory on pages 149–151, and the explanation of the R chart on pages 154–156. If the patterns are still complex when separated by source, follow the directions under Method B.

Method B: Elimination of variables

This method is used where there is no prior basis for separating the data. An example of such a case is given on pages 66–71. The engineer proceeds as follows:

(1) The original pattern is used to discover some variable (usually a single variable) which needs to be eliminated. This requires a knowledge of control chart patterns and the ability to interpret these patterns as outlined in Engineering Part F. Study the explanations given on pages 66–71.

(2) As soon as the first variable is discovered, do what is necessary to eliminate this variable. Then collect more data and make, in effect, a second process capability study. The patterns in the second study will be simpler because of the removal of one of the large variables. See page 67.

(3) Continue this process until the patterns become natural or until they consist of (a) simple shifts in level or (b) simple trends. Then make the calculations shown in paragraph A-3.10.

This method of simplifying patterns can be used in any situation. It may be the only method possible if there are complicated variables or many engineering unknowns.

Methods C and D: Rearrangements of data and formal designed experiments

If the data used in the study have been

identified in enough different ways, it may be possible to simplify the pattern by merely rearranging the data. An example of this is given on pages 72–73. Correlation studies, scatter diagrams and "trend arrangements" of the measurements, and formal designed experiments, are all methods of classifying and rearranging the data.

These methods simplify the pattern by arranging the data in various ways, thus making it possible to identify certain causes. For correlation and similar studies see pages 143–148. For designed experiments see pages 75–117.

A-3.9 Checking to determine whether you have found the real cause

If the causes affecting the pattern have been properly identified, there should be an obvious correspondence between the presence or absence of the cause and subsequent changes in pattern. It should be possible to put the cause in or take it out at will and make the pattern behave correspondingly. In addition, there must be some logical engineering reason for believing that such a condition might be the cause. Be careful not to assume that one condition causes another merely because it precedes the other in time.

A-3.10 Calculations from a pattern showing only very simple shifts and trends

If the cause of the shift or trend has been conclusively identified, calculations may be made from simple patterns in much the same manner as in paragraph A-3.6. In the case of a shift, make the calculations separately for each distinct level. In the case of a trend, make the calculations for one or more levels along the slope of the trend line.

A-4 MAKING AN ESTIMATE OF THE PROCESS CAPABILITY

The capability of a process may be expressed numerically in two different ways:

(a) as a distribution having a certain center, shape and spread; or
(b) as a percentage outside of some specified limit.

In the first case the capability is estimated from an $\bar{X}$ and R chart; in the second, from a p-chart.

By a simple calculation, information from the $\bar{X}$ and R chart can also be translated into percentages. It is not possible to work in the opposite direction and get distribution information from a p-chart.

A-4.1 Estimating center, shape and spread from an $\bar{X}$ and R chart

At the conclusion of the process capability study, you have obtained a set of controlled patterns. From these patterns it is possible to find the distribution that the process is capable of producing.

- **Center.** The center of the distribution will be the centerline on the $\bar{X}$ chart ($\bar{\bar{X}}$).
- **Shape.** The shape can be judged for most practical purposes by making a frequency distribution of the data which produced the controlled patterns. Several hundred measurements may be necessary to give reliable evidence about the shape.
- **Spread.** The spread can be calculated by using the factors given on page 131. Proceed as follows:
  (a) For a normal* distribution, estimate the spread of individuals as $\pm 3\bar{R}/d_2$. Be sure to use the d_2 factor (from page 131) which corresponds to the sample size used to obtain R.
  (b) For a non-normal** distribution, estimate σ as $\bar{R}/d_2$. The distribution may spread more than 3 σ on one side and less than 3 σ on the other side. The total spread may be more or less than 6 σ.

Note that the estimate of spread, as well as shape, will be affected if the distribution is skewed.

A-4.2 Permanent and non-permanent skewness

In many processes the degree of skewness is subject to change even when the center and

* See pages 131–134.
** See pages 134–136.

spread of the distribution are reasonably constant. If you wish to base specifications or changes in specifications on the fact that the distribution is skewed, be sure that there is a good engineering reason to account for the skewness in the first place and also for arguing that it is a permanent feature of the process.

Some of the causes which tend to introduce skewness and make it permanent are:

(1) Parts coming up against a positive stop.

(2) Measurements reaching the physical limits of the material, as in strength of welds.

(3) Manual control of operations such as grinding, where the tendency is to grind just inside the limits in order to minimize work.

(4) Characteristics such as eccentricity, warpage, unbalance, runout, etc. where the natural limit is zero.

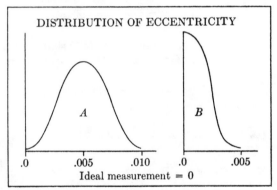

Fig. 53. *B* is a better distribution than *A*.

In many processes a skewed distribution is desirable. See Figure 53. Engineers should not jump to the conclusion that properly run processes, or processes in good control, will have "normal" distributions.

There are also certain mathematical reasons for skewness, an example of which is the following:

Suppose we are making a product consisting of square pieces. We measure the sides of a large number of squares and find that their distribution is symmetrical.

If the *sides* of the squares form a symmetrical distribution, it is obvious that the *areas* of the squares cannot form a symmetrical distribution. If we measured the areas (or volume or weights or anything related to the sides by a square or cubic relationship), the distribution would evidently be skewed. See Figure 54.

The above causes tend to introduce skewness as a permanent characteristic of the distribution. In addition, the following causes may introduce temporary skewness:

(1) Some skewness is created artificially by a sorting or screening operation. Such distributions are said to be "truncated." The truncation generally takes place at a specified maximum or minimum limit as in Figure 55.

(2) When skewness is associated with out-of-control patterns on a control chart, it is likely to be the result of a mixture of two

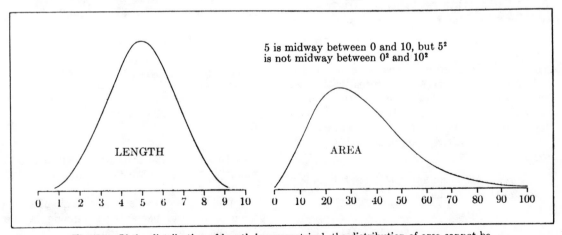

Fig. 54. If the distribution of length is symmetrical, the distribution of area cannot be.

or more distributions. This type of skewness tends to be nonpermanent and unstable. See Figure 56.

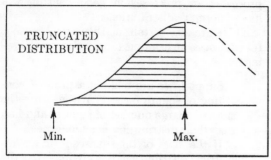

Fig. 55. Nonpermanent skewness due to screening.

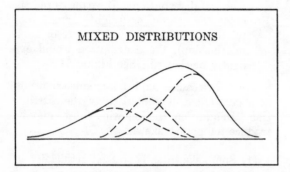

Fig. 56. Nonpermanent skewness due to mixture.

Occasionally skewness may be the result of "freaks" which cause a long tail to spread out on one side. In such cases, before deciding whether to treat the distribution as a skewed distribution, you must decide whether to consider the freaks as a regular part of the process.

A-4.3 Estimating percentages from an $\bar{X}$ and R chart

The percentage outside of a given limit can be estimated from $\bar{X}$ and R charts that show control. This requires a knowledge of the distribution center, shape and spread. If you have reason to believe the distribution is reasonably normal (symmetrical, not too flat on top, and not too peaked), the percentage can be estimated with reasonable accuracy as follows:

(1) Estimate "sigma prime" from the centerline of the R chart.

$$\sigma' = \frac{\bar{R}}{d_2}$$

Values of d_2 are given on page 131.

(2) Calculate "t" according to one of the following formulas, depending on whether you are interested in a maximum or minimum limit.

$$t = \frac{\bar{X} - \text{Max.}}{\sigma'}$$

$$t = \frac{\text{Min.} - \bar{X}}{\sigma'}$$

(3) Read the percentage outside of limits from Table I on page 133.

Example

In a process capability study on thickness of a core plate, $\bar{R}$ for samples of five was found to be .0030 and $\bar{\bar{X}}$ was .7512. Both patterns were in control. The engineer felt that the distribution was "reasonably normal." He calculated sigma as follows:

$$\sigma' = \frac{\bar{R}}{d_2} = \frac{.0030}{2.326} = .0013$$

The specification for core plate thickness was .750 ± .003. Consider the two specification limits separately as follows.

Taking first the upper specification limit (.7530):

$$t = \frac{\bar{\bar{X}} - \text{Max.}}{\sigma'} = \frac{.7512 - .7530}{.0013} =$$

$$\frac{-.0018}{.0013} = -1.38$$

Looking up −1.38 in the table on page 133 (under "Percentage Outside of Max."), we find the percentage is 8.4%.

Now considering the lower specification limit (.7470):

$$t = \frac{\text{Min.} - \bar{\bar{X}}}{\sigma'} = \frac{.7470 - .7512}{.0013} =$$

$$\frac{-.0042}{.0013} = -3.23$$

Looking up −3.23 in the table on page 133 (under "Percentage Outside of Min."), we find the percentage is 0.1%.

To find the *total* percentage outside of specification, add the percentages outside of the upper and lower specification limits.

58

$$8.4\% + 0.1\% = 8.5\% \text{ total}$$

Before deciding that a distribution is "reasonably normal," compare the plotted frequency distribution with the one on page 132 by eye. See also page 133 on the use of probability paper and various other tests for normality. The shape of the distribution is more important in estimating percentages than in most other applications.

Non-normal distributions

If the distribution has a moderate skew, follow the procedure outlined above; but in Step 3 read the percentages from Table II or Table III on pages 135 and 136, depending on the direction of the skew.

Example

Suppose the following have been calculated from data (and the data are in control on an $\bar{X}$ and R chart):

$$\bar{\bar{X}} = .12225$$
$$\sigma' = .00045$$

A frequency plot of these data (Figure 57) indicates that we should use Table III (negative skew, $k = -1$ approx.).

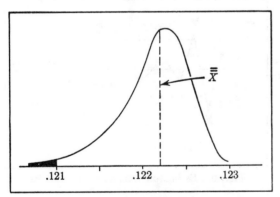

Fig. 57. Frequency distribution of some data which show control. A smooth curve has been drawn by eye around the tallied data.

Problem:

Determine the percentage outside $\bar{\bar{X}} \pm .001$.

(1) For percent outside $\bar{\bar{X}} + .001$ (.12325):

$$t = \frac{.12225 - .12325}{.00045} = -2.22$$

Find -2.22 in Table III (under "Percentage Outside of Max.") and read 0%.

(2) For percent outside $\bar{\bar{X}} - .001$ (.12125):

$$t = \frac{.12125 - .12225}{.00045} = -2.22$$

Find -2.22 in Table III (under "Percentage Outside of Min.") and read 3.6%.

Total percentage outside of $\bar{\bar{X}} \pm .001 = 3.6\%$.

If the distribution has a very pronounced skew, the best guide is an estimate based on the frequency distribution of observed results. In doubtful cases, it may be advisable to run a p-chart in the shop in conjunction with your $\bar{X}$ and R chart, in order to determine whether the percentage in the tail is controlled.

A-4.4 Estimating a percentage from a p-chart

At the conclusion of the process capability study, you have obtained a long series of points that show control. The process capability in terms of percentage (that is, the percentage outside of whatever limit was used in determining what would be called "defective") is merely the centerline on the p-chart. This estimate must always be considered as tentative unless the p-chart represents one source of data only.

If the p-chart does not represent one source of data, the sources should be studied separately before attempting to estimate the overall capability. Break the data down according to source, type of defect, or other obvious contributors to the composite pattern. Percentages should be estimated separately for the various contributors and later combined into an overall estimate.

A-4.5 Estimating capability from a pattern that is not in control

The following discussion applies to either $\bar{X}$ and R charts or p-charts.

Occasionally it is necessary to estimate the capability of a process prior to the time when it has been possible to bring the pattern into control. In such cases, the estimates can be only rough and tentative since the average of uncontrolled data cannot be taken to be the true capability.

However, estimates based on the early patterns in a capability study, even when out of control, will be better than estimates arrived at without such studies. While out-of-control patterns will not show the true capability, they permit us to make a more intelligent guess as to where it lies. In addition, they show us how far we are at present from reaching the desired state of control.

To obtain the best estimate from uncontrolled patterns, proceed as follows:

(1) If the pattern shows a trend, determine the cause of the trend and decide which portion of it represents the way in which the process will be run in the future. Estimate the capability in the manner described in paragraph A-4.1, basing your estimates on the selected portion of the pattern only. See Figure 58.

(2) If the pattern is interrupted by periodic lack of control, this can sometimes be recognized as indicating the presence of two or more separate patterns in the data. It should be possible to run the process at any one of the indicated levels provided we are able to identify the causes and bring the process, at some later time, into a state of control. See Figure 59; also Figure 207 on page 194.

Wherever it is possible to pick out such probable levels by eye, this provides a reasonable basis for estimating capability. Use engineering judgment in deciding which points are likely to indicate separate patterns.

(3) If the pattern is erratic in such a manner that it is not possible to pick out the separate patterns by eye, it may be that the best available estimate of capability will be the center of the out-of-control pattern. If this estimate is used for want of a better one, keep in mind that it is a very uncertain estimate. See Figure 60.

When estimates are based on out-of-control patterns, always explain the basis for the estimate and show the pattern of the data from which the estimate came. Also remember that

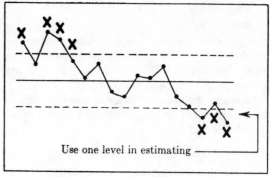

Fig. 58.   Estimating from a trend.

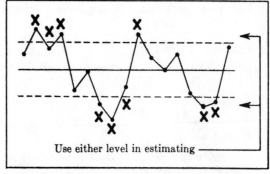

Fig. 59.   Estimating from an interrupted pattern.

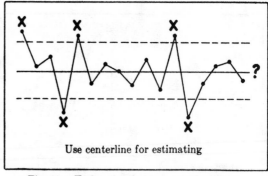

Fig. 60.   Estimating from an erratic pattern.

no estimate from uncontrolled data is reliable. Reliability comes from knowledge that the data show control.

A-4.6 Wrong ways of estimating the process capability

There are two common practices in estimating capability which have no valid statistical foundation. Engineers should avoid using either of them in arriving at estimates or set-

60

ting standards. The things to avoid are the following:

I. Do not attempt to use a distribution without a control chart.

A distribution will not give a reliable estimate of the process capability unless the data making up the distribution came from a controlled process. This can only be determined by plotting the data on a control chart. To use a distribution correctly in determining capability, proceed as follows:

Plot the data on a control chart (in the order of production, if possible), and determine whether there were any significant changes during the time when the data were accumulated. If there were significant changes, the distribution should not be used to determine capability.

II. Do not attempt to use the average of past data without a control chart.

Even a long and intimate knowledge of the job cannot show whether the average of past data is anything like the real process capability.

To use the past data from a job correctly in estimating capability, proceed as follows:

First check the data statistically by means of a control chart to determine whether it shows significant changes. If significant changes are found, the data should not be used without modification to determine capability.

These two points have important implications in engineering planning and in process control. Unless the true capability is determined, acceptance of past performance could merely authorize and allow a continuation of questionable conditions and practices.

A-4.7 Meaning of "short-term" and "long-term" capability

The "short-term" capability of a process refers to its normal behavior at any given instant of time. The "long-term" capability of a process includes the normal effect of toolwear, minor variations from batch to batch of material, and similar small and expected variations. Process control charts are set up, wherever possible, on the "long-term" capa-

bility of the process. See page 64.

The short-term capability of the process includes, among other things, the concept of its "natural tolerance." In the case of symmetrical distributions, the natural tolerance is usually taken to be a spread of ± 3 sigma from the center. In the case of unsymmetrical distributions the spread in either direction may be more or less than 3 sigma, and the use of the term "natural tolerance" is likely to cause confusion. The engineer will probably find it safer to use the term "natural spread" for distributions of all kinds, and to define it always as plus so much and minus so much from the distribution center. For example, "The natural spread of the process is estimated to be $\pm .003$." "The natural spread of the process is estimated to be $+.004, -.002$." When used in this manner, the term "natural spread" always refers to the short-term capability.

A-5 USING THE INFORMATION FROM A PROCESS CAPABILITY STUDY

The first step in using the information from a process capability study is to see whether the capability, as revealed by the study, is what we want it to be.

A process may be in control but at an entirely wrong level. It might be in control and still be 50% outside of specifications. It might be in control and well inside of specifications, and still be at a point that would cause the shop unnecessary trouble in adjusting or assembly. It might be in control but have such a wide spread that it would be virtually impossible to reach a high yield. In addition to this, serious measurement problems may have been encountered, or it may be necessary to get more data or different data in order to obtain a permanent solution to the problem. It is sometimes found that a specification needs to be added, reworded, narrowed, widened, modified or removed.

In any event there will be action of some sort which is required as a result of the study. The required action may be:

    a. Action on the process.
    b. Action on the data.
    c. Action on the specification.

To determine what action is necessary, first do the following:

- Make sure that the chart is in statistical control.
- Check the level of the $\bar{X}$ chart or p-chart to see whether it is in a desirable place.
- In a case of an $\bar{X}$ and R study, check the centerline on the R chart also to make sure that the process does not have too wide a spread. See page 56 for method of calculating the "spread of individuals" in the process. It is good practice to sketch the probable spread of individuals on the $\bar{X}$ chart as shown on page 31.

Then on the basis of the above information take the following steps.

Action on the process

(1) Decide what to do about the known assignable causes. It is possible to eliminate them or leave them in the process. Some of the causes you might not wish to eliminate are:

- Normal toolwear.
- Reasonable variations in the machine settings.
- Unavoidable variations in batches of material.
- Ordinary differences between operators, etc.

If you leave these causes in the process, it will generally require a shop control chart to keep them within bounds. If you wish to keep them out of the process, it may require a control chart also.

(2) Decide whether it would pay to set up a better process having a narrower capability. It may be possible to realize savings by holding the process closer than the present specifications so as to cut down adjusting difficulties, etc. If you think it would pay to set up a narrower process, it may be necessary to run a designed experiment or make further capability studies.

(3) Find whether the present process can be relocated in such a way as to get better results or higher yields. Perhaps a change in material, the re-design of a tool or fixture,

a change in the operator's work pattern can move the process up or down. If the process can be relocated to advantage, will the new location be permanent? If not, and if the location will be under the control of the shop, you will need a shop control chart.

(4) Find whether it would be possible to get cost reduction by using a more economical process. No capability study should be considered complete until this possibility has been investigated.

(5) If the process at the end of the study is in control with a satisfactory level and spread, and if none of the above actions are necessary, take steps to see that this desirable condition is made permanent. This in itself may require a shop control chart.

Note that many of the actions that may be required on a process tend to result in installing shop charts. See Paragraph A-6 for the method of setting up shop charts to complete the action in a process capability study.

Action on the data

This may be of two different kinds:

(1) Error of measurement. There may be indications that the measurements are not reproducible. In that case the engineer may need to make an error of measurement study before collecting further data.

(2) Inadequate amount of data. The patterns on the chart may still be inconclusive. If so, more data are needed to solve the original problem.

Action on the specification

This may take at least six different forms.

(1) Attempt to widen specifications which are found to be narrower than the process capability.

(2) Attempt to narrow specifications, if by so doing you can obtain economic advantages or a reduction in complaints. Investigate the value of using tighter tolerances on piece parts or components in order to reduce trouble in later assemblies.

(3) Take off specifications found to be unnecessary.

(4) Add specifications found to be necessary or desirable.

(5) Shift the nominal of specifications found to be in the wrong place.

(6) Re-word specifications found to be in need of modification or clarification.

Do not be discouraged if you find that one process capability study merely leads to another study and that one to a third study, etc. The problems you are tackling may have existed for many years. It may not be possible to resolve such a tangled situation overnight. Some process capability studies may extend for a period of many months. See the example on pages 66–71.

The determining factor is whether the study continues to reveal information which leads to a reduction in cost or improvement in quality or both.

A-6 TRANSLATING A PROCESS CAPABILITY STUDY INTO A SHOP CONTROL CHART

Having obtained certain information from a process capability study, the engineer knows what distribution or range of distributions can be maintained economically. He now wishes to set up a process control in the shop which will enable the shop to maintain the desired distribution and obtain the desired benefits. Very often the control which is needed in the shop will be a standard shop control chart.

The engineer should keep in mind that while the control chart technique is used for both capability studies and shop charts, the two applications are entirely different. Some of the differences are shown in Figure 61. Study these differences before attempting to set up a shop chart.

Preparation for setting up the chart

Properly speaking, before a shop chart is set up, the engineer should have experimented with all elements of the process. He should have studied the effect of changes in material, methods, personnel and tools. He should also have weighed the economics of each change so that the shop standards arrived at will have real economic meaning. However, it is seldom possible for an engineer to carry a study to this point prior to the installation of the shop chart.

CHARACTERISTIC	PROCESS CAPABILITY STUDY	PROCESS CONTROL CHART
PURPOSE	To obtain information.	To maintain a predetermined distribution.
SAMPLES	Relatively few.	A running series.
ANALYSIS	Very careful analysis and interpretation.	Shop watches only the more obvious changes in pattern.
ACTION	Any change may be important, either good or bad.	The shop acts only on unwanted changes.
INFORMATION	Distribution shape is studied as well as average and spread.	Attention focused mainly on average and spread (or percent defective).
CENTERLINES	Centerlines are calculated from the data to reflect the distribution of the process being studied.	Centerlines are set to represent a balance between quality and cost. They show where we want the process to run.
RELATION TO SPECIFICATION	Relation to specification is carefully checked. The study may lead to a change in either the process or the specification.	Proper relationship to specification is allowed for when the control chart is set up.

Fig. 61. Difference between a process capability study and a process control chart.

In fact, if he did so, it would postpone the immediate benefits which the shop could obtain from the chart. Consequently the usual procedure in setting up a shop chart is the following:

(1) The engineer makes a short intensive study with enough experimentation to effect the biggest improvements immediately.

(2) He then installs a chart in the shop, and the study is continued as a routine application of charting.

Continued use in the shop results in steady improvement and in time determines the ultimate capability of the process. In the meantime the engineer is making other studies.

A-6.1 Engineering a shop chart into the job on the basis of a process capability study

The following procedure is used in translating process capability information into permanent shop form.

(1) Base the shop control chart on the "long-term" capability of the process, as shown by your present studies, rather than its "short-term" capability. (See page 61.)

(2) Decide whether it is necessary to maintain a single level as nearly as possible, or whether it would be satisfactory to let the distribution shift. If it is to be permitted to shift, determine whether the amount of shifting should be limited on the high side only, on the low side only, or on both sides. Set the centerlines in accordance with this decision.

(3) Calculate control limits for the shop charts using the $\bar{R}$ or $\bar{p}$, as the case may be, from the controlled patterns in your process capability study. The mechanical details of installing the chart should be handled jointly by the Quality Control Team. See pages 187–199 and 228–229.

(4) Work with the shop regularly and at frequent intervals in using the information which develops from the chart. The Shop Section of the Handbook contains a large amount of practical wisdom on this subject which has been accumulated through years of application of statistical quality control. This will be found useful to engineers as well as Operating people.

On an $\bar{X}$ and R chart, the presence of a specification limit on one side or both is frequently a factor in setting up the chart. Other economic considerations may also exert a strong influence on the engineer's decisions, as follows:

(1) Some processes are not capable, in the present state of engineering and manufacturing knowledge, of turning out product which is compatible with specified limits.

(2) Some specifications are not compatible with each other. If the process is run at a level which ensures meeting one set of limits, large quantities of product may be outside of another set of limits.

(3) Some processes have an optimum level which will minimize, say, later difficulties in assembly. In such cases the engineer may decide to run the process well inside of the present specifications. Or he may decide to run it on the high or low side of nominal.

(4) Some processes, such as soldering or impregnating, tend to cause shifts in the characteristics of certain distributions. It may be desirable to allow for such anticipated shifts in choosing the optimum levels for the prior operations.

(5) There are some unavoidable conditions in materials, piece parts etc. for which it is necessary to compensate at a subsequent point in the process.

(6) Some failures to meet specifications are economically less undesirable than others. It may be cheaper to repair units which fail on the low side than on the high; or we may prefer to have a number of spoolheads so tight that they fail to fit relay cores, rather than run the risk of having loose spoolheads in the field.

(7) Some processes have maximum stability and predictability when run at a particular level.

(8) Some characteristics need to be controlled although they have no specified limits.

(9) Specifications themselves sometimes need to be changed as a result of the information developed from shop control charts.

A-6.2 Typical example of the installation of a shop chart

Figure 62 shows a typical shop chart derived from a process capability study. A representative portion of data from the capability study is shown at the left-hand side of the chart. This is useful guidance for the shop. It is reproduced from a master chart along with the scales, headings and control limits, so as to be a permanent part of every chart. The lines on the right-hand side of the chart represent the engineer's economic decision as to where the process should run.

The right-hand side of the chart will be used for the shop's samples. Note that the engineer has provided two centerlines on the $\bar{X}$ chart, to allow the shop the greatest possible leeway in running the process. The shop will ignore any patterns which form between the two centerlines, but will apply the usual tests for unnatural patterns to any points which fall between one of the centerlines and its control limit. Note that only one control limit is shown for each centerline.

If new control limits should be calculated later as a result of new studies, a portion of the new capability information will be shown at the left-hand side of the chart in place of the old information. This allows the shop people to see at all times what is expected of them, and to compare the current process with the engineering study on which the chart has been based.

Further information on shop charts will be found in the Shop Section on pages 187–229.

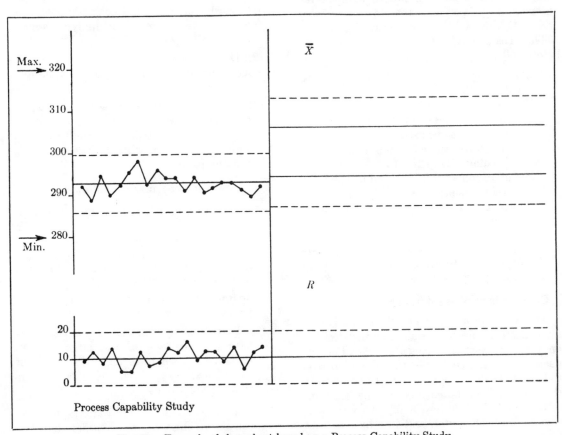

Fig. 62. Example of shop chart based on a Process Capability Study.

A-7 SIMPLE EXAMPLES OF PROCESS CAPABILITY STUDIES

The following are typical examples of process capability studies. They illustrate (a) the use of $\bar{X}$ and R charts and (b) the use of c-charts. In the first case the study is carried through to completion. In the second it is only begun. Both studies illustrate the simplification of complex patterns which was described on pages 54–56.

First process capability study: $\bar{X}$ and R charts

This problem involved an electrical characteristic on a certain type of switch. The switch was manufactured on a machine with 12 different heads. Performance was erratic, there seemed to be large differences among the heads, and a large percentage of product was being rejected because of failure to meet requirements. A process capability study was undertaken by the Quality Control Team.

The Team made the following decisions before collecting the original data:

> Characteristic to be plotted: Operate value of the switch
> Number of switches per sample: 5
> Number of samples in the study: 50
> Type of chart to be used: $\bar{X}$ and R chart
> Sources to be studied: Individual source of product (Head No. 6)
> Person to collect the data, and instructions to this person: Machine setter to take data and make a note of all known changes in the process during the period of study
> Period of time to be covered, and amounts of data: 10–15 samples on each of several different days

Comments on these decisions

The Team properly made plans in advance for collecting suitable data. For the decision on type of chart, see pages 47–48. For the decisions on source to be studied and person to collect the data, see page 49. In addition to the instructions noted above, the machine setter should be told how many measurements to take on each switch and just how to take them.

For the period of time to be covered, see page 50. The period should be long enough to make sure that the data will fairly represent the cause system. For example, if there are monthly production cycles, the study should cover at least a month.

For the point at which the data should be collected, see pages 49 and 51.

Control chart

The control chart obtained from the initial data is shown in Figure 63. This chart has many points out of control. It is typical of the complex patterns often obtained at the beginning of a study.

Statistical analysis of Figure 63

This is a complex pattern. It is just as important for the Team to know what not to do with it as what to do with it. The following are examples of what not to do with this pattern:

(1) Do not give up, and conclude that this is not a suitable area for applying statistical quality control.

(2) Do not decide to ignore this pattern, collect more data and see if the trouble disappears.

(3) Do not waste time trying to find assignable causes for the out-of-control points in this pattern. It will be virtually impossible to find them with the pattern in its present form.

Do, however, recognize the following:

(1) To interpret a complex pattern properly, we must be able to interpret the R chart. Here the pattern on the R chart is "masked" or obscure. This means that it is inflated by the presence of hidden variables. It will be necessary to reduce or remove this inflation in order to interpret the R chart.

(2) To reduce the inflation we must eliminate at least one of the large process variables. (See page 55.) The pattern will almost always give a clue as to what this variable should be.

In the present case we see that the fluctuations on the $\bar{X}$ chart are much wider than the fluctuations on the R chart. This indicates

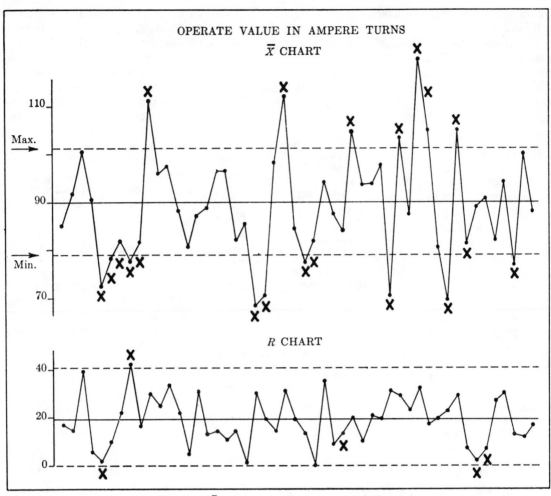

Fig. 63. First $\bar{X}$ and R chart in a process capability study.

over-adjustment. (See pages 153 and 203.) We therefore look for some obvious process adjustment and eliminate this before collecting further data.

Action taken as a result of this analysis

The Team found, on checking the machine setter's notes, that a meter had been adjusted from time to time to keep the process from "drifting." They instructed the machine setter not to make any adjustments of this meter while they were collecting the next data. The result of this action is shown in Figure 64 on the following page.

Statistical analysis of Figure 64

The chart on page 68 shows the effect of eliminating one adjustment. The $\bar{X}$ pattern is more stable, showing that the meter adjustment was one of the controlling variables. The R chart, however, shows just the opposite effect. There are 23 x's on this R chart where there were only 5 in Figure 63. To those who are not experienced in reading control charts, this pattern may look worse than the one in Figure 63.

Nevertheless this R chart contains the key to solving the problem. This can be seen by a more careful comparison of the R charts in Figures 63 and 64. The first pattern was obscure and could not be interpreted. The second is sharp and clear and can easily be interpreted. *The increased sharpness, which is reflected in the x's, results from the fact that we have eliminated one of the major variables.*

This is equivalent to filtering out noise in an electrical circuit. When some of the noise, or inflation, has been eliminated, this permits the signal, or hidden pattern, to come through more clearly.

Proceed as follows to interpret the R chart in Figure 64:

(1) This can be recognized at once as a pattern of "Instability." (See page 166.) Check the material in the Handbook on the subject of Instability (pages 166–167). We find that this pattern is characterized by unnaturally large, erratic fluctuations. There may be a single cause operating on the process erratically, or there may be a group of causes operating in conjunction with one another. We find that the first thing to do is check the process for *unstable mixtures.*

(2) Now check the material in the Handbook on Unstable Forms of Mixture (pages 179–180). We find that these are caused by having several distributions in the product at the same time. When the mixtures appear on the R chart, as in Figure 64, this indicates that the samples are coming at random from the various sources combined. In our own case we are not sampling deliberately from more than one source at a time. If mixtures exist in this process they are due to something that the people are not aware of.

Note the statement that unstable mixtures may show up as interactions, grouping, bunching or freaks. All of these are evident on the R chart in Figure 64.

(3) Now check the causes which are listed under "R Chart" on page 180. Among these we find the following:

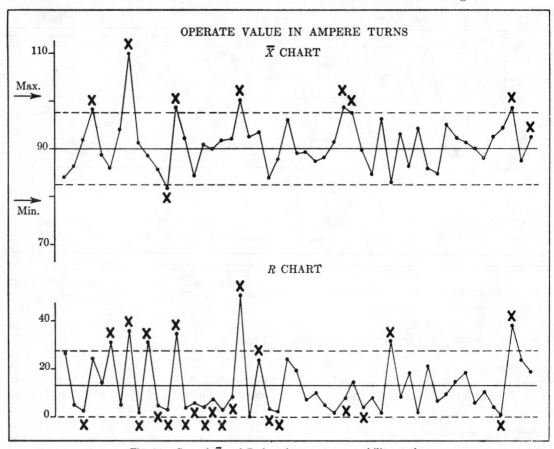

Fig. 64. Second $\overline{X}$ and R chart in a process capability study.

Two or more materials, operators, etc.

Too much play in a fixture.

Holding or locking devices unreliable.

Looseness of a chuck.

Machine in need of repair.

Fixtures or holders not holding the work in position.

Lack of alignment.

Etc.

Some of these possibilities can be eliminated at once, since they would not apply to this job. Any which cannot positively be eliminated should be carefully checked. Here we would look with particular care at any devices for holding the parts.

Action taken as a result of this analysis

The Team checked all the mechanical devices which had to do with positioning or holding the assemblies. They changed one of the fixtures and provided for magnetic alignment of certain parts. The result of this action is shown in Figure 65.

Statistical analysis of Figure 65

This chart shows the effect of the improvements in positioning and alignment. Much of the instability on the R chart has disappeared. The $\bar{X}$ chart also shows smaller fluctuations, and *these are now seen to be repeating themselves in more or less regular cycles*.

Cycles were present in the original pattern also (Figure 63) and again in the second pattern (Figure 64). But it would have been almost impossible to recognize them in the presence of larger, more erratic variables.

The causes for cycles are fairly easy to trace. (See page 162.) These were found to be associated with the *time allowed for cooling* before the assemblies were removed from a certain chuck.

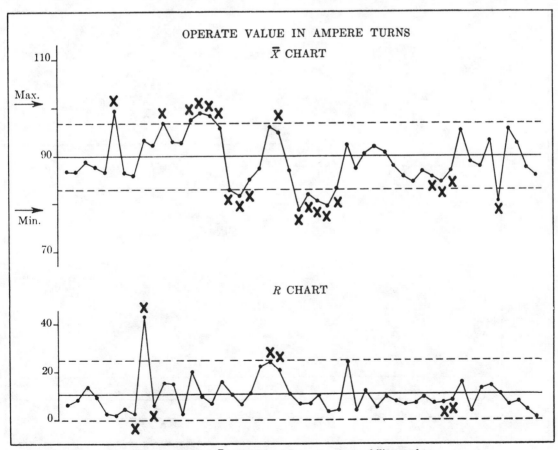

Fig. 65.   Third $\bar{X}$ and R chart in a process capability study.

Many things can be read from the control chart as the patterns become simpler. In this case, for example, the cycles on the $\bar{X}$ chart tend to "follow" those on the R chart. In a very large number of instances the fluctuations follow each other point to point. This indicates skewness in the distribution of product. (See page 156.)

In a manually controlled process, one of the common causes of skewness is the operator's tendency to short-cut an operation. (See page 57.) This is consistent with the above cause of cycles.

"Freaks" on the R chart or $\bar{X}$ chart can also be checked. These were found to occur immediately before or after rest periods, lunch periods etc. This again is consistent with the cycles.

Action taken as a result of this analysis

The engineer installed an automatic timer to prevent the operator from removing the switches too soon. The result of this is shown in Figure 66.

Statistical analysis of Figure 66

This chart shows the effect of installing the automatic timer. Only an occasional point is now out of control. This indicates that most of the large assignable causes have been eliminated. On the other hand, any cause which is still outstanding will show up very plainly, since it now occurs singly rather than in combination with others. In the present example several of the high points were found to be caused by tightness or "binding."

Action taken as a result of this analysis

The engineer relocated the individual motors on each head (from a position in front to one

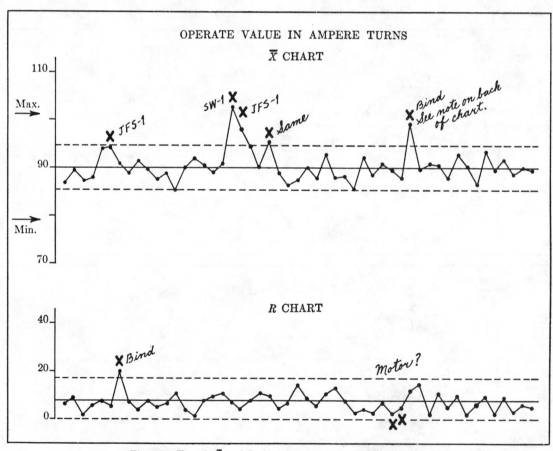

Fig. 66.   Fourth $\bar{X}$ and R chart in a process capability study.

at the back of the head). This alleviated a binding condition in the sliding portions of the head. The result of this action is shown in Figure 67.

Statistical analysis of Figure 67

This is the fifth chart in the study. It shows little change from the fourth. The level on the R chart has dropped slightly, showing the effect of relocating the motors. Ordinary production variables now come and go, leaving easy traces on the chart. The shop is able to find causes when out-of-control points appear.

These things indicate to the engineer that the process is probably approaching its capability.

Capability of this process

The capability of this process is calculated as follows:

$\bar{\bar{X}}$ = 90 amp. turns. Can be held consistently.

$\sigma = \bar{R}/d_2 = 6.5/2.326 = 2.8$ amp. turns
Spread of distribution = $\bar{\bar{X}} \pm 3\sigma = 90$ amp. turns ± 8.4.

Specification calls for 90 amp. turns ± 11.

The process is capable of meeting this specification easily and economically.

Notes on results

Original distribution (prior to process capability study) had spread of at least ± 25, and up to 40% of product might be outside of specification. Compare this with the capability calculated above.

Cost reduction was realized through (a) fewer defectives, (b) shop now making more assemblies per hour, and (c) reduced inspection.

Reliability of the product was also greatly improved.

Information on Head No. 6 was carried over

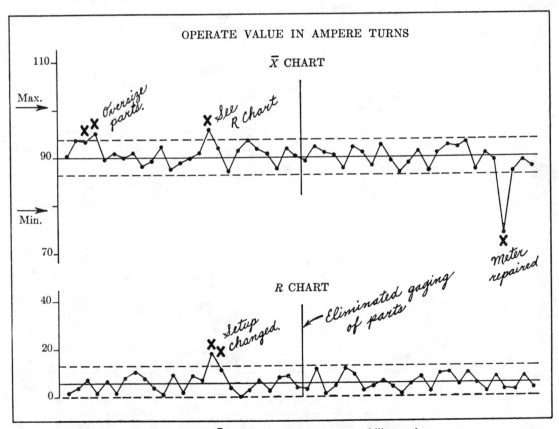

Fig. 67. Fifth $\bar{X}$ and R chart in a process capability study.

to the other heads. Similar shop charts provided for all heads.

Charts can now be used to evaluate the effect of process changes. For example, the shop wished to eliminate the 100% gaging of certain parts. When the chart showed no adverse effect (Figure 67) this change was made a permanent part of the process.

Conclusion

This was a relatively lengthy process capability study. In some cases the causes are simple enough to show up on the first chart.

A-7.2 Second process capability study: c-charts

The following is an example of the use of *c*-charts to study the work of operators. The original pattern is complex. (See Figure 68.) The control limits appear to be much too narrow for the fluctuations in the pattern, and the fluctuations are erratic. We recognize this at once as a pattern of "Instability." (See pages 166–167.)

As in all complex patterns, this must be simplified before it can be interpreted. (See page 55.) Simplification of this pattern would require the following steps:

(1) Complex patterns mean that the variable used as a basis for plotting the points in sequence is not the most significant variable. In Figure 68 the points are plotted by "operator." To simplify the pattern, select some other variable which is likely to be significant and show this on the bottom scale. For example, the defects might vary according to shift, or according to length of time on the job. Set up a scale which is arranged according to these possibilities.

(2) Re-plot the original data using the new bottom scale. Retain the same control limits that were used in the original chart. If the pattern tends to break up into simple shifts or trends, the variable used in the bottom scale is an important variable.

(3) If the pattern does not break up and become simpler, select some other variable for the bottom scale. If the pattern becomes simpler but you wish to simplify it still further, sub-divide the bottom scale according to some second significant variable.

Continue this simplification until the pattern consists of (a) simple shifts in level or (b) a simple trend. The following two charts are plotted from the data in Figure 68.

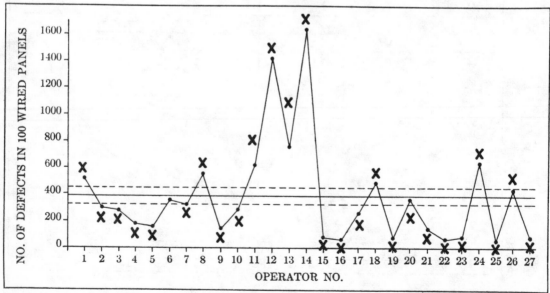

Fig. 68. Process capability study using a *c*-chart. Each point is the number of defects found in a group of 100 wired panels. Each point represents the work of a different operator.

72

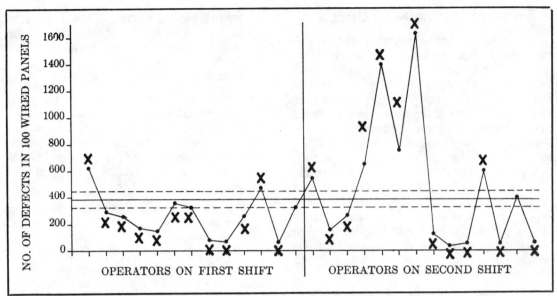

Fig. 69. First attempt to simplify complex pattern: data re-plotted according to shift.

The pattern remains complex. There is some other variable more important than shift.

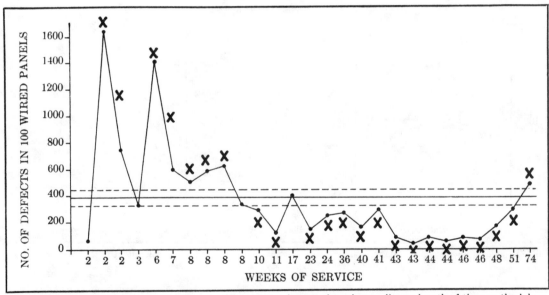

Fig. 70. Second attempt to simplify complex pattern: data re-plotted according to length of time on the job.

Now the pattern becomes simpler. Time on the job is an important clue to the cause of defects.

At this point it is possible to make tentative estimates of the capability of this process for operators with about 44 weeks of experience. The change in pattern for the operators with longest service (74 weeks) should also be investigated.

Note that, in Figure 70, the original control limits no longer appear to be unreasonably narrow. Complex patterns on a p-chart are simplified in much the same way as patterns on a c-chart.

73

A-8 PERFORMANCE STUDIES

"Performance studies" are temporary substitutes for process capability studies which are made by selecting data for a certain period, calculating control limits and determining whether the data show control. This permits the engineer to draw some of the conclusions he would draw from a formal capability study, and is sometimes useful until a more complete study can be carried out.

A series of performance studies over a period of time may be the practical equivalent of a process capability study, provided the necessary tracing and elimination of causes is carried out as the successive studies are made. Engineers frequently take advantage of this in setting up a program of shop control charts. The procedure is as follows:

(1) Obtain sufficient data to provide about twenty plotted points. Calculate control limits and determine whether the pattern is in control. Set up a temporary shop control chart in accordance with this information.

(2) Work with the shop to bring the chart into control or improve its pattern. When the pattern improves, select a period of data consisting of about twenty points and calculate a new set of control limits. Use this new set of limits as a second temporary shop control chart.

(3) Repeat this step from time to time in order to take advantage of progressive improvements.

Figure 71 shows how a performance study compares with a complete process capability study.

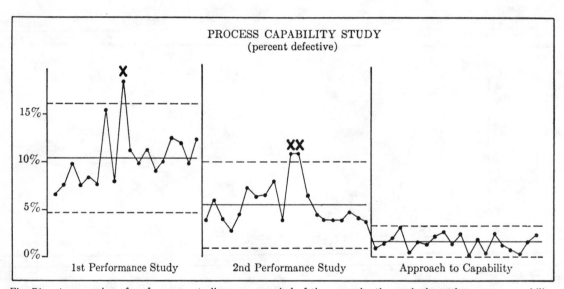

Fig. 71. A succession of performance studies over a period of time may be the equivalent of a process capability study.

PART B
Designed Experiments

This part of the Handbook covers some of the elementary principles involved in Design of Experiment. The engineer is presumed to be familiar with the making of process capability studies as covered in Part A. It is assumed that he has an acquaintance with the basic fact of variation, the fact that apparent differences in data may or may not be significant, and the need for applying statistical tests to data to discover whether a significant effect exists.

The following pages describe three types of designed experiment which engineers and shop people are called upon to handle more frequently than any others:

(1) Simple comparisons.
(2) Error of measurement.
(3) Four or five factor experiments to study main effects and interactions.

While reference will be made to statistical methods other than control charts, the principal emphasis in this section will be on the control chart analysis. Detailed information on other methods will be found in the references listed on pages 277–278.

This section will treat Design of Experiment as one of the steps in a process capability study. Particular emphasis will be placed on the tracing of causes in process capability studies which are hidden so deeply that they could not easily be discovered by other methods.

————————— ✦ —————————

B-1 PLACE OF DESIGNED EXPERIMENTS IN A PROCESS CAPABILITY STUDY

B-1.1 Review of the theory of a Process Capability Study

The theoretical basis for a Process Capability Study was described on pages 35–36. The total variation in the process is separated by control charts into natural and unnatural portions. The unnatural portion is then studied for the purpose of identifying and eventually removing its causes. When these causes are removed the process is reduced to its true capability. It is clear that the crucial step in such a study is the *tracing and identification of causes*. If the engineer is unable to complete this step, he will be unable to get results from the capability study.

In a majority of cases, when the engineer looks at the plotted patterns in such a study, he finds there are obvious reasons for the pattern changes. All he has to do is draw on his knowledge of the job to tell what is causing the unnatural variation. In other cases he learns to identify and interpret the 15 different types of control chart pattern which are explained on pages 161–180. An example of this is given on pages 66–71.

If this is not sufficient the engineer may resort to the so-called "breakdown" techniques. He separates the data according to different sources or production paths. He uses scatter diagrams or trend arrangements to pick up correlations. A discussion of this is given on pages 54–56.

Finally, if all ordinary resources fail and the causes remain so deeply hidden that he is unable to find them, he may use a Designed Experiment to break up the variation into component parts and find the answer. The information obtained in the previous steps of analysis is a vital factor in properly designing the experiment. Omission of the previous steps often leads to failure in using the experimental techniques.

B-1.2 Comparison between Design of Experiment and Process Capability Study

A Process Capability Study can be thought of as a one-factor designed experiment. The one broad factor being studied is time (or production path, source of material, or any other factor which forms the basis for the plotting of points in sequence.) A Designed Experiment on the other hand may include a number of factors which are being studied all at once. The data are arranged and rearranged for study according to these factors. The feature which makes it a "designed experiment" is the fact that the data have been collected in such a manner as to make these re-arrangements possible.

From another point of view, Design of Experiment is a much more limited technique than a Process Capability Study. Process Capability Studies are concerned with the effect of any and all factors on the characteristic being studied. The rule that capability studies should cover a number of different points in time arises from the fact that it is necessary to allow sufficient opportunity for unanticipated and unintentional changes (or variables) to appear in the process. In a Designed Experiment we try to eliminate all factors except the few which have been selected for study.

Design of Experiment is a powerful technique, one which is very useful when employed in the appropriate circumstances and when surrounded with appropriate precautions. It is, however, a technique to be used with reserve and never under any circumstances substituted for the broader Process Capability Study.

B-1.3 Meaning of "experiment" and "experimental techniques"

Every Process Capability Study can be thought of as an experiment. The principal object of the study is to learn what a given process is able to do. By changing one or more elements in the process and observing the effect on the charts, it is possible to use the Process Capability Study as an experimental technique.

Ordinarily, however, when we speak of "experiments" on a process we mean something which is, at the same time, more formal and more limited than a capability study, and more concerned with research or with delving into the unknown. We sometimes conduct experiments before we have even set up a process in order to discover what the best process would be. By using the formal experimental techniques it is possible to study the effect of several variables simultaneously and also to study any inter-relationships or interactions between them. The techniques are useful for deliberately disturbing causes which are in balance, for breaking apart the effects of hidden variables in a going process, and for studying the possible effects of variables during development and design.

B-1.4 Types of experiment

Experiments on industrial processes run all the way from informal and unofficial changes, introduced on a more or less hit-and-miss basis, to carefully planned formal experiments which may involve months of effort on the part of a group of people and which consist of an integrated set of plans using complicated mathematical and statistical designs. If we arrange some of these experiments in the order of increasing formality we might have a list something like this:

(1) Trial and error methods: introducing a change into the process and then watching to see whether an effect shows up in the results.

(2) Running "special lots," more or less carefully identified with respect to the conditions under which the special lots were made.

(3) Pilot runs, in which certain process elements are deliberately set up with the expectation of producing a desired effect. Results are then studied to see how close they come to what was anticipated.

(4) A planned experiment involving a simple comparison of two methods.

(5) A somewhat more complicated experiment involving more than one factor. For example, an error-of-measurement study where we wish to separate the effect of the measuring instrument from the effect of variables in the product.

(6) A more complicated experiment involving several factors, set up in such a way as to make it possible to study interactions between these factors.

(7) Experiments containing more factors and arranged in still more complicated designs.

(8) A comprehensive experimental plan embracing broad problems and including many experiments. Some "operations research" projects are of this type.

In using experiments of Types 1 and 2 (trial and error methods or running special lots) the informal conclusions reached should be checked on process control charts. Pilot runs (Type 3) should be analyzed with a standard process capability study. Experiments of Types 4, 5 and 6, which involve a limited number of factors and simple interactions, will be discussed in the present section.

This Handbook will not attempt to give information on the more complicated types of experiment such as No. 7 and No. 8.

B-1.5 Dangers and pitfalls in non-statistical experimentation

The ordinary type of experiment is subject to many pitfalls and dangers. Among the most serious of these are the following:

(1) Unless the experiment is carefully planned and the results studied statistically, conclusions may be wrong or misleading.

(2) Even if the answers are not actually wrong, non-statistical experiments are often inconclusive. This may cause the experimenters to fail to recognize a proper and productive course of action. It may also send them off experimenting along the wrong lines.

(3) In non-statistical experimenting, many of the observed effects tend to be mysterious or unexplainable. A given procedure may not yield the same results a second time. The results may be in conflict with job knowledge or shop experience.

(4) Time and effort may be wasted through studying the wrong variables or obtaining too much or too little data.

By planning his experiments statistically and analyzing them with control charts, the engineer is able to avoid many experimental problems and obtain solutions for others.

(1) He can save time and money.

(2) He can carry out the experiment with less interruption to the shop.

(3) He can drop out statistically the effects of unwanted variables.

(4) He can evaluate the results when experiments fail to repeat.

(5) It is easier to reconcile his new results with previous knowledge.

(6) He can plan scientifically how much data to collect and what variables to include.

B-2 EXPERIMENT I
(Comparison of Two Methods)

B-2.1 Background

The simplest experiment which an engineer is called upon to conduct, and also the most common type of experiment performed in industry, involves the comparison of two machines or two methods. The background for an experiment of this type might be as follows:

The engineer has designed Method 1 in the hope that it will be superior to Method 2. The variable in which he is interested is a certain electrical property. He wants the measurements to be high and as uniform as possible. The engineer sets up the two methods and obtains a certain amount of data for each.

By a casual comparison of the two sets of data he is unable to tell conclusively whether Method 1 is better than Method 2. He decides to test the data statistically in order to find which method is better.

His real purpose is to be able to make a further decision: that is, whether to change over to Method 1 or forget about Method 1 and try something else.

The measurements obtained for one such experiment were as follows:

Method 1		Method 2	
8.6	−9.3	−3.9	4.6
12.7	3.8	11.9	−3.0
8.2	7.0	2.9	1.5
10.0	−4.7	−4.0	2.3
5.8	−8.2	0.7	−2.0
5.5	0.8	−9.4	−8.4
12.5	−8.7	0.4	8.6
10.1	3.5	−7.6	5.6
8.7	1.7	−1.9	−6.9
9.1	−9.0	14.4	4.8

(The left side is labelled "Time" with a downward arrow.)

Fig. 72. Data for an experiment: comparison of two methods.

B-2.2 Methods of analysis

The analytical method recommended in this Handbook will be the control chart. However, the engineer should be acquainted, at least briefly, with various other techniques which are often used to analyze experimental data. Among these are:

(1) Observation of the data.

(2) Tests for normality.

(3) F-test (variance ratio test).

(4) Bartlett's test.

(5) Tests for constancy of the system of causes.

(6) t-Test.

(7) The analysis of variance.

B-2.3 Observation of the data

The following comparisons may be made without applying statistical tests:

(1) Visual comparison

Do the measurements under Method 2 appear to the eye to be different from Method 1?

(2) Average of the measurements

The measurements for Method 1 average +3.405. Those for Method 2 average +0.53. Should this be considered a significant difference in average?

(3) Observed range of measurements

The measurements for Method 1 range from −9.3 to +12.7. The measurements for Method 2 range from −9.4 to +14.4. Does this indicate a significant difference between methods?

(4) Simple observed proportions

There are 5 negative measurements in Method 1 and 9 in Method 2. Is this difference significant?

(5) Distributions

The following are the frequency distributions of the measurements in Method 1 and Method 2.

Measurements	Method 1	Method 2
+11.0 to +14.9	//	//
+ 7.0 to +10.9	THL ///	/
+ 3.0 to + 6.9	////	///
− 1.0 to + 2.9	//	THL
− 5.0 to − 1.1	/	THL
− 9.0 to − 5.1	//	///
−13.0 to − 9.1	/	/

Fig. 73. Distribution of measurements: Method 1 and Method 2.

The distributions may or may not be significantly different. We would hesitate to say, without a statistical test, that these two groups of measurements could not have come from the same population.

B-2.4 Analysis by formal statistical methods

The formal statistical methods require certain assumptions, the most common of which are the following:

(1) Normality of the distribution.

(2) Equivalence of the variances.

(3) Constancy of the cause system.

The following are some of the methods commonly used to check these assumptions:

(1) Tests for normality

For reasonably large amounts of data it is possible to use the "chi-square test" to test the normality of the observed data. (See Reference No. 13.) Another method would be to use normal probability paper on which the cumulative percentages could be plotted. (See Reference No. 13.) The present experiment does not include enough measurements to justify the use of either of these methods. In fact there is no satisfactory test for normality which involves so small an amount of data.

If either of the above tests were used in spite of the small quantity of data, they would not indicate any significant departure from normality, either in the case of Method 1 or Method 2, or both methods combined. Ordinarily, therefore, in a formal statistical analysis, we would assume that the data could be treated as having come from a normal population.

(2) F-test

This is a test for equivalence of the variances (also known as the variance ratio test). This test is used when there are only two variances to be compared. The calculations are shown in Figure 74.

To apply this test, look up the value of F for degrees of freedom 19 and 19 in a Variance Ratio Table (see Reference No. 5). The value of 1.29 is definitely not significant. Consequently, the variances may be considered equal.

(3) Bartlett's test

This is an alternative test for equivalence of the variances. It can be used for any number of variances. The calculations are given in Figure 75.

To apply this test, look up the value of χ^2 for $(k - 1)$ degrees of freedom in a Chi-square Table (see Reference No. 5). The value of .296 is definitely not significant. Consequently, the variances can be considered equal. This agrees with the variance ratio or F-test.

(4) Testing the assumption of constancy of the cause systems

There is no convenient way of doing this except by using control charts. In a classical analysis, we ordinarily assume that the cause systems did not change provided we feel that we have kept all conditions constant while collecting the data for Method 1 and Method 2.

	F-Test			
	Method 1		*Method 2*	
ΣX	68.1		10.6	
$[\Sigma X]^2$	4637.61		112.36	
Divided by 20 to obtain correction factor	231.88		5.62	
ΣX^2	73.96	86.49	15.21	21.16
	161.29	14.44	141.61	9.00
	67.24	49.00	8.41	2.25
	100.00	22.09	16.0	5.29
	33.64	67.24	.49	4.00
	30.25	.64	88.36	70.56
	156.25	75.69	.16	73.96
	102.01	12.25	57.76	31.36
	75.69	2.89	3.61	47.61
	82.81	81.00	207.36	23.04
	883.14	411.73	538.97	288.23
		883.14		538.97
		1294.87		827.20
Subtract correction factor		231.88		5.62
$\Sigma(X - \bar{X})^2$		1062.99		821.58
		$\div$ 19		$\div$ 19
σ^2		55.94		43.24
F		$\dfrac{55.94}{43.24} = 1.29$ at df (19, 19)		

Fig. 74. F-test for equivalence of the variances.

Bartlett's Test

Method	$\Sigma(X)$	$\Sigma(X^2)$	$(\Sigma X)^2$	$(\Sigma X)^2 \div n$	$\Sigma(X - \bar{X})^2$	σ_i^2	$\log_e(\sigma_i^2)$
1	68.1	1294.87	4637.61	231.88	1062.99	55.94	4.025
2	10.6	827.20	112.36	5.62	821.58	43.24	3.767
						99.18	7.792

Mean variance $= S^2 = 49.590$

$\log_e(S^2) = 3.904$

$k = 2$ (number of methods)

$df = 19$

$$B = k(df)\log_e S^2 - (df)\,\Sigma\,(\log_e \sigma_i^2)$$

$$= 2(19)(3.904) - 19(7.792) = 148.352 - 148.048 = .304$$

$$C = 1 + \frac{k+1}{3k(df)} = 1 + \frac{3}{114} = \frac{117}{114} = 1.026$$

$$\frac{B}{C} = .296$$

Note: $\frac{B}{C} = \chi^2$

Fig. 75. Bartlett's test for equivalence of the variances.

(5) Conclusions reached by the foregoing methods

We conclude from the foregoing tests that the data may be treated as having come from a normal population, that the variances of the two methods may be considered equal and that the two cause systems may be considered constant. Under these assumptions, it is possible to test for a significant difference between the averages by using either a *t*-test or the analysis of variance.

(6) t-Test

The calculations for one form of *t*-test are shown in Figure 76.

Look up the value of "*t*" for 38 degrees of freedom in a "*t*" Table (see Reference No. 5). The value of 1.32 is definitely not significant. Consequently, the averages can be considered equal.

(7) Analysis of variance

This is an alternative test which can be used for any number of averages. It depends on finding the variance of the entire set of numbers, subtracting the variance due to the observed difference between averages, and using the remaining variance (or residual) to test

"*t*"-Test

Method 1

$$\bar{X}_1 = \frac{\Sigma X}{n} = \frac{68.1}{20} = 3.4$$

$$\sigma_1 = \sqrt{\frac{\Sigma X^2}{n} - \bar{X}^2} = \sqrt{\frac{1294.6}{20} - 11.6}$$

$$\sigma_1 = \sqrt{53.1} = 7.3$$

Method 2

$$\bar{X}_2 = \frac{\Sigma X}{n} = \frac{10.6}{20} = .53$$

$$\sigma_2 = \sqrt{\frac{\Sigma X^2}{n} - \bar{X}^2} = \sqrt{\frac{827.4}{20} - .28}$$

$$\sigma_2 = \sqrt{41.0} = 6.4$$

Let σ_D be the standard deviation of the difference between averages.

$$\sigma_D = \sqrt{\frac{(\sigma_1)^2}{n1} + \frac{(\sigma_2)^2}{n2}} = \sqrt{\frac{(7.3)^2}{20} + \frac{(6.4)^2}{20}} = \sqrt{2.65 + 2.05} = 2.17$$

$$t = \frac{\bar{X}_1 - \bar{X}_2}{\sigma_D} = \frac{3.40 - .53}{2.17} = \frac{2.87}{2.17} = 1.32$$

Fig. 76. *t*-Test for significant difference between averages.

whether the observed difference between averages is significant.

This method can be extended to test a number of variables and interactions in a much more complicated experiment. (See pages 93–97.) The calculations for the present data are shown in Figure 77.

To apply this test, look up the value of F for degrees of freedom 1 and 38 in a Variance Ratio Table (see Reference No. 5). The value of 1.67

is definitely not significant. Consequently, the averages can be considered equal. This agrees with the t-test.

Practical result of using the above methods

Since none of the above tests have shown a significant difference between methods, the engineer would have to conclude that Method 1 is no different and therefore is no better than Method 2.

$n = 40$
T (grand total) $= 78.7$ Analysis of Variance $C = \dfrac{T^2}{n} = 154.842$

Source	No. of ind. (i)	No. of Totals	Totals to be Squared						Grand Total
Individuals	1	40	8.6	12.7	8.2	10.0	5.8	5.5	
			12.5	10.1	8.7	9.1	−9.3	3.8	
			7.0	−4.7	8.2	0.8	−8.7	3.5	
			1.7	−9.0	−3.9	11.9	2.9	−4.0	
			0.7	−9.4	0.4	−7.6	−1.9	14.4	
			4.6	−3.0	1.5	2.3	−2.0	−8.4	
			8.6	5.6	−6.9	4.8			78.7
Methods	20	2	68.1	10.6					78.7
Residual	—	—	—	—	—	—	—	—	—

Source	Σ Squares	$\div i$	Corrected Σ Squares*	df	Mean Square
Individuals	2122.07	2122.070	1967.228	39	
Methods	4749.97	237.498	82.656	1	82.656
Residual	—	—	1884.572	38	49.594
			*Obtained by subtracting C		
	$F = \dfrac{82.656}{49.594} = 1.67$ at (1,38) degrees of freedom				

Fig. 77. Analysis of variance to test for a significant difference between averages.

B-2.5 Control chart analysis

The control chart has certain advantages over other methods of analysis in the treatment of experimental data.

(1) It takes account of the order in which the measurements were made. In this it differs from the chi-square test, the F-test and Bartlett's test.

(2) It does not require assumptions of normality, equivalence of the variances or constancy of the cause systems. In this it differs from the t-test and the analysis of variance. The control chart sets up *hypotheses* of normality, equivalence and constancy, but the data in the experiment are able to make us reject any of these hypotheses.

The control chart will therefore, under certain circumstances, give different results from other methods.

For a control chart analysis of the foregoing

Method 1		8.6	8.2	5.8	12.5	8.7	−9.3	7.0	−8.2	−8.7	1.7
		12.7	10.0	5.5	10.1	9.1	3.8	−4.7	0.8	3.5	−9.0
	$\bar{X}$	10.65	9.10	5.65	11.3	8.90	−2.75	1.15	−3.70	−2.60	−3.65
	R	4.1	1.8	.3	2.4	.4	13.1	11.7	9.0	12.2	10.7
Method 2		−3.9	2.9	0.7	0.4	−1.9	4.6	1.5	−2.0	8.6	−6.9
		11.9	−4.0	−9.4	−7.6	14.4	−3.0	2.3	−8.4	5.6	4.8
	$\bar{X}$	4.00	− .55	−4.35	−3.60	6.25	.80	1.90	−5.20	7.10	−1.05
	R	15.8	6.9	10.1	8.0	16.3	7.6	.8	6.4	3.0	11.7

Fig. 78. Calculations for an $\bar{X}$ and R chart. Method 1 and Method 2.

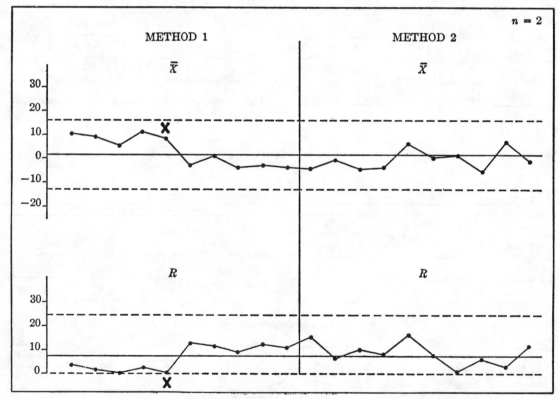

Fig. 79. Control chart plotted for Method 1 and Method 2.

data, take the measurements in the order in which they were obtained. Since the quantity of data is limited, break it up into samples of two. In calculating control limits use the ordinary control chart factors which are given on page 12.

Plot both sets of data against the same set of control limits, as shown in Figure 79. In marking x's on the R chart, use the tests for samples of two which are given on page 182.

The chart is interpreted like any other control chart.

B-2.6 Conclusions reached from studying the control chart

In Method 1, the $\bar{X}$ chart and the R chart are both out of control. We therefore arrive at the following statistical conclusions from this chart:

(1) Since Method 1 shows a definite shift in both average and spread, its data cannot be treated as having come from a normal population.

(2) Since the variability in Method 1 is out of control, its variance cannot be treated as equal to that of Method 2.

(3) The data for Method 1 did not come from a constant system of causes.

(4) Method 1 will evidently be superior to Method 2 *provided we maintain the conditions which existed during the earlier portion of the experiment.*

Note that, in this experiment, the control chart contradicts all the assumptions made in other methods.

On the practical side, it is evident that the early data in Method 1 must have come from a very desirable distribution. Its average was significantly higher than the general average of the data and its spread was extremely narrow. If the engineer is able to discover the variable which entered the process later and disturbed the results, it is clear that Method 1 will be much more uniform than Method 2 and will also give higher readings.

There is no similar indication of possible improvement in the case of Method 2.

B-2.7 Practical results from studying the control chart

The engineer investigated what had happened in Method 1. He found there was trouble with a small locating device which had jammed. This accounted for the drop in average and the immediate increase in spread. By making a modification which would virtually eliminate the possibility of jamming, the engineer was able to get consistently superior results from Method 1.

When experimental data are plotted on control charts, the results often reach farther than the experiment itself. In the above case the engineer had found a mechanical condition which was able to affect an electrical measurement. This caused him to investigate various other conditions having to do with the mechanical location and feeding of the parts. Eventually, by studying successive sets of data with control charts, he was able to get the average electrical measurement up to almost 16 and still retain the very uniform spread which had been indicated originally by his R chart.

B-2.8 Comparison between the control chart and other statistical methods

In spite of the fact that different conclusions were reached in this experiment, there is no theoretical conflict between the control chart and other sound statistical methods. If these had been reliable averages for Method 1 and Method 2 ($\bar{X}$ charts in control) and if the variability had been constant and equal (R charts in control), the control chart and the other methods would have agreed very closely.

In general, the control chart will agree with an F-test or Bartlett's test provided the patterns on the $\bar{X}$ chart and R chart would not show any unnaturalness if the individual factors were plotted separately. It will agree with a "t" test or analysis of variance if, in addition to the conditions cited above, none of the R patterns would show any evidence of unnaturalness when plotted on the same R chart. However, if a control chart pattern shows instability, freaks, stratification, etc., the control chart analysis is likely to disagree with other methods. In such cases, the information given by the control chart will cause us to modify any conclusions arrived at by other methods.

For this reason it will be desirable to use control charts in analyzing the experiments described in this Handbook.

B-3 EXPERIMENT II
(Error of Measurement)

B-3.1 Background

This is a somewhat more complicated experiment than Experiment I. It involves two different factors whose effects are to be separated and studied. The background for this experiment is as follows:

> Two instruments are available for measuring a certain product. Instrument 1 is believed to be a finer piece of equipment than Instrument 2. However, the engineer and others have measured the product with both instruments and attempted to compare them. It does not appear from the initial results that either instrument is superior. We wish to test the two instruments statistically to determine which is better for measuring this product.

To solve this problem it is necessary to "design an experiment" which will separate the error of measurement from the variations in the product. This is different from Experiment I where we were concerned only with variations in the product.

B-3.2 Original data

The following example shows why a poorly designed experiment may fail to give proper conclusions. Originally, a number of units of product were measured on Instrument 1. The same units were then re-measured in the same order on Instrument 2. All measurements were made by the same experienced operator. The measurements are given in Figure 80.

The engineer took these in groups of 5, preserving the order in which the measurements had been taken. The first sample consisted of 20, 24, 19, 21 and 25. The other samples followed in order. He labeled the chart Instrument 1 and Instrument 2. See Figure 81.

On studying this chart he was disappointed

to find that there was apparently no difference between the instruments. As a matter of fact, note that there is remarkable correspondence between the two halves of the chart. The pattern of Instrument 1 is repeated very closely under Instrument 2.

Interpretation of this chart

A little consideration will show that the above chart is not really comparing instruments. This chart shows certain pieces of product measured on Instrument 1 (first half of the chart) and then the same pieces of product measured on Instrument 2 (second half of the chart). The similarity between the two halves of the chart tells us that we had the same pieces of product measured in the same order in both cases; also that the effect of the measuring instrument, whatever it may have been, was not large enough to hide the variations that actually existed in the product. This is a chart on product rather than a chart on instruments. There is nothing in the "design" or planning of this experiment that makes it possible to compare instruments or to study the measurement error.

B-3.3 Design for an error of measurement study

The design of an experiment for this type of study is very simple. All that is necessary is to

	Instrument 1					Instrument 2				
	20	24	28	26	18	21	28	27	28	23
	24	23	28	26	21	26	27	32	27	20
Time	19	22	21	18	24	23	20	23	19	24
	21	15	29	16	24	19	15	30	14	24
↓	25	22	27	25	25	22	13	26	23	25
	18	29	24	24	21	17	24	23	19	25
	19	26	22	20	18	23	24	19	20	15
	27	32	24	20	25	31	33	22	23	24
	21	20	23	23	28	24	22	25	23	32
	25	24	17	22	20	22	25	18	22	19

Fig. 80. Data for an experiment: error of measurement study.

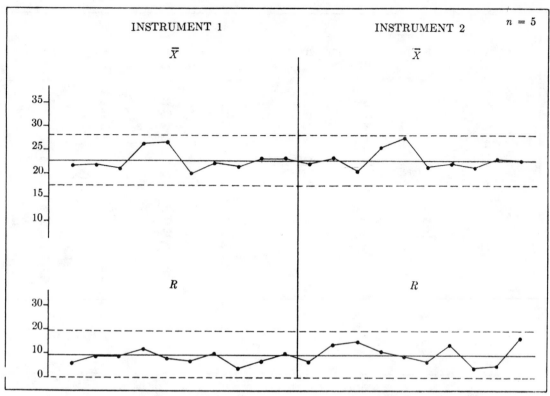

Fig. 81. Does this chart show a comparison of Instrument 1 and Instrument 2?

measure the same parts again, as follows:

Retain the 50 measurements already recorded under Instrument 1. This time however, they should be identified as Measurement A.

Then take the same parts and measure them a second time in the same order on the same instrument. Record the new set of measurements as Measurement B.

This procedure is repeated for the second instrument in the same way.

The two sets of measurements must be taken under the "same essential conditions." (See pages 89–90.)

The measurements obtained for the two instruments are shown in Figure 82.

This is now a "designed experiment" because it is possible to plot the data in more than one way. If we form samples as we did in Figure 81, by grouping the data vertically, we will obtain, as before, a chart on product. How-

ever, it is now possible to form samples by taking the measurements horizontally instead of vertically, so that Measurement A and Measurement B are included in one group. We can use these horizontal groups to plot an ordinary $\bar{X}$ and R chart for samples of two. This will make it possible to compare instruments, and also to obtain some interesting information about the suitability of the instruments for measuring this type of product.

B-3.4 Chart for the error of measurement study

Figure 83 on page 86 shows the $\bar{X}$ and R values for horizontal samples of two. Plotting these values on a control chart (Instrument 1 only), we obtain Figure 84.

Note that the $\bar{X}$ chart is out of control throughout the data. This type of chart requires a special interpretation which is very different from the interpretation given to the ordinary shop chart or the ordinary process capability study.

Instrument 1				Instrument 2			
A	B	A	B	A	B	A	B
20	21	24	23	21	18	23	23
24	24	22	21	26	29	19	22
19	18	24	25	23	22	22	23
21	20	23	23	19	21	25	23
25	25	17	18	22	25	18	15
18	20	26	26	17	19	28	16
19	20	26	25	23	23	27	25
27	27	18	15	31	21	19	18
21	20	16	16	24	23	14	13
25	25	25	24	22	27	23	23
24	26	24	24	28	19	19	26
23	22	20	21	27	23	20	22
22	21	20	23	20	21	23	24
15	16	23	25	15	20	23	23
22	22	22	21	13	25	22	18
29	28	18	18	24	37	23	22
26	27	21	20	24	25	20	24
32	32	24	25	33	31	24	25
20	20	24	24	22	19	24	26
24	22	25	27	25	26	25	20
28	27	21	20	27	29	25	13
28	29	18	17	32	31	15	21
21	21	25	25	23	21	24	23
29	30	28	29	30	33	32	29
27	27	20	20	26	24	19	24

Fig. 82.   Simple design for an error of measurement study: data on instruments.

Instrument 1				Instrument 2			
$\bar{X}$	R	$\bar{X}$	R	$\bar{X}$	R	$\bar{X}$	R
20.5	1	23.5	1	20.5	3	23.0	0
24.0	0	21.5	1	27.5	3	20.5	3
18.5	1	24.5	1	22.5	1	22.5	1
20.5	1	23.0	0	20.0	2	24.0	2
25.0	0	17.5	1	23.5	3	16.5	3
19.0	2	26.0	0	18.0	2	22.0	12
19.5	1	25.5	1	23.0	0	26.0	2
27.0	0	16.5	3	26.0	10	18.5	1
20.5	1	16.0	0	23.5	1	13.5	1
25.0	0	24.5	1	24.5	5	23.0	0
25.0	2	24.0	0	23.5	9	22.5	7
22.5	1	20.5	1	25.0	4	21.0	2
21.5	1	21.5	3	20.5	1	23.5	1
15.5	1	24.0	2	17.5	5	23.0	0
22.0	0	21.5	1	19.0	12	20.0	4
28.5	1	18.0	0	30.5	13	22.5	1
26.5	1	20.5	1	24.5	1	22.0	4
32.0	0	24.5	1	32.0	2	24.5	1
20.0	0	24.0	0	20.5	3	25.0	2
23.0	2	26.0	2	25.5	1	22.5	5
27.5	1	20.5	1	28.0	2	19.0	12
28.5	1	17.5	1	31.5	1	18.0	6
21.0	0	25.0	0	22.0	2	23.5	1
29.5	1	28.5	1	31.5	3	30.5	3
27.0	0	20.0	0	25.0	2	21.5	5

Fig. 83. $\bar{X}$ and R calculations: error of measurement study.

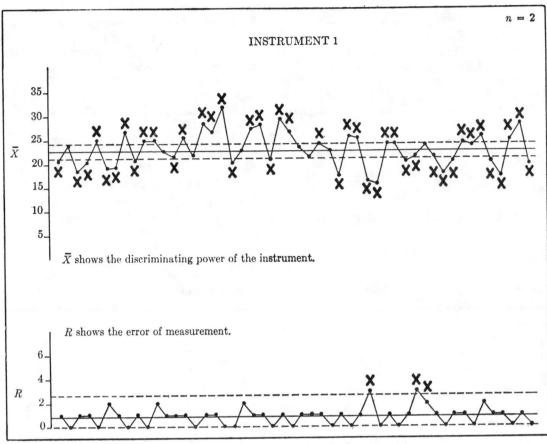

Fig. 84. Error of measurement chart for Instrument 1.

B-3.5 Interpretation of the error of measurement chart

The R chart shows, directly, the magnitude of the *error of measurement*. This is because the R values represent differences between successive measurements made by the same instrument on the same piece of product. When the R chart shows instability, as this one does in the latter portion, it means that the operator of the instrument is having difficulty in taking the measurements consistently. This in itself may be one of the factors which the engineer will wish to consider in deciding which instrument to use for a given purpose. In general, a good instrument should have a low centerline on the R chart and the indications of instability should be as few as possible.

The $\bar{X}$ chart, on the other hand, shows the *discriminating power* of the instrument. The plotted points represent different pieces of product. The control limits, being derived from the error of measurement chart, represent the inability of the instrument to tell one piece from another—that is, the area over which this instrument is not capable of discriminating. If the $\bar{X}$ points stayed in control, it would mean that the measuring instrument could see no difference between the pieces of product.

A good measuring instrument, suitable for measuring this product, should have such narrow control limits that all or most of the $\bar{X}$ points will be thrown out of control. Note that this is quite different from the ordinary control chart. *In an error of measurement study we want the $\bar{X}$ points to go out of control.*

The chart shown above should be interpreted as follows:

Instrument 1 is capable of reproducing its results very closely and can readily distinguish between units of product. It is suitable to use for the purpose being considered. The instrument is also capable of being used with consistent results. Its present good performance can even be improved somewhat as the operator using the instrument learns how to improve his technique and eliminates the indications of instability on the R chart.

B-3.6 Calculation of measurement error

To calculate the actual magnitude of the measurement error proceed as follows:

$$\bar{R} \text{ from Fig. 84} = \text{approx. 0.8 unit}$$

$$\sigma' = \frac{\bar{R}}{d_2} = \frac{0.8}{1.128} = \text{approx. 0.7 unit}$$

where d_2 is the standard control chart factor for samples of 2. See page 131.

The distribution of measurement errors is known to be approximately normal. Consequently, the spread of these errors (assuming that the R chart can be brought into control) will be approximately $\pm 3\ \sigma'$. Individual measurements can be expected to vary as much as ± 2.1 units (on repeated measurements) in extreme cases.

About two-thirds of the measurements will vary less than ± 0.7 unit ($\pm 1\ \sigma'$).

B-3.7 Comparing instruments

Taking the $\bar{X}$ and R values in the same way for Instrument 2, we obtain Figure 85. Again the R chart shows, directly, the error of measurement. We see at a glance that this is much higher than in the case of Instrument 1. Not only is it at least four times as large, but there are many more indications of instability. The operator using this instrument will have

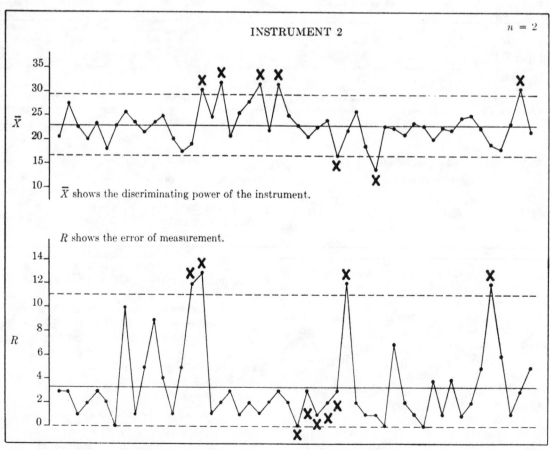

Fig. 85. Error of measurement chart for Instrument 2.

much more trouble reproducing his results (unless, of course, the operator can be trained to use the instrument much more consistently than he is doing now).

Again the $\bar{X}$ chart shows the discriminating power of the instrument. This time, however, because of the high value of $\bar{R}$, the control limits on the $\bar{X}$ chart are very wide. This means that the inaccuracies of measurement are large enough to swallow up most of the variations from unit to unit in the product. Only the very largest units or the very smallest can be reliably distinguished from the others.

It is not possible to calculate the actual magnitude of the measurement error of Instrument 2, because the R chart is out of control. A rough estimate, however, would be that σ' must be close to 3. ($\bar{R}/d_2 = 3.4/1.128 =$ approx. 3.) Since individual errors are likely to spread about $\pm 3\sigma'$, the measurements made by this instrument may vary in extreme cases as much as ± 9 units. Two-thirds or more of the measurements can be expected to vary up to ± 3 units.

B-3.8 Comparing the error of measurement with the variability of the product

Consider the case of Instrument 1, where the error of measurement was essentially in control. From the first half of the chart on product, which was shown on page 85, we observe that $\bar{R}$ for the product as measured was 8.2 units. The total variability, therefore (including both product variability and measurement variability), can be expressed in terms of σ' as follows:

$$\sigma'_{total} = \frac{\bar{R}}{d_2} = \frac{8.2}{2.326} = \text{approx. 3.5 units}$$

Note that, since the chart in question was based on samples of 5, we must use the d_2 factor for samples of 5 rather than for samples of 2.

We know that the measurement variability of Instrument 1 (in terms of σ') is about 0.7 unit. See paragraph B-3.6. By the law of the addition of standard deviations or variances, as given on page 123, we have:

(Total Variability)^2 = (Product Variability)^2
$\qquad$ + (Measurement Variability)^2

This can be solved to find the product variability, x.

$$
\begin{aligned}
(3.5)^2 &= (x)^2 + (.7)^2 \\
12.2 &= (x)^2 + .5 \\
(x)^2 &= 11.7 \\
x &= 3.4 \text{ units}
\end{aligned}
$$

Therefore, the standard deviation of the product is approximately 3.4 where the standard deviation of Instrument 1 is approximately 0.7. The standard deviation of the instrument is about $^1/_5$ as great as the standard deviation of the product.

The measurement error can also be expressed as "percentage of the total variance" as follows:

$$\frac{(\text{Measurement variability})^2}{(\text{Total variability})^2} = \frac{(.7)^2}{(3.5)^2} =$$

0.040, or 4% of the total variance.

This is sometimes spoken of as finding the "components of variance."

In all cases involving error of measurement, the observed distribution of product is the statistical sum of the real distribution of product, whatever that may be, and the distribution of measurement error. If the measurements are precise, the distribution of measurement errors will be narrow. If the measurements are accurate, the center of the distribution of measurement errors will be zero.

The above discussion covers the effect of measurement precision on the observed *variability*. It does not cover the effect of measurement accuracy on the observed distribution *center*. Measurement accuracy is discussed on pages 90–91.

B-3.9 Meaning of "measurement error." Positional variability, drift, etc. vs. the error of actual measurement

Before leaving Experiment II the engineer should note that the "measurement error" referred to above is really a combination of the instrument error itself and the error of the operator using the instrument. It would be possible to carry the experiment one step further by designing it in such a way as to separate the operator error from the instrument error. The experiment would then become a "three-factor" experiment—product, instrument and operator.

In the same way, there may be more than one source of variability in the product itself. For example, if the parts are tapered, we will obtain a different measurement from place to place on the same part, and this will be in addition to the normal variability from one part to another. If the parts are out of round, there will be a similar difference from place to place, depending on the position or point where the measurement is taken. Variability from position to position on the same piece is called "positional variability." We can eliminate it from the experiment by taking the repeat measurements in exactly the original place.

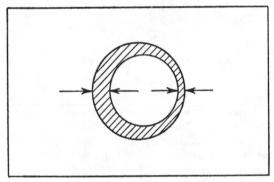

Fig. 86. Positional variability.

If we wish to study the amount of taper, out-of-round etc., as well as the error of measurement, we should take repeat measurements at *both* ends or *both* sides, and compare the two positions just as we would compare two methods or machines.

If the product is one which can drift or change from one measurement to the next (as in certain electrical properties) or if the mere act of measurement may change it (for example, by causing distortion), it will not be possible to obtain repeat measurements under the "same essential conditions." In that case it is necessary to consider the drift or distortion as if it were an additional variable—that is, we set up a three, four or five factor experiment, as explained on pages 91–101, instead of treating it as a simple Error of Measurement study.

Positional variability, or variability due to drift, distortion etc., may increase either the apparent variability of the product or the apparent error of measurement.

B-3.10 Amount of data required for the experiment

In the preceding experiment the engineer measured 50 parts. It is a general rule that the more measurements are available the more information we will be able to get from the experiment. On the other hand, the major conclusions from the experiment are likely to show up with only a moderate amount of data.

It is also a rule that the amount of data required for the experiment is governed by the amount needed to obtain the necessary precision in the estimate of variability.

If a good estimate of variability is already available before the experiment is started (for example, from process capability studies), or if there is reason to believe that the variability is not different in different parts of the experiment, then only a small amount of data will be needed. Where the variability is not known in advance, and especially where there is a possibility that there may be more variability in certain portions of the experiment, considerably more data will be needed.

B-3.11 Measurement accuracy

Experiment II was concerned with precision of measurement rather than with measurement accuracy. Precision refers to the reproducibility of the measurements: that is, the ability of the measurer or the measuring instrument to repeat or duplicate readings. Accuracy on the other hand refers to the absolute correctness of the measurements as compared with some known standard. The accuracy of measurement can be checked in either of two ways.

(1) Obtain a standard whose true value is known or has been fixed by authority: for example, a standard Jo-block, a line of standard length or width etched in glass, an oscillator of known frequency, etc. Make a series of measurements on this standard using the measurement technique which is to be studied. Plot an $\bar{X}$ and R chart. As in Experiment II the R chart will show the error or precision of measurement. However, since all measurements have been obtained on the same standard, the $\bar{X}$ chart should stay in control. The accuracy of measurement is checked by comparing the centerline on the

$\bar{X}$ chart with the known true value of the standard.

(2) If no standard of the above type is available it is necessary to have a method of measurement which is itself considered to be a standard. For example, a specific test set, master gage or micrometer may constitute the standard method of measurement. Check one or more pieces of product repeatedly using the standard method and plot an $\bar{X}$ and R chart. Check the same unit or units of product repeatedly using the method which is to be studied, and plot a similar $\bar{X}$ and R chart. The accuracy of the measurements is determined by comparing the centerlines on the two $\bar{X}$ charts.

The $\bar{X}$ chart for any one piece of product should stay in control.

In either of the above two methods, if lack of control is indicated on the R chart or $\bar{X}$ chart, check for assignable causes and eliminate them before attempting to determine the measurement accuracy. In particular, observe the basic rule which applies to all $\bar{X}$ and R charts: Do not attempt to draw conclusions from an $\bar{X}$ chart when the R chart is out of control.

B-3.12 Other statistical methods

Error of measurement data can be analyzed by other statistical methods, including the "sum of squares" method of analysis of variance. The control chart, however, has the usual advantages of

(a) Simplicity.
(b) The R chart.
(c) A plotted pattern.

B-4 EXPERIMENT III
(Four Factor Experiment)

B-4.1 Background

This is a more complicated experiment than either Experiment I or Experiment II. It involves four different factors whose effects are to be separated and studied. The background for this experiment is as follows:

A certain shop is manufacturing a product which has a relatively low yield. There already are charts in the shop, and a number of process capability studies have been made. These studies indicate that one reason for low yields is the fact that a certain parameter tends to run at too low an average. If a suitable way to raise the average could be found, this would increase the yield.

Raising the average, however, is not a simple problem. Many things have been tried by the shop and engineers with no consistently good effects. There are many conflicting opinions on what should be done to produce the desired results. Among these conflicting ideas are the following:

The design engineers reported good results some time ago by using a special cleaning procedure. The Western Electric engineers have not been able to get similarly good results. On the other hand, since the trouble seems to be worse recently, they feel that it may be related to the thickness of plating on certain parts. (The plating was made thinner a short time ago in connection with certain other design changes.)

It is also possible that the trouble may be due to Western's method of activation, since this is different from the method used during laboratory development. The shop has added further confusion to the picture by claiming that it is possible to improve the yields by lengthening the drying period at a certain stage in the process. The engineers see no reason to believe that drying should be a factor, and at least one engineering experiment has indicated that longer drying may make matters worse.

In short, the results so far have been inconclusive and in some cases contradictory. A number of factors seem to be involved here, which may or may not be important individually and which may or may not be interrelated with each other.

This situation calls for a special kind of Designed Experiment, which will make it possible to study several variables simultaneously.

B-4.2 Old style experiment (without statistical design)

Originally, the engineers on this job made no attempt to design the experiment statistically. They tried to find answers to these problems by running "special lots" as follows:

(1) They held all conditions constant except the method of cleaning. They processed a certain number of units with special cleaning and a similar number with ordinary cleaning. They then measured the parameter in question and compared the results.

They found that results were slightly in favor of special cleaning.

(2) Having finished the first experiment, they ran a second "special lot." They held all conditions constant except the method of activation. They processed a certain number of units with the laboratory method and a similar number with the Western Electric method. They then measured the parameter in question and compared the findings.

They found that the Western Electric method gave slightly better results.

(3) In the same way, they held all conditions constant except the plating thickness and ran an experiment to determine the effect of this factor.

They found that thicker plating appeared to give better results.

(4) Finally, they held all conditions constant except the drying period and found that there seemed to be very little difference between the short and long drying.

(5) On the basis of the above results, they decided to use in the process:

(a) Special cleaning.
(b) The Western Electric method of activation.
(c) Thick plating.
(d) Short drying.

To arrive at these conclusions, the engineers had to process a large number of pieces of product in each of four separate experiments. This involved the wasting of many experimental pieces as well as the expenditure of large amounts of effort and time. Furthermore, when they introduced the above combination of variables into the process, they did not obtain the anticipated good results. The process continued to run with a low yield and it became obvious that the experiment had not produced the correct answers.

The engineers then designed an experiment statistically with the results shown below.

B-4.3 Designed experiment

By proper planning or design of this experiment it was possible to study all four of the above variables in a single experiment involving only 16 pieces of product. First the variables were labeled A1, A2, B1, B2 and so forth as shown in Figure 87. This is a "balanced block design" in the form of a 4 x 4 square. The design is arranged in such a way that half of the squares are reserved for condition A1 and the other half for A2 (in this example, the left and right halves of the design respectively). At the same time, using some other method of division, half of the squares are reserved for B1 and half for B2 (in this example, the first and

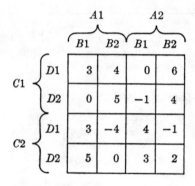

MEASUREMENTS ON A CERTAIN
PARAMETER OF A CERTAIN PRODUCT

		A1		A2	
		B1	B2	B1	B2
C1	D1	3	4	0	6
	D2	0	5	−1	4
C2	D1	3	−4	4	−1
	D2	5	0	3	2

A1—Original plating
A2—Thin plating
B1—Laboratory activation
B2—Western Electric activation
C1—Regular cleaning
C2—Special cleaning
D1—Short drying period
D2—Long drying period

Since we wish to raise the value of the measured parameter, we will consider effects good if they tend to result in higher values.

Fig. 87.   Simple example of a Designed Experiment.

third columns for B1, the second and fourth for B2). By dividing the space horizontally instead of vertically, it is possible to reserve half of the squares for C1 and C2 respectively, and similarly for D1 and D2. This results in a completely balanced statistical design with eight squares reserved for each of the eight conditions to be studied. This completely balanced design is called a "factorial design."

With this design each variable can be studied separately if we wish, just as if the other variables were not present. At the same time, it is possible to study the variables in combination. For example, the special cleaning may have a certain effect when the plating is thin, and it may have a totally different effect when combined with thicker plating. Effects like this, which are due to a combination of variables, are called "interactions."

In the above design, it is possible to study the following variables and combinations of variables:

> A alone
> B alone
> C alone
> D alone
>
> A combined with B
> A combined with C
> A combined with D
> B combined with C
> B combined with D
> C combined with D

A combined with various conditions
> of both B and C
A combined with various conditions
> of both B and D
A combined with various conditions
> of both C and D
B combined with various conditions
> of both C and D, etc.

There will also be certain effects not attributable to any combination of variables. These additional (unidentified) effects are known as "residual."

In running the experiment, the engineers processed one unit under the combination of conditions A1B1C1D1—that is, using the original plating thickness, the laboratory method of activation, the regular cleaning method and a short period of drying. They measured the parameter in question on this unit and recorded the result in the first box or square. In the same way they processed another unit under A1B2C1D1—that is, with original plating, the Western method of activation, regular cleaning and a short period of drying—and recorded this in the second box. All the other boxes in the experiment were filled in similarly, using a random order for filling the boxes as explained on pages 114–115.

The above example shows the minimum amount of data which can be used to study four variables at two levels each. If possible, more than one unit should be processed for each box.

B-4.4 Method of analysis

A designed experiment of this type is analyzed by the method known as "Analysis of Variance." This method involves studying all the variability (or "variance") found in the data and partitioning it off into a number of separate parts in such a way that it is possible to distinguish the variability associated with each variable or combination of variables in the experiment.

There are two methods of performing the "Analysis of Variance."

(1) *Sum of squares method.* This involves rather complicated calculations, together with the application of various statistical tables. There are many articles on this in the statistical literature.

(2) *Control chart method.* This accomplishes the same results as the sum of squares method, but does it by means of addition and subtraction plus the plotting of one or more control charts.

The following is a comparison between these two methods.

SUM OF SQUARES METHOD

The method of calculating the Sums of Squares is shown in Figure 88.

The following notes relate to the numbered columns.

(1) In this column list (a) the individuals, (b) the 4 main effects, (c) the 6 first order interactions, (d) the 4 second order interactions and (e) the residual. Each of these is a possible source of variation.

| | | | Data for the Experiment Shown in Figure 87 | | | |

n (the number of observations in the experiment) $= 16$
T (the grand total of all observations) $= 33$
C (the correction factor) $= \dfrac{T^2}{n} = \dfrac{(33)^2}{16} = 68.0625$

(1)	(2)	(3)	(4)		(5)	(6)
Source of Variation	No. of Ind. (i)	No. of Totals	Numbers to Be Squared		Grand Total	Sum of Squares
Individuals	1	16	3 4 0 6 0 5 −1 4		33	183.0000
			3 −4 4 −1 5 0 3 2			
Main Effects A	8	2	16 17		33	545.0000
B	8	2	17 16		33	545.0000
C	8	2	21 12		33	585.0000
D	8	2	15 18		33	549.0000
First Order Interactions AB	4	4	11 5 6 11		33	303.0000
AC	4	4	12 4 9 8		33	305.0000
AD	4	4	6 10 9 8		33	281.0000
BC	4	4	2 19 15 −3		33	599.0000
BD	4	4	10 5 7 11		33	295.0000
CD	4	4	13 8 2 10		33	337.0000
Second Order Interactions ABC	2	8	3 8 9 −4 −1 7 10 1		33	321.0000
ABD	2	8	6 0 4 5 5 5 2 6		33	167.0000
ACD	2	8	7 6 5 3 −1 3 5 5		33	179.0000
BCD	2	8	3 10 −1 9 7 −5 8 2		33	333.0000
Residual	—	—	— — — — — — — —		—	—

Fig. 88. Sum of squares method: sheet for calculations.

(2) In this column list the number of individual measurements in each level, or combination, associated with the source listed in column (1). For example, variable A has 8 measurements in each level. Each of the A and B combinations (such as A1B1) has 4 measurements. Each of the A, B, C combinations (such as A1B1C1) has 2 measurements, etc.

(3) In this column list the number of levels, or combinations, associated with each source. The product of (2) and (3) should in each case be equal to "n."

(4) In this column list the totals separately for each level or combination. In the case of individuals, list the individual observations. In the case of variable A, list the total of A1 and the total of A2. For the combination AB list separately the totals of A1B1, A1B2, A2B1 and A2B2. Similarly for all other variables.

(5) In this column write the total of all the numbers in column (4). In each case this should be equal to the grand total of all the data.

(6) In this column write the total obtained by squaring all the numbers in column (4) and then adding the squares. For example, taking the source listed as "individuals":

$(3)^2 + (4)^2 + (0)^2 + (6)^2 + (0)^2 + (5)^2 + (-1)^2 + (4)^2 + (3)^2 + (-4)^2 + (4)^2 + (-1)^2 + (5)^2 + (0)^2 + (3)^2 + (2)^2$
$= 9 + 16 + 0 + 36 + 0 + 25 + 1 + 16 + 9 + 16 + 16 + 1 + 25 + 0 + 9 + 4$
$= 183$

Carry out the same number of decimal places as in the correction factor at the top of the sheet.

For variable A:

$(16)^2 + (17)^2 = 256 + 289 = 545.0000$

Source of Variation	(7) Sum of Squares ÷ i	(8) Col. (7) − C	(9) Subtract Other Corrections		(10) Corrected Sum of Squares	(11) df	(12) Mean Square	(13) Significance
Individuals	183.0000	114.9375		—	114.9375	15	—	—
A	68.1250	.0625		—	.0625	1	.0625	None
B	68.1250	.0625		—	.0625	1	.0625	—
C	73.1250	5.0625		—	5.0625	1	5.0625	—
D	68.6250	.5625		—	.5625	1	.5625	None
AB	75.7500	7.6875	(A)	.0625				
			(B)	.0625				
				.1250	7.5625	1 x 1	7.5625	None
AC	76.2500	8.1875	(A)	.0625				
			(C)	5.0625				
				5.1250	3.0625	1 x 1	3.0625	None
AD	70.2500	2.1875	(A)	.0625				
			(D)	.5625				
				.6250	1.5625	1 x 1	1.5625	None
BC	149.7500	81.6875	(B)	.0625				
			(C)	5.0625				
				5.1250	76.5625	1 x 1	76.5625	⟨0.1%⟩
BD	73.7500	5.6875	(B)	·.0625				
			(D)	.5625				
				.6250	5.0625	1 x 1	5.0625	None
CD	84.2500	16.1875	(C)	5.0625				
			(D)	.5625				
				5.6250	10.5625	1 x 1	10.5625	None (or "not quite")
ABC	160.5000	92.4375	(A)	.0625				
			(B)	.0625				
			(C)	5.0625				
			(AC)	3.0625				
			(AB)	7.5625				
			(BC)	76.5625				
				92.3750	.0625	1 x 1 x 1	.0625	None
ABD	83.5000	15.4375	(A)	.0625				
			(B)	.0625				
			(D)	.5625				
			(AB)	7.5625				
			(AD)	1.5625				
			(BD)	5.0625				
				14.8750	.5625	1 x 1 x 1	.5625	None
ACD	89.5000	21.4375	(A)	.0625				
			(C)	5.0625				
			(D)	.5625				
			(AC)	3.0625				
			(AD)	1.5625				
			(CD)	10.5625				
				20.8750	.5625	1 x 1 x 1	.5625	None
BCD	166.5000	98.4375	(B)	.0625				
			(C)	5.0625				
			(D)	.5625				
			(BC)	76.5625				
			(BD)	5.0625				
			(CD)	10.5625				
				97.8750	.5625	1 x 1 x 1	.5625	None
					111.8750			
Residual = 114.9375 − 111.8750 = 3.0625						15−14	3.0625	—

Fig. 89. Sum of squares method: table of components of variance.

and similarly for all the other sources of variation.

No Sum of Squares is calculated for the residual.

The Sums of Squares must now be tested for significance as shown in Figure 89.

The following notes relate to the numbered columns.

(7) To obtain the values in this column divide column (6) by column (2).

(8) For this column subtract the correction factor C from column (7).

(9) In this column list any of the values from column (10) which are associated with the source of variation in question. Leave column (9) blank in the case of individuals, main effects, and residual. In the case of the interaction AB, fill in the column (10) values for A and B. In the case of the interaction ABC, fill in the column (10) values for A, B, C, AC, AB and BC. Add these values to obtain the total as indicated.

(10) To obtain the values in this column, subtract the total in column (9) from column (8).

(11) In this column list the number of degrees of freedom. In the case of individuals, the degrees of freedom are $n - 1$. For a main effect, the degrees of freedom are the number of levels minus 1. For a first order interaction, the degrees of freedom will be the product of the degrees of freedom associated with the two variables involved. In the case of a second order interaction, the degrees of freedom will be the product of the degrees of freedom for the three variables involved. The number of degrees of freedom in the residual will be the degrees of freedom for individuals minus the total of all degrees of freedom for the other sources of variation.

(12) To obtain the values in this column divide column (10) by column (11). These are "components of variance" for each of the possible sources of variation.

(13) To find the significance of the different sources of variation, use the "F-test" as follows:

F-test:

Form various ratios consisting of
$$\frac{\text{Mean Square to Be Tested}}{\text{Residual}}$$

Start by testing the second order interactions. If these are found to be nonsignificant, pool them with the residual, obtain a new residual and use this to test the first order interactions.

In testing the first order interactions, start with the smallest. Pool those which are nonsignificant to obtain various new residuals, and proceed in this manner until all the mean squares have been tested or until one is found to be significant. When a first order interaction is significant, do not test the main effects associated with that interaction.

The method of making an F-test is explained in Reference No. 5. See also the example in this book on page 79.

While the rules for pooling the residual will not be given here in detail, the following calculations will show how the pooling is done.

Pooled Residual =	3.0625	Res.
	.5625	BCD
	.5625	ACD
	.5625	ABD
	.0625	ABC
	3.0625	AC
	1.5625	AD
7	9.4375	
	1.3482	

To test for BD:
$$\frac{5.0625}{1.3482} = 3.76 \text{ at } df \ 1, 7$$
Not significant.

Second Pooled Residual =	9.4375	Former Residual
	5.0625	BD
8	14.5000	
	1.8125	

To test for AB:
$$\frac{7.5625}{1.8125} = 4.17 \text{ at } df \ 1,8$$

Not significant.

Third Pooled
Residual   =   14.5000 Former Residual
                   7.5625 AB
              9| 22.0625
                   2.4514

To test for CD:

$$\frac{10.5625}{2.4514} = 4.31 \text{ at } df \ 1,9$$

Not significant.   (Or "not quite significant.")

Fourth Pooled
Residual   =   22.0625 Former Residual
                 10.5625 CD
             10| 32.6250
                   3.2625

To test for BC:

$$\frac{76.5625}{3.2625} = 23.47 \text{ at } df \ 1,10$$

Significant at 0.1% level.

For tables of the Variance Ratio and for a detailed discussion of pooling, significance testing and other calculations involved in the Sum of Squares method, see Reference No. 5, pages 77–97 and 146–149.

Effects which are found to be "significant at the 5% level" are usually called merely "significant"; those at the 1% level "very significant"; and those at the 0.1% level "extremely significant." Some workers identify these with one, two and three asterisks respectively.

Conclusions from this analysis

The result of this analysis is that there is something "extremely significant" about the BC interaction. The Sum of Squares method does not tell us just what combination is significant, or how the B and C effects are related to each other or to the other variables. To obtain this information, it is necessary to go back and study the original data.

CONTROL CHART METHOD

A large amount of information is available on the use of control charts in analyzing multifactor experiments. The control charts have the general advantages of (a) simplicity and (b) the information contained in patterns. The control charts are usually much easier to understand and interpret than other forms of analysis. However, it is necessary to learn certain new techniques in connection with (a) the calculation of control limits and (b) plotting the data.

The following material covers only that part of the control chart analysis which is directly comparable to the Sum of Squares method shown above. Further information is available in the advanced Engineering Courses on this subject which are given from time to time in the various manufacturing locations.

Basis of control chart analysis

When control charts are used in multifactor experiments, it is customary to base the control limits on the "Residual" rather than on a series of sample ranges. This is the only essential difference between this and other uses of control charts. The Residual is the same value which is obtained in the Sum of Squares method, but in plotting the control chart it can be obtained very rapidly. The following instructions apply to a four factor experiment with each factor at two levels.

(1) Visualize the boxes in the experiment as shaded or unshaded according to the following diagram.

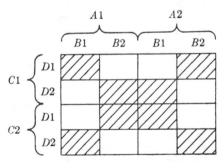

Fig. 90.   Diagram for calculating residual: control chart method.

(2) Add the numbers in the shaded squares, subtract from these the numbers in the unshaded squares, and divide by 4. In the present example,

$$\frac{20 - 13}{4} = +1.75$$

97

The absolute value of this Residual (disregarding signs) is called σ' and is used as the basis for calculating control limits. Note that if we take the square root of 3.0625 (the mean square for the Residual which was obtained at the end of the calculations in Figure 89) we obtain this value of 1.75.

For the control chart analysis, it is not necessary to make the other calculations which were used in the Sum of Squares method. However, if it is desired to reproduce all the other numerical effects, this can be done as indicated under the heading "Optional Calculations" below.

To obtain a value of $\bar{R}$ for use on the range chart, first multiply σ' by the appropriate d_2 factor for the sample size to be used. In the present example we would probably decide to use samples of 2.

$$\bar{R} = d_2 \times \sigma' = 1.128 \times 1.75 = 1.97$$

Then use this value of $\bar{R}$ in the usual way to obtain standard control limits. Complete directions are given on pages 107–109.

Optional calculations

To reproduce the numerical effects obtained in Figure 89, proceed as follows:

(1) Identify each box in the experiment as shown in Figure 91.

(2) Calculate the numerical effects as shown in Figure 92. "Res." stands for the algebraic value of Residual already calculated (+1.75). Add or subtract as indicated, using the values in the designated boxes. For example:

		A1		*A2*	
		B1	*B2*	*B1*	*B2*
C1	*D1*	*a1*	*a2*	*a3*	*a4*
	D2	*b1*	*b2*	*b3*	*b4*
C2	*D1*	*c1*	*c2*	*c3*	*c4*
	D2	*d1*	*d2*	*d3*	*d4*

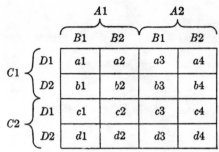

Fig. 91. Identification of boxes in a four factor experiment.

$$\text{A effect} = +1.75 + 1/2(-3 + 0 - 5 + 4 - (-4) - 1 - 5 + 3) = +.25$$

Each of these values is the square root of the corresponding value in Figure 89.

These calculations show that the largest potential effect is the BC interaction. This information is useful, but not essential, in plotting the control charts.

Method of plotting

The following procedure may be used in plotting the control charts.

	Main Effects
A	Res. + ½(−a1 + a3 − b2 + b4 − c2 + c4 − d1 + d3) = + .25
B	Res. + ½(−a1 + a2 − b3 + b4 − c3 + c4 − d1 + d2) = − .25
C	Res. + ½(−a1 − a4 − b2 − b3 + c1 + c4 + d2 + d3) = −2.25
D	Res. + ½(−a1 − a4 + b1 + b4 − c2 − c3 + d2 + d3) = + .75
	First Order Interactions
AB	Res. + ½(+b1 − b2 − b3 + b4 + c1 − c2 − c3 + c4) = +2.75
AC	Res. + ½(+a2 − a4 + b1 − b3 − c2 + c4 − d1 + d3) = +1.75
AD	Res. + ½(+a2 − a4 − b2 + b4 + c1 − c3 − d1 + d3) = −1.25
BC	Res. + ½(+a3 − a4 + b1 − b2 − c3 + c4 − d1 + d2) = −8.75
BD	Res. + ½(+a3 − a4 − b3 + b4 + c1 − c2 − d1 + d2) = +2.25
CD	Res. + ½(+a2 + a3 − b2 − b3 − c2 − c3 + d2 + d3) = +3.25
	Second Order Interactions
ABC	Res. + ½(−a1 + a2 + a3 − a4 + c1 − c2 − c3 + c4) = + .25
ABD	Res. + ½(−a1 + a2 + a3 − a4 + b1 − b2 − b3 + b4) = − .75
ACD	Res. + ½(−a1 + a3 + b1 − b3 + c1 − c3 − d1 + d3) = − .75
BCD	Res. + ½(−a1 + a2 + b1 − b2 + c1 − c2 − d1 + d2) = + .75

Fig. 92. "Effects" or components of variance: control chart method.

(1) Select two of the factors in the experiment which you particularly wish to study. These may be (a) factors in which you are particularly interested for engineering reasons, (b) factors which appear, in the original data, to be associated with large numerical effects, or (c) factors which show the largest main effects or interactions when calculations are made as in Figure 92. In the present example we would select B and C.

(2) Look up these factors in the Plotting Guide on page 109. The Guide will show (a) the headings to put at the top of the chart, (b) the identification to put at the bottom of the chart and (c) the order in which to plot the data. The order is shown by the series of symbols

$$a1b1a3b3 \text{ etc.,}$$

each symbol referring to one of the experimental boxes in Figure 91.

	B1		B2	
	C1	C2	C1	C2
	a1 b1 a3 b3	c1 d1 c3 d3	a2 b2 a4 b4	c2 d2 c4 d4
	A1 A1 A2 A2	A1 A1 A2 A2	A1 A1 A2 A2	A1 A1 A2 A2
	D1 D2 D1 D2	D1 D2 D1 D2	D1 D2 D1 D2	D1 D2 D1 D2

Fig. 93. Plotting guide for factors B and C.

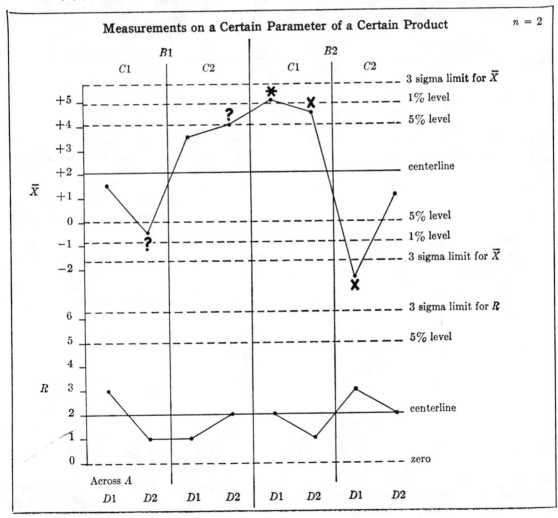

Fig. 94. Control chart analysis: $\bar{X}$ and R chart. Three sets of limits are shown (1% and 5% levels in addition to the 3 sigma limits).

Directions for making this chart are given on pages 107–109.

In plotting the control chart, it is customary to show one or two sets of "inner control limits" in addition to the standard 3σ limits which are used on other control charts. These inner control limits are explained on page 107.

To interpret the chart, first look at the standard 3σ limits and mark x's in accordance with the usual tests. The x's are interpreted as in the case of any other control chart. Then look at the inner control limits and mark any significant points with an asterisk or a question mark as explained on pages 107 and 109. The asterisks and question marks are interpreted in the same way as x's, except that we recognize that the conclusions are less certain.

Drawing conclusions

The conclusions from the experiment are usually obvious, once the chart has been plotted, since each point is completely identified in terms of the variables being studied. However, a detailed analysis of the present example is given below to serve as a guide in interpreting other experiments.

Detailed analysis of the chart in Figure 94

$\bar{X}$ chart

(1) Looking at the 3σ control limits on this chart, we note that one point is out of control on the low side. A check of the headings at the top of the chart and the identification at the bottom shows that the low point is B2C2D1. Since we wish to avoid low readings on the parameter being studied (page 91), this means that we should avoid the combination B2C2D1.

By checking the list of variables on page 92 we find that the combination to be avoided is Western activation, special cleaning, and short drying.

(2) Still looking at the 3σ limits, we note that the four points at the top of this chart react to a test for "4 out of 5." This means that these four points are significantly higher than the rest of the data. The desirable combinations are B1C2 (laboratory activation with special cleaning) and B2C1 (Western method with regular cleaning).

The above points, which react to the 3σ limits, have been marked in the usual way with x's.

(3) Looking now at the inner control limits, which represent lesser degrees of certainty, we note the following:

At the 1% level (that is, with less certainty than if we were basing this on 3σ limits), the first point under B2C1 is significant. There is a little more evidence of the desirability of B2C1 than there is of the desirability of B1C2.

At the 5% level (that is, with less certainty than if we were basing this on the 1% limits), the point marked B1C1D2 is significant. It may be that, if we are already using the combination B1C1, longer drying will make matters worse.

R Chart

The $\bar{X}$ chart was plotted in such a way as to show the effect of variables B, C and D. The R chart will show the effect of the remaining variable, A. The R chart compares this variable (plating) directly with the Residual. The Residual is represented by the centerline on the R chart.

Since none of the R points are significantly different from the Residual, this indicates that there is no significant effect due to plating. If there had been a significant effect in some portion of the R chart (for example, in the portion marked B1C2), this would have warned us that there was an interaction between variables A, B and C.

Summary

The conclusions from this experiment are summarized as follows:

(1) It is desirable to use the Western Electric method (B2) but only if it is to be followed by regular cleaning (C1).

(2) Very bad results may be obtained by using tne Western method in combination with special cleaning (B2C2).

(3) If by any chance it should be necessary

to use the Western method with special cleaning, at least we should try to make the best of a bad situation by using longer drying (D2).

(4) It does not matter whether we use thick or thin plating.

(5) If we decided to adopt the laboratory method (B1), it would probably be necessary to use special cleaning.

(6) If we wished to use the laboratory method without going to special cleaning, it would probably not be advisable to use prolonged drying.

B-4.5 Comments on this experiment

(1) The control chart explains the conflicting ideas described on page 91. The design engineers said that special cleaning was better. This checks with one part of the chart. The Western engineers did not agree with this idea. This checks with another part of the chart. The shop said longer drying would improve the yield. This is true—provided we are unfortunate enough to be using the combination B2C2. The engineers found just the opposite effect with longer drying. This would be true if they were using B1C1.

(2) The best combination of variables in this process would be Western activation and ordinary cleaning. Note that this was not the conclusion reached in the non-statistical experimenting on page 92.

(3) As a result of this experiment, the variables chosen for the process were:

a. Western activation.
b. Ordinary cleaning.
c. Thin plating (desired for other reasons).

The drying time was not changed.
This combination improved the average considerably, and helped to bring about a significant increase in yield.

B-4.6 General comment

Before attempting to analyze an experiment by the method shown above, study the "Directions for Plotting" on pages 107–109 and the material on "Drawing Conclusions" on pages 111–112.
For further information on the Sum of Squares method, see References No. 5, 15, 16, 17 and 41. For further information on the Control Chart method, see References No. 7, 32, 33, 40 and 47.

B-5 EXPLANATION OF THE FOUR FACTOR ANALYSIS
(With Special Reference to the Control Chart Method)

The following explanation is not essential for the analysis, but will aid in understanding the theory of the factorial design. The engineer is asked to imagine a process which contains initially no variation whatsoever. As the example proceeds, variables are deliberately introduced into this process in such a way that their separate and combined effects can be studied. This will help to show:

(a) The meaning of "balance" in a factorial design.
(b) The fact that it is possible to study the factors separately, even though many factors have been combined in the same experiment.
(c) The meaning of "residual."
(d) The meaning of "interactions."

Because the example starts with zero variation, it is easy to check the effects and also to cross-check the calculations.

B-5.1 Explanation of "factorial design"

Imagine a process which contains no variation whatsoever. A series of measurements from this hypothetical process could be represented as follows:

0	0	0	0
0	0	0	0
0	0	0	0
0	0	0	0

Fig. 95. Original measurements from a hypothetical process containing zero variation.

When variables are introduced into an experiment on this process, they will tend to produce changes in the original numbers. For

101

example, suppose we introduce a change in a certain alloying temperature, the effect of the change being equivalent to adding 2 to each of the basic measurements. To represent this, divide the experiment vertically into two halves, label the halves A1 and A2, and add 2 to each of the A2 measurements as shown below.

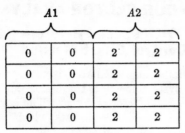

A1		A2	
0	0	2	2
0	0	2	2
0	0	2	2
0	0	2	2

Fig. 96. Introduction of Variable A: +2 added to all A2 measurements.

A second variable could be introduced into the same experiment as follows:

Suppose, in addition to alloying temperature, we are interested in the effect of curing in a bake-out oven overnight. Let the effect of baking be equivalent to subtracting 6 from each of the original measurements. Introduce this second variable into the experiment in the following way:

Let B1 represent the units processed without baking and B2 the units which have been baked. Divide the experiment vertically into quarters. Label the first and third quarters B1 and the second and fourth quarters B2. Now subtract 6 from each of the B2 measurements as shown below. These measurements will contain the combined effect of variables A and B.

A1		A2	
B1	B2	B1	B2
0	−6	2	−4
0	−6	2	−4
0	−6	2	−4
0	−6	2	−4

Fig. 97. Introduction of Variable B: −6 added to all B2 measurements.

In the same way, let C1 represent a certain

capacitance level and C2 another. The data below would be obtained by adding 4 to each of the C2 measurements:

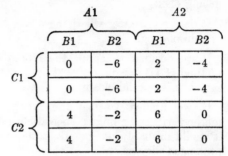

	A1		A2	
	B1	B2	B1	B2
C1	0	−6	2	−4
	0	−6	2	−4
C2	4	−2	6	0
	4	−2	6	0

Fig. 98. Introduction of Variable C: +4 added to all C2 measurements.

Finally, let D1 represent a "bright dip" finish and D2 the regular finish. The data below would be obtained by subtracting 2 from each of the D2 measurements:

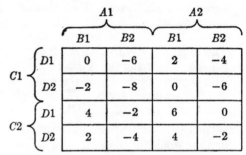

		A1		A2	
		B1	B2	B1	B2
C1	D1	0	−6	2	−4
	D2	−2	−8	0	−6
C2	D1	4	−2	6	0
	D2	2	−4	4	−2

Fig. 99. Complicated data containing four different variables.

We now have a number of variables introduced into the same data. It would be difficult to tell, by looking at the numbers, just what effect was contributed by each variable.

B-5.2 Method of separating the effects of the variables

To separate the effects of the different variables, proceed as follows:

Starting with the complicated data in Figure 99, calculate the average for each level of each variable and record these averages as shown in Figure 100. The "Effect" of the variable is the amount obtained by subtracting Level 1 from Level 2.

Note that these are the numbers which we added to the data originally.

It would now be possible to "remove" the

Variables		Averages		Main Effects
A2 − A1	=	0 − (−2)	=	+2
B2 − B1	=	−4 − (+2)	=	−6
C2 − C1	=	+1 − (−3)	=	+4
D2 − D1	=	−2 − 0	=	−2

Fig. 100.   Main effects.

effect of any variable from the data by subtracting the calculated difference in average from each of its Level 2 measurements. For example, to remove the effect of Variable B, start with the data in Figure 99 and subtract −6 from (or add +6 to) each of the B2 measurements.

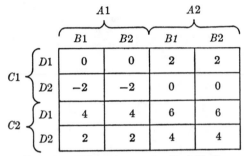

		A1		A2	
		B1	B2	B1	B2
C1	D1	0	0	2	2
	D2	−2	−2	0	0
C2	D1	4	4	6	6
	D2	2	2	4	4

Fig. 101.   Effect of removing Variable B.

To remove the effect of Variable C (in addition to B) start with the data in Figure 101 and subtract 4 from each of the C2 measurements.

		A1		A2	
		B1	B2	B1	B2
C1	D1	0	0	2	2
	D2	−2	−2	0	0
C2	D1	0	0	2	2
	D2	−2	−2	0	0

Fig. 102.   Effect of removing Variable C.

To remove the effect of Variable D (in addition to B and C) start with the data in Figure 102 and subtract −2 from each of the D2 measurements. See Figure 103.

This uncovers the original simple effect of Variable A, uncomplicated by any other variable. If we now removed Variable A also, in the same manner, all the numbers would be reduced to the original zeros.

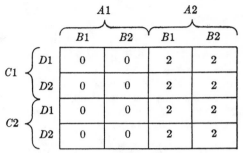

		A1		A2	
		B1	B2	B1	B2
C1	D1	0	0	2	2
	D2	0	0	2	2
C2	D1	0	0	2	2
	D2	0	0	2	2

Fig. 103.   Effect of removing Variable D: all variables are now removed except A.

B-5.3 Meaning of "Residual"

Suppose we had started, not with zeros, but with other numbers such as 1, 2 and 3. Assume that these numbers are scattered more or less uniformly through the experiment, in such a way that the numbers in one portion of the experiment are about the same as the numbers in other portions of the experiment. It would be possible to introduce variables into this experiment just as we did before, then calculate the effect of each variable and remove these effects from the data. This time the numbers would be reduced, not to zero, but to something closely approximating the original 1's, 2's and 3's.

In the same way, we could start with any set of numbers (provided only they are uniformly scattered) and reproduce these numbers more or less closely by calculating and removing effects.

In a real experiment we assume that we start with random variation (uniformly scattered). We add several variables to this in conducting the experiment. We calculate the effects of these variables in the manner shown above. *When the effects are removed, we obtain an estimate of the original random variation.*

The variability left in the numbers after the known effects are removed is called the "Residual." It is a measure of random variation. Some writers refer to the Residual as the "experimental error."

If any of the identified variables in the experiment are significantly larger than the Residual, this is statistical evidence that these variables must have a real effect. If any of the variables are not significantly larger than the Residual, we conclude that their apparent effects may be due to chance, or to ordinary random fluctuation.

103

B-5.4 Interactions

When variables have a simple direct effect like those introduced in paragraph B-5.1 (that is, when we can represent the effect of A2 by adding or subtracting a constant amount from all the A2 measurements) such variables are said to have a "main effect." When the effect of a variable is more complicated, it is said to exhibit "interaction." A simple example of interaction would be the following:

In paragraph B-5.1 we introduced a certain variable, B, representing the effect of curing in a bake-out oven overnight. This variable had a "main effect" indicated by subtracting 6 from all B2 measurements. Imagine now that the effect of baking is not always the same. Suppose it normally tends to *increase* the measurements by 6, but if the material has already been processed at alloying temperature A2, then baking will *reduce* the measurements by an amount equal to 12. We then say that there is an "interaction" between Variable B and Variable A.

Interaction is defined as the effect of one variable acting on another. It can also be defined as the effect produced by two variables acting in combination where the effect would not be produced by either variable acting alone. These are two ways of saying the same thing.

To represent the above interaction between B and A, start with the hypothetical data in Figure 95 and add 6 to all of the B2 measurements. Then subtract 12 from the A2B2 measurements only (those in the last column). Then introduce the main effects of variables A, C and D in the same manner as in paragraph B-5.1.

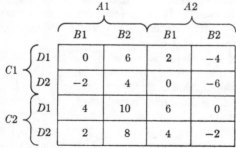

		A1		A2	
		B1	B2	B1	B2
C1	D1	0	6	2	−4
	D2	−2	4	0	−6
C2	D1	4	10	6	0
	D2	2	8	4	−2

Fig. 104. Effect of introducing 3 main effects and one interaction.

The results of this further complication of the data are shown in Figure 104.

By working backward from Figure 104, the numerical effect of the interaction can be discovered as follows. First find the averages of all possible combinations of B and A. There are four of these:

$$A1B1 = +1$$
$$A1B2 = +7$$
$$A2B1 = +3$$
$$A2B2 = -3$$

Then take the difference between the A1B2 average and the A1B1 average:

$$A1B2 - A1B1 = 7 - 1 = 6$$

This is the effect of B, considering the A1 data only.

Now take the difference between the A2B2 average and the A2B1 average:

$$A2B2 - A2B1 = (-3) - 3 = -6$$

This is the effect of B, considering the A2 data only.

Finally take the difference between these two differences. This is the interaction.

$$(A2B2 - A2B1) - (A1B2 - A1B1) =$$
$$(-6) - 6 = -12$$

This shows that the A2B2 measurements must have been reduced by 12.

The above expression is usually written as follows:

Interaction between A and B:
$$A2B2 - A2B1 - A1B2 + A1B1$$
$$(-3) - (+3) - (+7) + (+1) = -12$$

In the same way, it would be possible to calculate the interactions between all other combinations of variables. In the present example we did not actually introduce any other interactions. Consequently these interactions should all turn out to be zero.

Between A and C:
$$A2C2 - A2C1 - A1C2 + A1C1$$
$$(+2) - (-2) - (+6) + (+2) = 0$$

Between A and D:
$$A2D2 - A2D1 - A1D2 + A1D1$$
$$(-1) - (+1) - (+3) + (+5) = 0$$

Between C and B:
C2B2 − C2B1 − C1B2 + C1B1
(+4) − (+4) − (0) + (0) = 0

Between C and D:
C2D2 − C2D1 − C1D2 + C1D1
(+3) − (+5) − (−1) + (+1) = 0

Between D and B:
D2B2 − D2B1 − D1B2 + D1B1
(+1) − (+1) − (+3) + (+3) = 0

B-5.5 How to remove the effect of interactions

To remove from the data the effect of an interaction, subtract the indicated amount from the measurements which represent Level 2 for both variables. For example, to remove the AB interaction found above, subtract −12 from (or add +12 to) the A2B2 measurements.

B-5.6 Correcting the "main effects" by taking account of interactions

When main effects were calculated in paragraph B-5.2, these were not complicated by the presence of any interactions. If interactions are present, however, they will tend to "throw off" or distort the corresponding main effects. An example of this is the following: Suppose we try to determine the main effect of variable A in Figure 104. We find

$$A2 − A1 = 0 − 4 = −4$$

This is not the effect which we really introduced into variable A. *The A2 average has been changed by the presence of the interaction.*

A simple additional calculation, however, can easily remove this difficulty. Merely subtract from the A2 average one-half of any interactions involving A.

Corrected "A" main effect =

$$A2 − A1 − \frac{\text{(the sum of any interactions involving A)}}{2}$$

$$= 0 − 4 − \left(\frac{−12}{2}\right)$$

$$= −4 + 6$$

$$= +2$$

This is the true main effect which we introduced into Variable A.

In the same way, corrected effects can be calculated for all the other variables. This has been done in Figure 105. Note that in all cases we obtain the values which were originally introduced.

	Corrected Main Effects	
Variable	Level 2 − Level 1 − $\frac{1}{2}$ of any interactions which involve this variable	
A	$0 − (+4) − \left(\dfrac{−12}{2}\right)$	$= +2$
B	$+2 − (+2) − \left(\dfrac{−12}{2}\right)$	$= +6$
C	$+4 − 0 − 0$	$= +4$
D	$+1 − (+3) − 0$	$= −2$

Fig. 105. Corrected main effects for all four variables.

Since all of these effects are the true values (those actually introduced), it would be possible to subtract them all from the data and thus get back to the original zeros. To do this, start with Figure 104, subtract 2 from the A2 measurements, 6 from the B2, 4 from the C2 and (−2) from the D2. Finally, subtract (−12) from the A2B2 column. All the numbers will now be reduced to zero.

In a real experiment, they would be reduced to the Residual.

B-5.7 Higher order interactions

It is possible for the data to be complicated by other interactions than the simple one shown above. For example, it may take a combination of three or more variables to produce a certain effect on the process. Interactions involving more than two variables are called "higher order interactions." First order interactions involve two variables, second order interactions involve three variables, third order interactions involve four variables, etc. In a four factor experiment it is possible to calculate (a) Main Effects, (b) First Order interactions, (c) Second Order interactions and (d) the Third Order interaction involving all four factors. While these calculations will not be given in detail, the method is a simple extension of the method already explained.

Second Order interaction between A, B and C = A2B2C2 − A2B1C2 + A2B1C1 − A2B2C1 + A1B1C2 − A1B2C2 − A1B1C1 + A1B2C1.

Using the data in Figure 104, (−4) − (+6) + (0) − (+2) + (+8) − (−2) − (+2) + (+4) = 0.

This shows that we did not introduce any Second Order interaction ABC.

Third Order interaction between A, B, C and D = A1B1C1D1 − A1B2C1D1 − A2B1C1D1 + A2B2C1D1 − A1B1C1D2 + A1B2C1D2 + A2B1C1D2 − A2B2C1D2 − A1B1C2D1 + A1B2C2D1 + A2B1C2D1 − A2B2C2D1 + A1B1C2D2 − A1B2C2D2 − A2B1C2D2 + A2B2C2D2.

Using the data in Figure 104, (0) − (+6) − (+2) + (−4) − (−2) + (+4) + (0) − (−6) − (+4) + (+10) + (+6) − (0) + (+2) − (+8) − (+4) + (−2) = 0.

This shows that we did not introduce any Third Order interaction ABCD.

As before, interactions would tend to complicate the other effects of the variables, but this could be corrected by a simple calculation similar to that in paragraph B-5.6. In each case we would be able to find the real (corrected) effect of each variable; and if all these effects were removed, the data would be reduced to the original zeros.

B-5.8 How this can be used in analysis

If we actually went through all this, calculating the effects and obtaining their true values, we would be able to remove any effects from the data at will and study the remainder. In a four factor factorial experiment containing only one measurement per box, we might choose to remove

    All 4 Main Effects
    All 6 First Order interactions
    All 4 Second Order interactions

and leave only the Third Order interaction. (We would not attempt to remove the Third Order interaction because it would not be possible to separate this from the Residual.)

The data from which all possible effects have been removed are called the "fully reduced data".

The reader would be able to verify, by calculating the effects, correcting them and actually

removing them from the data, that

$\bar{R}$ for samples of 2 from the fully reduced data would be ABCD/8*, and

σ for the same data would be $\bar{R}/2$.

The calculated σ should be multiplied by $\sqrt{n}$ (where n is the number of boxes in the experiment) to take care of the restrictions imposed on the data in removing so many effects.

$$\text{Residual} = \sigma \times \sqrt{n} = \bar{R}/2 \times \sqrt{16} = \text{ABCD}/16 \times \sqrt{16}$$

$$= \text{ABCD}/4$$

This gives the same value of Residual that is obtained in the Sum of Squares method. The shaded boxes shown in Figure 90 are merely a convenient way of calculating ABCD.

B-5.9 Other possibilities

In the control chart method it is not necessary to remove all the main effects and interactions in the manner shown above. It is possible to remove any desired variables or combinations of variables and study the effect of this on the remainder. This makes the control chart a very flexible method.

Estimates of Residual will involve larger or smaller numbers of degrees of freedom depending on the number of effects that are removed. The method shown above is the one which corresponds directly to the Sum of Squares method prior to the pooling of any effects with the Residual.

B-5.10 Summary of technical terms

(1) The *"characteristic to be plotted"* is the characteristic which is actually measured and whose measurements are recorded in the boxes provided for data.

(2) A *"factor"* is a variable which may or may not have an effect on the characteristic to be plotted, but which has been selected as an object of study in the experiment. We run the experiment to discover the possible effect of one or more factors. An experiment containing four variables is called a four-factor experiment.

---

* This will be true regardless of which variable is "summed across". See page 107.

(3) A *"level"* is a particular condition or state of one of the factors being studied. The different conditions or states of the same variable are called its different "levels." For example, the variable C may appear in the experiment at two levels, C1 and C2. The *presence* of a certain condition may be considered one level, and its *absence* may be considered another level.

(4) The *"Residual"* in the experiment refers to the basic data which existed (or might have existed) in the process prior to the introduction of any of the factors in the experiment. The Residual is the estimated variability in the original basic data. See paragraphs B-5.3 and B-5.9.

(5) A *"main effect"* is a simple, direct, consistent effect on the characteristic being plotted. For example, if changing from D1 to D2 has a definite tendency to make the measurements higher, regardless of the presence or absence of other variables, there is a D main effect.

(6) Sometimes variables do not have a particular effect when acting alone, but produce that effect only when acting in combination with other variables. Such variables are said to exhibit *"interactions"* rather than main effects. Interactions were discussed in paragraphs B-5.4 to B-5.7.

(7) The different methods of forming samples in an experiment are spoken of as *"summing across"* variables. We say we are "summing across" a variable when we include, in the same sample, measurements representing different conditions of the same variable. For example, if the experiment covers conditions C1 and C2, we are summing across C when we include a C1 measurement and a C2 measurement in the same sample. Each different method of forming samples from the boxes (horizontally, vertically, skipping one box, etc.) may result in summing across a different variable.

B-6 DIRECTIONS FOR PLOTTING

The following are directions for plotting control charts in simple factorial experiments. The instructions include not only the calculation of standard 3 σ limits, but also the calculation of "inner control limits" at various "significance levels." The significance of the inner control limits is as follows. (All percentages are based on a normal distribution.)

On the $\bar{X}$ chart:

3 sigma limits correspond to 0.1% level (approx.)

2.33 sigma limits correspond to 1% level (approx.)

1.65 sigma limits correspond to 5% level (approx.)

On an R chart for samples of 2:

3 sigma limits correspond to 1% level (approx.)

2 sigma limits correspond to 5% level (approx.)

The inner control limits are used as follows:

(1) Points which react at the 5% level are less certain than those which react at the 1% level (1 in 20 chances of being wrong as compared with 1 in 100). In the same way, points at the 1% level are less certain than points at the 3 σ limits.

(2) Points which react to the 3 σ limits are marked with an "x" in the usual way. Points which react at the 1% level are marked with an asterisk (*) and points at the 5% level with a question mark (?) to distinguish them from points which react to the standard 3 σ limits.

B-6.1 Experiment with four factors, two levels, one measurement per box

Preliminary calculations

(1) Calculate the Grand Average of all the data ($\bar{\bar{X}}$).

(2) Calculate the Residual. This can be done by using the shaded boxes in Figure 90.

(3) Take σ' as the absolute value of the Residual, disregarding signs.

$\bar{X}$ and R chart for n = 2

(1) Calculate the centerline for the R chart

as follows:

$$\bar{R} = d_2 \times \sigma' = 1.128 \, \sigma'$$

(2) Calculate control limits for the R chart as follows:

Upper 3 sigma limit $= 3.267 \, \bar{R}$ (or 3.68 σ').

Upper 1% limit: The 1% limit in this case is so close to 3 σ that no separate 1% limit is calculated.

Upper 5% limit $= 2.51 \, \bar{R}$ (or 2.83 σ').

Lower control limit $= 0$.

(3) Calculate control limits for the $\bar{X}$ chart as follows:

Upper 3 sigma limit $= \bar{\bar{X}} + 1.88 \, \bar{R}$ (or $+ 2.12 \, \sigma'$).

Upper 1% limit $= \bar{\bar{X}} + 1.46 \, \bar{R}$ (or $+ 1.65 \, \sigma'$).

Upper 5% limit $= \bar{\bar{X}} + 1.03 \, \bar{R}$ (or $+ 1.16 \, \sigma'$).

The lower control limits are obtained similarly, except that the quantities are subtracted from $\bar{\bar{X}}$ instead of being added to it.

(4) Plot the control chart as follows:

(a) Decide on two factors which you particularly wish to study.

(b) Select the appropriate diagram from page 109.

(c) Set up a control chart which shows, at the top, the combination of variables given at the top of the diagram.

(d) Before plotting the chart, consider the two variables shown at the bottom of the diagram. Decide which of these variables is probably less important. Strike out the line of identification corresponding to the less important variable.

Show at the bottom of the control chart the identification which remains.

(e) Finally, consider the row of symbols at the center of the diagram. These symbols refer to the boxes in the experiment, as shown in Figure 91. Each symbol can be translated into one of the numbers in the original data.

If, in step (d), you struck out the *last* line of identification, form samples by taking these symbols (or numbers) in successive pairs. That is, use the first two numbers for the first sample, the next two numbers for the second sample, etc.

But if, in step (d), you struck out the *next to the last* line of identification, form samples by taking the symbols alternately. That is, use the first and third numbers for the first sample; the second and fourth numbers for the second sample; the fifth and seventh numbers for the third sample, etc.

(f) Calculate $\bar{X}$ and R for each sample in the usual way, and plot these values on the control chart.

Example

Consider the experiment shown in Figure 87 on page 92.

$$\bar{\bar{X}} = 2.06$$
$$\sigma' = 1.75$$
$$\bar{R} = 1.128 \times 1.75 = 1.97$$

Control limits for R chart:

$$3.68 \times 1.75 = 6.44 \text{ (3 sigma level)}$$
$$2.83 \times 1.75 = 4.95 \text{ (5\% level)}$$

Control limits for $\bar{X}$ chart:

$2.06 \pm (2.12 \times 1.75) = 2.06 \pm 3.71$ (3 sigma level)

$2.06 \pm (1.65 \times 1.75) = 2.06 \pm 2.89$ (1% level)

$2.06 \pm (1.16 \times 1.75) = 2.06 \pm 2.03$ (5% level)

Points are plotted as follows. The steps are lettered to correspond to the instructions given above.

(a) We have previously decided that we would like to plot B and C.

(b) We therefore select Diagram No. 3.

(c) We set up a control chart in accordance with this diagram as shown on page 99.

(d) The two variables at the bottom of the diagram are A and D. Suppose we decide we are least interested in A. Strike out the upper line of identification, consisting of A's, and show only the D's on the control chart. See page 99.

(e) Since the next to the last line of identification was eliminated, we must form samples by taking the data alternately. The symbols in Diagram No. 3 are:

a1b1a3b3   c1d1c3d3   a2b2a4b4   c2d2c4d4

Our samples will therefore be:

| a1 | b1 | c1 | d1 | a2 | b2 | c2 | d2 |
| a3 | b3 | c3 | d3 | a4 | b4 | c4 | d4 |

Note that this results in "summing across A"—that is, including in one sample an A1 measurement and an A2 measurement. This will cause variable A to appear in the R chart but not in the $\bar{X}$ chart. Label the R chart "Across A."

When we translate these symbols into the data in Figure 87 we get the following:

| 3 | 0 | 3 | 5 | 4 | 5 | −4 | 0 |
| 0 | −1 | 4 | 3 | 6 | 4 | −1 | 2 |

These are the samples which will be plotted on the control chart.

(f) The $\bar{X}$ and R points for the above samples are:

| $\bar{X}$ | 1.5 | −0.5 | 3.5 | 4.0 | 5.0 | 4.5 | −2.5 | 1.0 |
| R | 3 | 1 | 1 | 2 | 2 | 1 | 3 | 2 |

These are the points which are plotted on page 99.

Marking x's and other significant points

In looking at these charts, consider first the $3\,\sigma$ limits. Apply the standard tests for unnatural patterns and mark any significant point with an "x". See pages 182–183.

Next, consider the 1% and 5% limits. Do not apply the tests for "2 out of 3" or "4 out of 5", but consider it significant if

(a) a single point exceeds the limit in question, or

(b) the average of two related points would be more than $7/_{10}$ of the distance from the centerline to the limit in question.

Rule (b) is derived from the fact that, if we plotted the averages of samples having twice as much data, the control limits applying to these averages would have their width divided by $\sqrt{2}$.

$$\frac{1}{\sqrt{2}} = \text{approximately } .7$$

Use asterisks or question marks for these special significant points as indicated on page 107.

Guide for plotting

The diagrams referred to in the preceding instructions are shown at the bottom of this page. The symbols in the center refer to boxes, as in Figure 91 on page 98.

Diagram 1.   A and C.

A1		A2	
C1	C2	C1	C2
a1 b1 a2 b2	c1 d1 c2 d2	a3 b3 a4 b4	c3 d3 c4 d4
B1B1B2B2	B1B1B2B2	B1B1B2B2	B1B1B2B2
D1D2D1D2	D1D2D1D2	D1D2D1D2	D1D2D1D2

Diagram 2.   B and D.

B1		B2	
D1	D2	D1	D2
a1 c1 a3 c3	b1 d1 b3 d3	a2 c2 a4 c4	b2 d2 b4 d4
A1A1A2A2	A1A1A2A2	A1A1A2A2	A1A1A2A2
C1C2C1C2	C1C2C1C2	C1C2C1C2	C1C2C1C2

Diagram 3.   B and C.

B1		B2	
C1	C2	C1	C2
a1 b1 a3 b3	c1 d1 c3 d3	a2 b2 a4 b4	c2 d2 c4 d4
A1A1A2A2	A1A1A2A2	A1A1A2A2	A1A1A2A2
D1D2D1D2	D1D2D1D2	D1D2D1D2	D1D2D1D2

Diagram 4.   A and D.

A1		A2	
D1	D2	D1	D2
a1 c1 a2 c2	b1 d1 b2 d2	a3 c3 a4 c4	b3 d3 b4 d4
B1B1B2B2	B1B1B2B2	B1B1B2B2	B1B1B2B2
C1C2C1C2	C1C2C1C2	C1C2C1C2	C1C2C1C2

Diagram 5.   A and B.

A1		A2	
B1	B2	B1	B2
a1 b1 c1 d1	a2 b2 c2 d2	a3 b3 c3 d3	a4 b4 c4 d4
C1C1C2C2	C1C1C2C2	C1C1C2C2	C1C1C2C2
D1D2D1D2	D1D2D1D2	D1D2D1D2	D1D2D1D2

Diagram 6.   C and D.

C1		C2	
D1	D2	D1	D2
a1 a2 a3 a4	b1 b2 b3 b4	c1 c2 c3 c4	d1 d2 d3 d4
A1A1A2A2	A1A1A2A2	A1A1A2A2	A1A1A2A2
B1B2B1B2	B1B2B1B2	B1B2B1B2	B1B2B1B2

B-6.2 Experiment with three factors, each factor at two levels, one measurement per box

Obtain the Residual as follows. Visualize the boxes in the experiment as shaded or unshaded according to the diagram shown below.

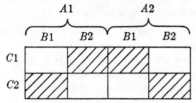

Fig. 106. Calculating residual for a three factor experiment.

Add the numbers in the shaded squares, subtract from these the numbers in the unshaded squares, and divide the result by $\sqrt{8}$.

Use this in the standard manner to obtain control limits. Follow the general method used for the Four Factor experiment as given on pages 107–109.

B-6.3 Experiment with five factors, each factor at two levels, one measurement per box

Obtain the Residual as follows. Visualize the boxes in the experiment as shaded or unshaded according to the diagram shown in Figure 107.

Add the numbers in the shaded squares, subtract from these the numbers in the unshaded squares and divide the result by $\sqrt{32}$.

Use this in the standard manner to obtain control limits. Follow the general method used for the Four Factor experiment as given on pages 107–109.

B-6.4 Experiments containing factors at more than two levels

When one of the factors in an experiment occurs at more than two levels, the experiment becomes, in effect, a combination of simpler experiments. For example, we might have an experiment containing three factors (A, B and C) with factor A occurring at three levels instead of two. This experiment can be regarded as a combination of three experiments —one comparing A1 with A2, another comparing A2 with A3, and a third comparing A1 with A3. The separate (simple) experiments are shown in Figure 108.

While 24 boxes are shown in Figure 108, it would only be necessary to obtain a total of 12 measurements. The four A1 measurements are entered first in section 1 and then copied for use in section 2. The same is done for A2 and A3.

This type of experiment may be analyzed in separate sections, if desired, following the method in paragraph B-6.2. It is also possible to calculate a "combination" Residual which can then be used for all three sections. The method is as follows:

(1) For each section, add the numbers in the shaded squares and subtract from these the numbers in the unshaded squares. Square the result and divide by 8.

(2) Average the values obtained in (1) and take the square root of the average.

This gives the same value of Residual which would have been obtained in the Sum of Squares method. There are other shortcuts for multi-level experiments, but these are beyond the scope of the present Handbook.

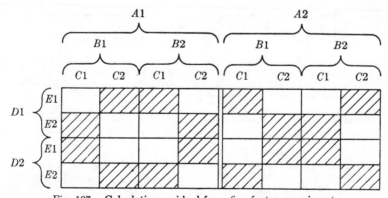

Fig. 107. Calculating residual for a five factor experiment.

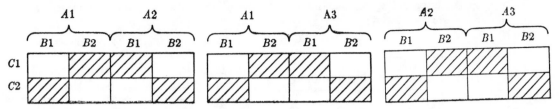

Fig. 108. Arrangement of data for a three factor experiment with Factor A occuring at three levels.

B-6.5 Experiments containing more than one measurement per box

The foregoing instructions were for experiments which have only one measurement per box. If more than one measurement is available for each box, the instructions are similar, except that it may be possible to use some other method of finding the Residual. In general, the data may be treated in three different ways, as follows. Before deciding on the appropriate treatment, use a control chart to test for the presence of assignable causes within boxes. If there are no assignable causes within boxes, use methods (1), (2) or (3). If assignable causes are found within boxes, use method (2) or (3) but not method (1).

(1) *Using the average of the measurements in each box.*

In this treatment, consider the average of each box as if it were a single measurement, and analyze the experiment in the same way as when there is one measurement per box. It is desirable to have the same number of measurements in each box. In drawing conclusions, remember that these are averages and that the conclusions will apply to averages also.

(2) *Forming samples within each box.*

In this treatment, use the measurements within a single box to form one or more "samples." Calculate $\bar{X}$ and R for each sample in the usual way. Add the values of R for all samples in the experiment and calculate $\bar{R}$. Use this value of $\bar{R}$ as if it were the $\bar{R}$ obtained from the Residual.

(3) *Treating the measurements as a separate factor in the experiment.*

In this treatment, identify the sets of measurements as M1, M2 etc., and treat "M" as an additional factor in the experiment. For example, if this is a four factor

experiment containing variables A, B, C and D, treat it as a five factor experiment containing variables A, B, C, D and M. In some cases there may be more variability from measurement to measurement than there is between boxes.

B-7 DRAWING CONCLUSIONS FROM EXPERIMENTAL CONTROL CHARTS

B-7.1 Preliminary analysis

Contrary to the expectation of many engineers, experimental charts are easy to interpret once they have been plotted. The patterns are marked with x's as in the case of any control chart. They are classified as stratification, mixture, freaks, sudden shift etc. as in any process capability study. The tracing of causes is generally simpler on the experimental charts, since changes in the pattern can be associated immediately with the particular variables included in the experiment. The interpretation is simplest when the analysis includes only one chart.

If a number of charts have been plotted, or a number of experiments have been run, it is sometimes helpful to combine the conclusions and reduce them to their simplest form. One method of doing this is the following.

(1) Considering each chart as a whole, read the patterns as in any process capability study.

(2) As each conclusion is reached, record it on a suitable form as shown in Figure 109. This form may contain the conclusions from an entire group of control charts.

(3) When duplicate conclusions are obtained, as shown by duplicate entries in the same column, strike out one of the duplicates so

111

as to keep the outstanding conclusions in as simple a form as possible. See Figure 109.

HIGH	LOW	MORE UNIFORM	LESS UNIFORM
A1D2 A1B1C1 A1B1C2 ~~A1D2~~	A2D2	C1	C2

Fig. 109. Form for recording significant effects found on control charts.

(4) If, in a single column, entries occur which are identical, except that they contain all possible levels of one of the variables, strike out the variable which occurs at all levels. Afterward, since this will leave duplicates in the same column, strike out all but one of the duplicates so as to leave the simplest possible conclusions.

This can be illustrated by an example. Suppose we have the following entries, all in the same column:

A1D2
A1B1C1
A1B1C2
A1D2

First strike out one of the "A1D2" entries, since this is a duplicate. This leaves:

A1D2
A1B1C1
A1B1C2

In two of the entries which are otherwise identical (A1B1C1 and A1B1C2), the variable C occurs at all possible levels. Since we find the same effect at all levels of C, it is obvious that this effect must be due to other variables and not C. Strike out C1 and C2. This leaves:

A1D2
A1B1
A1B1

Since we now have duplicates in the same column (two entries of A1B1), one of the duplicates should be eliminated. This leaves:

A1D2
A1B1

These are the conclusions reduced to their simplest possible form.

(5) After the analysis is completed and all conclusions have been noted and reduced to their simplest form, express the conclusions verbally in terms of the real variables. Check the conclusions by referring back to the plotted charts. Be sure you are fully aware of the evidence on which these conclusions are based.

B-7.2 Final conclusions

All experiments of the type discussed here involve minimum amounts of data. They should be used as a means of obtaining quick indications of the best avenues to explore further. Variables that are found to be significant in the experiment are probably important variables. They can be used to improve the process, reduce costs or explain effects that were previously baffling and unexplainable.

On the other hand, variables which do not show up as significant in the experiment are not necessarily unimportant. The amounts of data used in designed experiments may be sufficient to establish certain variables as significant, but it requires much larger amounts of data to establish the absence of significance. This is true whether the experiment is analyzed by control charts or by any other method.

In any case the engineer should design his experiments on the basis of previous process capability studies, and should check all conclusions from his experiments by making other process capability studies. He should guard against the temptation to substitute conclusions from this quick type of experiment for the broader and more reliable analysis of the process which is included in a process capability study.

B-8 SOME SUGGESTIONS ON PLANNING THE EXPERIMENT

B-8.1 The problem

Define the problem as specifically as possible before starting the experiment. Consult others who have expert knowledge of this job or of the planning of designed experiments. During the planning, decide whether to measure one or several characteristics on the experimental units. By measuring the units for a number of characteristics, it is often possible to select an optimum set of variables considering their effect on all characteristics simultaneously. If the problem is complicated, attempt to subdivide it and handle the subdivisions individually.

B-8.2 Type and quantity of data

The characteristics studied may be "variable" in nature (that is, capable of measurement along a continuous scale) or they may be discrete or non-variable in nature (that is, capable of being classified into limited categories only). Characteristics of the latter type include those which are measured with attributes gages on a go, no-go basis and those which are indicated only by the presence or absence of a given condition (for example, the units did or did not crack, did or did not fail on a life test, etc).

There is also a third type of characteristic which is intermediate between the continuously variable and the entirely discrete. These are the characteristics which are ordinarily considered discrete in nature but which can nevertheless be measured on some sort of crude "semi-variables" scale. Such characteristics may include cracks, burrs, extent of warpage or damage, depth of nicks or scratches and many other characteristics for which it is possible to distinguish degrees if not actual measurements.

If the characteristic is measurable on a continuous scale, it may be necessary to process only one unit for each "box" in the table of experimental results. If the characteristic is non-measurable, it will be necessary to produce a number of units under each designated set of conditions and record in the box the percentage or count which did or did not contain the characteristic in question. The number of units to be processed for each box depends on how many are needed to obtain usable counts or percentages. The number in each group should be large enough so that most of the boxes in the table will contain a number other than zero. It is desirable to process the same number of units for each box.

Attributes data may be analyzed with p-charts or c-charts, as explained in Reference No. 32; or it is possible to use an $\bar{X}$ and R chart as explained on page 198. Most engineers find it convenient to use the $\bar{X}$ and R chart, following the same procedures for both variables and attributes data.

Unless there is good reason for doing otherwise, the experiment should not be reduced to fewer than a total of sixteen observations. This is necessary to permit reasonable estimates of the residual or experimental error. Better estimates of residual may be obtained if the experiment provides more than one observation per box.

Occasionally it is convenient to process more units than will be needed for the experiment and select the experimental units at random from the larger group. In this event, use dice, shuffled cards or a table of random numbers as the basis for selecting the units, in order to avoid unconscious bias in making the selection.

B-8.3 Reliability of measurements

The person conducting the experiment should take special precautions to make sure that the measurements are reliable. In many process capability studies the initial measurements show erratic and unexplainable patterns, particularly on the R chart. These are likely to reflect problems in measurement at least as often as they reflect difficulties in the product.

In a designed experiment, measurement peculiarities are even more important because the amount of data is very small and all conclusions are based on a few measurements obtained in a brief period of time. If practice is necessary in using the measuring instrument (or using the standard adopted as a basis for classification), this should be carried out prior to the time when the experimental data are collected. In particular, make certain that the standards of measurement are not allowed to change during the experiment. If gages and test sets must be replaced, re-calibrated or overhauled, start again to collect the experimental data.

B-8.4 Selection of variables

In designing the experiment, make a list of all variables which are suspected of being able to influence the experimental results. This list will be an aid in setting up the original experiment and also in carrying the experiment further in case the original analysis shows that the important variables were not covered. In making up this list, the engineer should draw not only on his own technical information and knowledge of the job but also on information which can be contributed by shop supervisors and others. The list should include not only the theoretical variables but also the practical shop-type variables which experience or capability studies have indicated may be present.

In particular, be sure to include the variables which may be associated with processing operations such as cleaning, heat treating, method of stacking material in furnaces or boats, etc. The longer the list of possible variables, the better.

Select from this list four or five variables to be included in the experiment. The experiment will be most successful if the first variables chosen have fairly large effects. While we cannot be sure in advance just what these variables are, there are usually certain reasons to suppose that one variable is potentially more important than another. Attempt to select the variables in the order of their probable importance.

On the other hand, having made every reasonable effort to select important variables at the beginning, do not be unduly concerned about the possibility of choosing the wrong variables. The initial experiment will warn you, by showing a large residual, if there are variables in the process larger than the ones you have selected for study. In that case, go back to the original list, pick out another set of variables which may prove to be productive and set up another experiment.

Your judgment of the variables which should be included will be considerably sharpened after the first experiment is run.

B-8.5 Disposing of the variables not included in the experiment

All the variables which are not to be studied formally must be dropped out statistically so they will be unable to affect the conclusions. There are two methods of doing this:

(1) Randomize the order in which the ex-

perimental results are obtained so that any unidentified variables which happen to be present will have an equal chance of affecting all portions of the data. To do this, first set up the experiment in boxes as shown on page 92 and then use some random method of assuring that the boxes will be filled in an unbiased order. Methods of doing this are given in paragraph B-8.6.

(2) If it is convenient and practical, arrange to hold constant some of the variables which are not to be studied. For example, if you do not wish to study the possible effect of various machines, arrange to run the experiment on only one machine. Temperatures, pressures, the composition of chemical baths, etc., can often be held constant or essentially so.

On the other hand, the experimenter should be careful not to assume that variables are constant without sufficient evidence. A single machine may behave differently depending on how it is set up or on its state of repair. The experimenter himself may behave differently according to his physical or emotional state or according to the time of day. We frequently find that conditions which we believed to be constant were actually varying over quite a wide range.

Even where it is possible to hold some of the variables constant, it may be undesirable to do so because of the fact that all of the elements in the going process will not be represented.

B-8.6 Methods of introducing randomness into the experiment

(1) First Method

Throw a die or pair of dice and note the number which comes up. Start counting the boxes in the upper left-hand corner of the design and fill in first the box which corresponds to the number on the dice. This can be indicated by writing the word "first" in the appropriate box. Then throw the dice again and count off more boxes in accordance with the indicated number. Write in this box "second." When you have counted off all the boxes in the design, continue again with the upper left-hand corner but this time skip any boxes which have already been filled. Continue in this manner until all the parts of the experiment have been assigned.

In conducting the experiment, set up first the combination of conditions corresponding to the box marked "first" and run the necessary number of units. Then set up the conditions for the box marked "second" and run the necessary units, etc. This will tend to keep any particular portion of the data from being influenced by the known or unknown variables which come and go in a process with time. It is unlikely,

RANDOM NUMBERS

15	62	38	72	92	03	76	09	30	75	77	80	04	24	54	67	60	10	79	26	21	60	03	48	14
77	81	15	14	67	55	24	22	20	55	36	93	67	69	37	72	22	43	46	32	56	15	75	25	12
18	87	05	09	96	45	14	72	41	46	12	67	46	72	02	59	06	17	49	12	73	28	23	52	48
08	58	53	63	66	13	07	04	48	71	39	07	46	96	40	20	86	79	11	81	74	11	15	23	17
16	07	79	57	61	42	19	68	15	12	60	21	59	12	07	04	99	88	22	39	75	16	69	13	84
54	13	05	46	17	05	51	24	53	57	46	51	14	39	17	21	39	89	07	35	47	87	44	36	62
95	27	23	17	39	80	24	44	48	93	75	94	77	09	23	48	75	91	69	03	55	51	09	74	47
22	39	44	74	80	25	95	28	63	90	41	19	48	46	72	51	12	97	39	83	35	83	23	17	29
69	95	21	30	11	98	81	38	00	53	41	40	04	16	78	67	29	83	41	18	30	90	44	37	64
75	75	63	97	12	11	57	05	86	52	82	72	47	72	14	37	72	69	75	48	72	21	52	51	81
08	74	79	30	80	70	11	66	79	25	88	01	94	52	31	38	57	98	71	62	12	56	61	01	54
04	88	45	98	60	90	92	74	77	87	40	18	65	87	37	08	68	62	39	52	84	74	90	68	18
97	35	74	05	75	42	13	49	48	38	74	19	06	42	60	20	79	90	81	77	18	51	71	27	27
53	09	93	28	29	80	19	68	30	45	94	49	49	71	21	93	93	71	30	34	52	65	83	40	13
26	36	68	48	09	37	69	26	22	80	23	34	10	45	70	83	51	07	37	44	62	96	74	42	64
49	16	57	15	79	56	63	22	94	28	11	39	69	55	38	53	06	97	20	42	09	14	90	43	48
03	51	79	78	74	75	23	73	75	98	47	85	07	26	02	61	28	01	22	16	14	12	15	67	22
21	88	87	28	48	23	44	03	03	80	53	89	07	87	93	30	17	84	17	74	16	53	31	39	01
56	41	73	33	41	59	16	59	50	98	24	24	87	06	75	99	52	09	88	05	86	25	43	50	94
72	39	19	70	17	01	04	01	22	33	04	84	63	27	65	84	39	45	55	31	95	88	93	90	37
97	28	25	81	49	71	69	22	04	51	56	46	56	15	10	69	59	99	50	29	33	50	16	93	09
18	87	02	72	08	74	52	16	03	82	20	19	66	23	62	37	51	04	89	31	32	19	59	85	57
53	40	11	75	45	13	56	85	31	37	09	17	71	96	79	39	50	79	27	62	71	14	95	53	03
60	49	03	41	56	78	33	77	28	92	21	90	10	62	01	97	06	45	01	19	95	12	24	18	52
09	16	12	75	04	39	69	95	00	48	26	85	28	73	08	66	92	10	66	75	62	61	27	82	57
64	20	19	87	54	88	15	12	54	24	06	99	57	07	28	51	34	54	98	50	70	88	02	86	48
31	28	07	58	77	03	98	26	76	09	10	44	57	61	28	60	29	85	70	79	80	29	19	98	92
80	04	28	47	76	35	73	67	78	28	09	39	88	63	74	41	26	92	42	33	06	80	06	33	84
24	60	22	51	19	34	54	08	24	73	86	72	11	44	69	76	90	81	17	85	57	47	35	16	84
59	16	11	26	29	18	97	78	44	43	58	92	78	70	80	09	65	32	68	26	65	73	90	50	46
58	54	29	98	27	40	51	92	07	13	58	41	59	56	94	16	32	51	42	54	77	37	13	85	19
20	18	34	22	73	57	40	67	17	28	63	57	74	36	18	65	55	25	50	68	35	90	00	03	38
53	90	46	56	19	50	58	33	84	53	14	74	17	40	73	86	11	04	02	04	02	28	49	62	36
97	16	93	94	65	70	95	95	83	20	91	42	57	95	63	00	86	29	02	53	02	27	86	70	95
72	55	71	70	92	04	22	53	19	29	67	29	13	56	70	45	73	45	05	04	32	43	30	93	41
99	19	72	58	35	49	09	26	00	74	26	42	94	52	02	83	31	85	65	66	31	97	67	52	15
48	21	49	72	97	79	19	64	81	82	78	92	51	96	51	28	79	13	20	82	34	81	39	46	86
52	37	68	15	53	22	98	30	16	31	83	24	87	69	29	24	85	44	25	50	75	62	83	95	41
97	50	52	53	52	26	78	21	68	69	57	79	42	40	89	55	81	75	24	52	51	32	79	97	05
36	05	09	18	11	71	01	63	17	60	11	65	19	43	07	44	86	19	58	92	23	71	32	96	19
20	79	70	09	30	81	14	53	80	93	71	94	10	18	14	83	69	76	53	25	27	36	65	65	05
13	07	89	72	08	00	37	75	14	94	83	85	06	72	66	07	47	30	17	11	16	02	63	97	30
94	26	82	37	43	34	23	00	14	50	96	85	41	17	71	69	20	15	98	82	79	69	68	50	31
13	55	88	38	43	75	37	43	83	85	53	74	54	62	99	68	93	74	43	95	06	26	79	78	87
02	44	24	97	71	97	93	12	70	89	42	52	33	24	91	05	87	53	15	77	49	92	83	97	80

Fig. 110.   Table of random numbers.

for example, that one of the unknown variables would happen to affect all of the data under factor A1 and none of the data under factor A2.

(2) Second Method

Write on cards or slips of paper all the combinations of variables to be represented in the experiment. For example:

A1B1C1D1
A1B1C2D1,etc.

Shuffle the cards thoroughly and put them together to form a deck. Set up first the combination of conditions shown on the top card in the deck and run the necessary number of units. Then continue with the next card and so on. This will make sure that the data are obtained in random order and will help to keep unanticipated variables from introducing an unexpected bias.

(3) Third Method

Use a table of random numbers to determine the order in which the portions of the experiment should be run. A typical page from one of the published tables is shown in Figure 110. The table is used as follows:

Starting at random at any point in the table, take the first digit you find and count off that number of boxes in the experimental design. Write the word "first" in the indicated box. Then take the digit directly below and continue in this manner, using the digits in exactly the same way as the numbers which came up on the dice in Method (1).

The table of random numbers can also be used in other ways. Take the digits vertically or horizontally. Take the first column in the separated blocks of five columns or alternatively take the last column, the fourth column, etc. Take either the last digit, the next to the last digit, pairs of two digits in combination, and so on. It is also possible to take the numbers in diagonal rows: for example, 15, 81, 05, 63, etc. in Figure 110. One can start at the bottom and read up, start at the right-hand side and read across toward the left, skip numbers in any way desired, taking every fourth pair, every tenth individual digit, etc.

Because of the large number of ways in which the table can be used, a single table of the type shown in Figure 110 can be used indefinitely without introducing non-random patterns into the data.

Other methods of ensuring randomness in the results may occur to the engineer. He should avoid, however, attempting to make a "hit-and-miss" or haphazard assignment of the boxes. Because of the strong psychological tendency of a human being to repeat patterns, it is virtually impossible to ensure randomness without the aid of something which is dependent directly on the laws of chance. For example, a truly random set of numbers will repeat digits in succession, or alternate even and odd digits, more frequently than a person who is attempting to give numbers at random.

B-8.7 Methods of handling abnormal data

Experiments are frequently disturbed by the accidental loss of a unit which was to have been used for one of the boxes. Where possible, the experimenter should forestall this possibility by running more units than will be essential for the experiment and select from this group at random as described on page 113. Occasionally, however, it may be so expensive to produce the units or obtain measurements that provision for additional units is out of the question. In that case, the engineer should do one of the following things to take care of the gap in the data:

(a) Omit the measurement completely and leave a gap in the plotting.

(b) Fill in an arbitrary value if necessary by calculations based on other numbers in the experiment. See Reference No. 5.

A second common experience is the obtaining of a measurement which looks like a "freak." This should be handled as in the case of any data in a process capability study. (See pages

52–53). The experimenter should label the measurement in such a way as to identify it but should not, in general, attempt to eliminate it from the data.

In handling freaks on experimental charts, keep in mind the following points:

(1) In view of the small total quantity of data, each single measurement carries a large proportion of the information. Do not overlook the possibility that certain combinations of variables may tend to produce the condition you are tempted to call a "freak."

(2) Since the data in a designed experiment are arranged and rearranged many times in order to study the different factors in different combinations, a single freak is likely to appear in several different ways. Be careful not to conclude from this that the entire process is full of freaks.

B-8.8 Protecting the Identification of the experimental units

Since all the conclusions which will be obtained from the experiment depend upon careful and precise identification of the measurements, the experimenter must take constant precautions to preserve the necessary identification. Ordinarily at least part of the processing and handling will be done by the shop, or by other people who are not directly responsible for the experiment. An inadvertent mixup in the units, or the processing of the A1B2 units at the temperature which was planned for A1B1, may make it impossible to obtain useful conclusions.

In all cases, the experimenter should either follow through all units in the experiment himself, or make sure that others who are doing this for him have been carefully instructed. Precautions of this kind invariably pay off in more reliable and more conclusive results.

PART C
Specifications

---✦---

C-1 SPECIFICATIONS IN GENERAL

In manufacturing processes, we are interested in the characteristics of each and every unit produced. Even when we attempt to study the process by means of samples, as in process capability studies or shop control charts, we are really interested in the total distribution of individuals and are using the samples as a means to this end. Specifications are stated by design engineers or product engineers in an attempt to set up desirable restrictions on:

(a) the individual units, or
(b) the distribution of individual units,

or both.

Specifications tend to fall into three basic types.

Type A. The specification states a limit or other requirement which applies to each unit of product individually regardless of other units in the same product. For example: "The length of the part shall be .125″ ± .003″." "The width of the groove shall not exceed .375″." Product is considered to conform to such specifications if each individual unit is on or inside the limit, even if all units are exactly at the limit.

Type B. The specification defines the distribution which the product must have in order to be acceptable. For example: "The average of the product shall not be higher than .5 millivolt and the individual units shall be distributed in a natural manner around this average with a spread not to exceed ±.03 millivolt." Such specifications are sometimes spoken of as "distribution requirements." They may or may not be accompanied by limits of Type A which apply to the individual pieces.

Occasionally, requirements of this type are specified in terms of $\bar{X}$ and R charts. That is, the specification states the centerline and control limits for an $\bar{X}$ and R chart and the product is acceptable as long as random samples from the product show control on this chart.

Type C. The specification states a requirement which must be met by most of the product but allows a certain percentage of units to exceed the requirement. For example: "The resistance shall not exceed 173 ohms. However, product shall be considered acceptable if not more than 2% exceeds this limit provided no units exceed 178 ohms."

Such requirements are sometimes referred to as "product tolerance" requirements. When the Government specifies the AQL which a given product must meet, this is in effect a Type C specification.

On most products the majority of specifications are of Type A. However, the number of Type B specifications is gradually increasing. The engineer should be aware that many specifications are stated as if they were of Type A and yet the designer has in mind a distribution which he expects the product to meet. Such requirements are, in the mind of the designer, specifications of Type B.

In a quality control program there are many advantages in working with Type B specifications.

C-2 RELATIONSHIP BETWEEN PROCESS AND SPECIFICATION

To make a valid comparison between a process and a specification, it is necessary to have an $\bar{X}$ and R chart with both $\bar{X}$ and R in control. Follow the directions on page 56 to find how the process distribution is related to the specified limits. If necessary, make calculations as shown on pages 58–60 in order to determine, more or less accurately, how much of the distribution can be expected to fall outside of limits. There are four basic relationships which may exist between the process and its specifications, as follows.

(1) *The spread of the process may be less than the difference between the specified maximum and minimum, with the process safely centered.* See Figure 111.

Possible action:

a. Maintain control against these standard values.
b. Consider the use of modified control limits for shop charts as explained on pages 195–196.
c. Consider the possibility of reducing inspection as explained on page 274.

(2) *The spread of the process may be just equal to the difference between the specified maximum and minimum.* See Figure 112.

Possible action:

a. Provide for constant checking of the process to keep it centered.
b. Provide for sorting the product when the distribution shifts.
c. Attempt to reduce the process spread through a designed experiment.
d. If possible, get wider specifications.

(3) *The spread of the process may be less than the difference between the specified maximum and minimum, but the process may be off-center.* See Figure 113.

Possible action:

a. Try to center the distribution at a point safely within the specified limits. Maintain control at that point.
b. If the shop is unable to center the distribution within limits, and if the present level does not produce a good product, write this down as *unfinished business.* Put a control chart in the shop and study

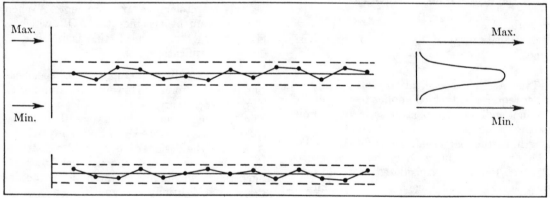

Fig. 111. Process narrower than specified limits.

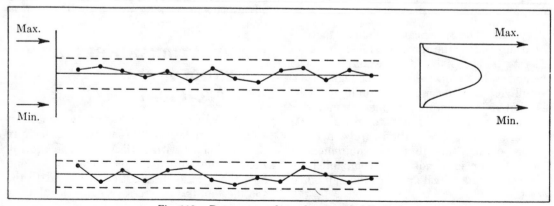

Fig. 112. Process spread equal to specified limits.

it regularly at your quality control meetings. If necessary, design an experiment to discover what can be used to make the process shift.

Meanwhile provide for operational sorting until the necessary information is obtained. Don't give up until you get this problem solved.

c. Determine whether the specification nominal can be shifted without adverse effect on the product. If so, take steps to get the specification changed.

It sometimes happens that a distribution cannot be shifted to meet one specification without causing failures to meet another specification. In that case, there may be correlation between the characteristics, and the two specifications may be incompatible. Put a control chart on each characteristic and study the charts together. Include both characteristics in any designed experiments which are conducted. This will make it possible to find the optimum combination of distributions and maximize yields on both characteristics simultaneously.

(4) *The spread of the process may be greater than the difference between the specified maximum and minimum.* See Figure 114.

Possible action:

a. Try to open the specifications.
b. Try to reduce the spread of the process by running a designed experiment.
c. Provide for 100% sorting of all product until the problem can be resolved.
d. Aim for a level that will set an economic balance between relative costs, including rework or scrap. Maintain control at that level.
e. Make fundamental changes in the process, such as: buy a new machine, design different tools or provide different methods.

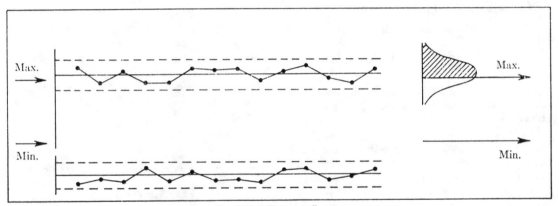

Fig. 113. Process offcenter.

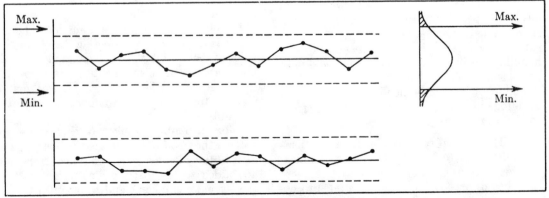

Fig. 114. Process wider than specified limits.

Non-normal distributions

The foregoing comparisons apply to any distribution, whether normal or not. However, if the distribution is not normal, the center of the distribution may need to be located closer to or farther from one of the specification limits in order to allow for the non-normal shape.

C-3 SPECIFICATION CONFLICTS AND WHAT CAN BE DONE TO AVOID THEM

If $\bar{X}$ and R charts show that the natural distribution of the process is too wide to fit between the specified limits (Condition 4), or if the process cannot be centered in the proper place (Condition 3), there is evidently a conflict between process and specification. As indicated above, there are three ways in which this conflict may be resolved:

(1) Change the process.

(2) Change the specification.

(3) Sort and repair the product which falls out of limits.

The first thing to attempt is to change the process. If making the necessary changes would be very expensive, or if no better way of making the product is known, the engineers should look carefully at the specification. The usual procedure is to ask to have the tolerances reviewed to see what effect a different set of tolerances would have on the assembly, functioning or interchangeability of the product.

In order to reduce manufacturing costs to a minimum, tolerances should be as wide as the design can permit rather than as narrow as the shop is able to meet.

Sorting and repair is a very expensive way of handling specification trouble, and should only be considered as a last resort.

The following will be helpful to engineers in avoiding unnecessary costs resulting from specification conflicts:

(1) The natural spread of a process is usually taken to be $\pm 3\ \sigma'$. For economical manufacture, the specified tolerances should accept the full natural process spread.

(2) In addition, it is seldom possible to keep a process running at exactly the same level month after month. Some allowance is needed to permit a slight shifting of the center. For most processes, it is considered desirable to allow the center to shift about $\pm 1\ \sigma'$. In that case, the specified tolerances should be about $\pm 4\ \sigma'$.

In some Western Electric processes where good control around the nominal is essential, the specified tolerance is $\pm 3\frac{1}{3}\ \sigma'$. This permits the process average to shift up or down about $\frac{1}{3}\ \sigma'$.

(3) If the natural spread of the process is more than about $\frac{2}{3}$ of the specified tolerances, it is probably great enough to cause occasional difficulty in meeting the requirements. If the spread is considerably less than the specified tolerances (say $\frac{1}{2}$ or $\frac{1}{3}$), it may be possible to reduce costs by using a more economical process.

In all cases where processes are to be compared with specifications, the processes must first be in control as shown by a process capability study. See paragraph A-3.10 on page 56. If an out-of-control condition is indicated by the study, identify the assignable causes and remove them (or allow for them) before comparing the process with the specification.

C-4 STATISTICAL ADDITION OF TOLERANCES

Whenever two or more parts are assembled together, the act of assembly creates new dimensions and new distributions that did not exist before the assembly was made. The engineer is interested in predicting the characteristics of the assembly, and in assigning suitable tolerances to the components so as to permit the most economical and trouble-free manufacture for both the components and the assembly.

Every assembly problem of this nature involves the *addition of distributions*. The distributions which exist on one component are added to the distributions which exist on the second component and so on until the assembly is completed.

Inasmuch as the addition of distributions is a statistical procedure, the engineer should be familiar with certain basic statistical laws in order to arrive at economical solutions.

C-4.1 Theory of the addition of distributions

The most important statistical laws which govern the addition of distributions are the following:

(1) *Law of the addition of averages.* If parts are assembled in such a way that one dimension is added to another, the average dimension of the assembly will be equal to the sum of the average dimensions of the parts.

Let $\bar{X}_A$ = the average dimension of Part A

$\bar{X}_B$ = the average dimension of Part B

$\bar{X}_C$ = the average dimension of Part C, etc.

Average dimension of assembly = $\bar{X}_A + \bar{X}_B + \bar{X}_C$, etc.

See Figure 115.

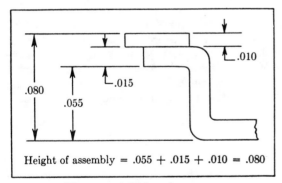

Height of assembly = .055 + .015 + .010 = .080

Fig. 115. Addition of averages.

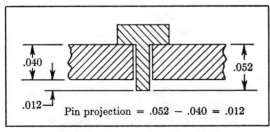

Pin projection = .052 − .040 = .012

Fig. 116. Subtraction of averages.

(2) *Law of differences.* If the parts are assembled in such a way that one dimension is subtracted from another, the average dimension of the assembly will be the difference between the average dimensions of the parts.

Let $\bar{X}_D$ = the average dimension of Part D

$\bar{X}_E$ = the average dimension of Part E

Average dimension of assembly = $\bar{X}_D - \bar{X}_E$ or $\bar{X}_E - \bar{X}_D$ as the case may be.

See Figure 116.

(3) *Law of sums and differences.* If the parts are assembled in such a way that certain dimensions are added to each other while certain dimensions are subtracted, the average dimension of the assembly will be the algebraic sum of the average dimensions of the parts.

Average dimension of assembly = $\bar{X}_A + \bar{X}_B + \bar{X}_C - \bar{X}_D + \bar{X}_E$, etc.

(4) *Law of the addition of standard deviations or variances.* If the components are assembled at random, the standard deviation of the assembly will not be the simple sum of the standard deviations of the parts. It will be the value obtained by squaring each of the component standard deviations, totaling the squares, and then taking the square root of the total.*

Let σ_A = the standard deviation of Part A

σ_B = the standard deviation of Part B

Standard deviation of the assembly $\sqrt{(\sigma_A)^2 + (\sigma_B)^2}$.

The fourth law should be carefully studied by the engineer, because the statistical addition gives a different result from the one which he would be likely to obtain intuitively.

In particular, the engineer should note that

---

* In special cases, where the dimensions do not combine linearly, or are not independent, more complicated calculations may be necessary to obtain the final dimension and its standard deviation.

123

the squares of the standard deviations are always *added* regardless of whether the average dimension is obtained by sums or differences. Never attempt to subtract one standard deviation from another as may be done in the case of averages.

The fourth law can also be expressed in terms of "variance" instead of standard deviation. The variance is the square of the standard deviation (σ^2). If $(\sigma_A)^2$ is the variance of Part A and $(\sigma_B)^2$ is the variance of Part B, the variance of the assembly will be $(\sigma_A)^2 + (\sigma_B)^2$.

C-4.2 Assembly tolerances

The law of the addition of standard deviations has important implications in assembly work, since the "square root of the sum of the squares" will always be less than the value that would be obtained if the standard deviations were merely totaled. For example:

$$\sigma_A = .0003$$
$$\sigma_B = .0004$$
$$\sigma_A + \sigma_B = .0007$$

But:

$$\sqrt{(\sigma_A)^2 + (\sigma_B)^2} = \sqrt{(.0003)^2 + (.0004)^2} =$$
$$\sqrt{.00000025} = .0005$$

The law of statistical addition gives .0005 while simple arithmetic addition gives .0007. This means that *random assemblies can be held to narrower spreads than would be indicated by totaling the spreads of the parts.* Designers take advantage of this in the condition known as "overlapping tolerances."

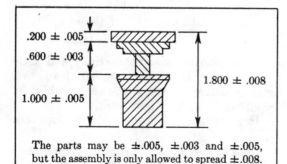

.200 ± .005
.600 ± .003
1.000 ± .005
1.800 ± .008

The parts may be ±.005, ±.003 and ±.005, but the assembly is only allowed to spread ±.008.

Fig. 117. Overlapping tolerances.

C-4.3 Overlapping tolerances

When we add up the tolerances on all component parts on a drawing and find that their total is greater than the tolerance allowed for the assembly, we have a condition known as "overlapping tolerances." See Figure 117.

This may or may not be a cause for concern since, by the law of the addition of standard deviations as given above, we know that the spread of random assemblies will be less than the total spread of all the parts.

Whether we will have trouble in assembly when using these "overlapping tolerances" depends on four factors:

(1) Whether the actual standard deviations of the components are really the same as implied in the tolerances on the drawing.

(2) Whether the actual averages of the components are the same as the nominals shown on the drawing.

(3) Whether the components are assembled at random.

(4) Whether the "square root of the sum of the squares" of the actual standard deviations, when calculated, is compatible with the tolerance specified for the assembly.

The information for points 1 and 2 must be obtained from process capability studies or shop control charts. Point 3 can be taken care of in setting up the assembly process. Point 4 can be calculated by the engineer from the information provided in 1 and 2.

C-4.4 Pitfalls in the use of overlapping tolerances

The law of the addition of standard deviations as given on page 123 applies in any case where the standard deviations of the various components are known. Engineers sometimes wish to take advantage of this law without having prior knowledge of what the standard deviations are likely to be. In such cases the engineer may reason as follows:

a. Assume that the components will all be normally distributed with a spread equal to the tolerance which is put on the drawing.

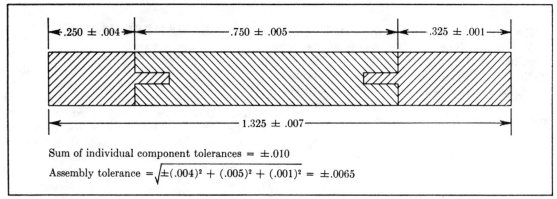

Sum of individual component tolerances = ±.010

Assembly tolerance = $\sqrt{\pm(.004)^2 + (.005)^2 + (.001)^2} = \pm.0065$

Fig. 118.   Wrong use of overlapping tolerances.

b. It would then be possible to substitute "specified tolerance" in place of "standard deviation" in the equation on page 123.

Figure 118 shows an example of assembly limits calculated in this manner.

The calculations were as follows:

Average of assembly should equal Nominal$_A$ + Nominal$_B$ + Nominal$_C$

.250 + .750 + .325 = 1.325.

Tolerance of assembly should equal

$$\sqrt{(\text{Tolerance}_A)^2 + (\text{Tolerance}_B)^2 + (\text{Tolerance}_C)^2}$$

$$\sqrt{(.004)^2 + (.005)^2 + (.001)^2} =$$

$$\sqrt{.000042} = .0065$$

On the basis of the above calculation the engineer fixed the assembly tolerance at ±.007. This is a dangerous way to use overlapping tolerances.

The danger in making calculations of this type is that the engineer has no way of checking his assumptions. If the components are not normally distributed around nominal, or if their spread is not equal to the tolerance, the shop may get into serious trouble when tolerances are calculated in this manner.

In particular, the shop will be likely to get into trouble if the spread of the process at any one time is considerably narrower than the tolerance. This is very likely to be the case in practice. To avoid such trouble the engineer should adopt the following rules.

(1) Always calculate the assembly tolerance from process capability information. If no information is available, use your best estimate of the probable capability and make ample allowance for the fact that your estimate may be inaccurate.

(2) In using specifications which include overlapping tolerances, always provide the shop with control charts which will show the actual distribution of the components. The assemblies will be the statistical sum of the distributions on the control charts, and this may be very different from the assumed distributions on the drawing.

C-4.5 Successful use of overlapping tolerances

Figure 119 shows an example of the successful use of overlapping tolerances, properly implemented with control charts.

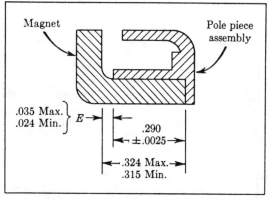

Fig. 119.   Correct use of overlapping tolerances.

The "E" requirement on the gap is only .035 − .024. The possible maximum clearance using extreme parts would be .324 − .2875 = .0365. The possible minimum clearance using extreme parts would be .315 − .2925 = .0225. Yet the shop consistently meets the tight "E" requirement.

Procedure

- The .290″ dimension is controlled by an $\bar{X}$ and R chart.
- The .324 maximum, .315 minimum dimension is controlled by an $\bar{X}$ and R chart.
- The .035 maximum E, .024 minimum E dimension is verified by an $\bar{X}$ and R chart.

The results have been economical manufacture, minimum inspection, virtually no rejections and good process control.

C-5 CLEARANCES AND FITS

"Statistical addition of tolerances" can be applied to advantage in dealing with clearances and fits. These are "mating" conditions expected of two or more parts having the same or different tolerances. The specified mating conditions vary from interference fits to running fits according to the functional design of the mating parts. See Figures 120 and 121.

Taking Figure 121 as an example, what will be the average clearance between shaft and bearing, and how much will it vary?

Let $\bar{\bar{X}}_B$ = the controlled average of the inside diameter of the bearing, and let σ_B = its standard deviation.

Let $\bar{\bar{X}}_S$ = the controlled average of the outside diameter of the shaft, and let σ_S = its standard deviation.

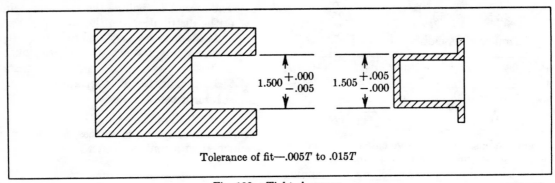

Tolerance of fit—.005T to .015T

Fig. 120. Tight clearance.

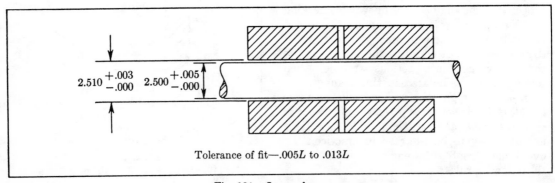

Tolerance of fit—.005L to .013L

Fig. 121. Loose clearance.

A process capability study has yielded the following values:

$$\bar{\bar{X}}_B = 2.5115 \qquad \bar{\bar{X}}_S = 2.502$$

$$\sigma_B = .0006 \qquad \sigma_S = .0007$$

The evidence indicates that the distributions are approximately normal.

Average assembly clearance

$$= \bar{\bar{X}}_B - \bar{\bar{X}}_S$$

$$= 2.5115 - 2.502$$

$$= .0095$$

Standard deviation of the assembly clearance

$$(\sigma_C) = \sqrt{(\sigma_B)^2 + (\sigma_S)^2}$$

$$= \sqrt{(.0006)^2 + (.0007)^2}$$

$$= \sqrt{.00000085}$$

$$= .0009$$

Minimum clearance $= .0095 - 3\,\sigma_C$
$= .0095 - .0027 = .0068$.
Maximum clearance $= .0095 + 3\,\sigma_C$
$= .0095 + .0027 = .0122$.

To find how much of the product can be expected to meet the specification (assuming normal distributions), proceed as follows:

$$t = \frac{.0095 - \text{Spec. Max.}}{\sigma_C} =$$

$$\frac{.0095 - .013}{.0009} = -3.9$$

Look up -3.9 in Table I on page 133, under "Percentage Outside of Max." Only one-hundredth of 1% of the product is likely to fail to meet the maximum tolerance. Similar calculations are made for the minimum tolerance. Follow the directions on page 132.

Comment

In order to take advantage of statistical solutions for such problems, two restrictions must be met:

(1) There must be a known distribution for each component. This ordinarily means that each component must come from a controlled process, or at least from a known process which is covered by $\bar{X}$ and R charts.

(2) The mating components must be assembled at random rather than by selection.

As in the case of overlapping tolerances, the engineer should *not* use the nominals or tolerances specified on the drawing. It is necessary to use the actual $\bar{X}$'s and standard deviations from controlled processes, as shown by a shop control chart or a process capability study.

PART D
Distributions

D-1 CHARACTERISTICS OF FREQUENCY DISTRIBUTIONS

Frequency distributions have three characteristics that provide useful information:

(1) Center, or average.
(2) Spread, or dispersion.
(3) Shape.

Each of these characteristics can be described by means of standard statistical measures.

D-1.1 Center or average

When observations are plotted in the form of a frequency distribution they usually tend to cluster near some central value, with fewer readings falling on either side. The point near which the measurements tend to cluster is called the "central tendency." Among the common measures of central tendency are the following:

(1) Arithmetic mean (commonly spoken of as "average").
(2) Median (or middlemost value).
(3) Mode (the value having the highest frequency).

The arithmetic mean or "average" is almost universally used in quality control. In a few cases the median is employed as a convenient substitute.

Arithmetic mean

This is denoted by the symbol $\bar{X}$. It is calculated as follows:

Add the observed values and divide the total by the number of observations.

Let X = an individual observation

$$X = \frac{X_1 + X_2 + X_3 + X_4 \ldots \ldots X_n}{n}$$

Median or middlemost value

This is denoted by the symbol MED. It is calculated as follows:

Arrange the measurements in ascending order of magnitude. Count off equal numbers of measurements from either end of the series until (a) a single value or (b) a pair of values is left at the center. If a single value is left, this value is the median. If two values are left, the median is the average of the two. For example:

a. 72   79   80   81   93
MED = 80.

b. 46 $\boxed{51 \qquad 54}$ 60

MED = the average of 51 and 54, or 52.5.

Mode

The mode is often used in referring to a skewed distribution. It represents the maximum point on the distribution curve. In a skewed distribution the median and the mode do not occur at the same point as the arithmetic mean.

D-1.2 Spread or dispersion

The "spread" of a distribution is the amount of variation or dispersion of the individual values around their average. Among the common measures of dispersion are the following:

(1) Variance (the mean square deviation of the values from their average).
(2) Standard deviation (the square root of the variance, or "root mean square" deviation of the values from their average).
(3) Range (the difference between the highest and lowest value in a set of observations).

All three of these measures are employed in quality control.

Variance

This is denoted by the symbol σ^2 (sigma squared). It is calculated as follows:

Obtain the average of the given values. Calculate the difference between each value and the average. Square these differences, total them, and divide by the number of given values.

Let X = an individual value

$\bar{X}$ = the arithmetic mean (or average) of the individual values

$$\sigma^2 = \frac{\Sigma[(X - \bar{X})^2]}{n}$$

Example:

Given the set of numbers:

10   14   6   2

$$\bar{X} = \frac{32}{4} = 8$$

Deviations from $\bar{X}$ are $+2$, $+6$, -2, -6. Squares of deviations are 4, 36, 4, 36.

Mean square deviation (or variance)

$$= \frac{4 + 36 + 4 + 36}{4} = 20$$

Standard deviation

The standard deviation is denoted by the symbol σ (sigma) or sometimes s. It is calculated as follows:

Obtain the variance as directed above. Extract the square root. This is the standard deviation.

$$\sigma = \sqrt{\frac{\Sigma[(X - \bar{X})^2]}{n}}$$

Example:

Given the set of numbers:

10   14   6   2

$$\bar{X} = 8$$

$$\sigma = \sqrt{\frac{(+2)^2 + (+6)^2 + (-2)^2 + (-6)^2}{4}}$$

$$= \sqrt{20} = 4.472$$

In calculating the standard deviation of a large number of measurements, it is convenient to group the data into cells as shown on page 139.

The standard deviation can then be calculated by a short-cut method as shown in Figure 122.

Proceed as follows:

(1) Record the observed frequency opposite the midpoint of each cell.

(2) Set up some convenient arbitrary scale which can be used for preliminary calculations.

(3) Fill in the columns "fx" and "fx^2" as indicated.

Data from Figure 130 on page 139. $n = 100$				
Mid-point of Cell	Observed Frequency, f	Arbitrary Scale, x	fx	fx^2
12.75	1	+10	+10	100
12.55	0	+ 9	0	0
12.35	3	+ 8	+24	192
12.15	1	+ 7	+ 7	49
11.95	3	+ 6	+18	108
11.75	2	+ 5	+10	50
11.55	4	+ 4	+16	64
11.35	10	+ 3	+30	90
11.15	10	+ 2	+20	40
10.95	8	+ 1	+ 8	8
10.75	11	0	0	0
10.55	7	− 1	− 7	7
10.35	4	− 2	− 8	16
10.15	15	− 3	−45	135
9.95	6	− 4	−24	96
9.75	6	− 5	−30	150
9.55	2	− 6	−12	72
9.35	3	− 7	−21	147
9.15	0	− 8	0	0
8.95	0	− 9	0	0
8.75	0	−10	0	0
8.55	1	−11	−11	121
8.35	3	−12	−36	432
	100		−51	1877
Divided by n			−.51 E1	18.77 E2

A = midpoint of zero cell = 10.75
m = cell interval (difference between midpoints) = .20
$\bar{X} = A + m\,(E1) = 10.75 + [.20 \times (-.51)] = 10.75 - .10 = 10.65$
$\sigma = m\,\sqrt{E2 - (E1)^2} = .2\,\sqrt{18.77} - .26 = .2\,\sqrt{18.51} = .86$

Fig. 122. Short method of calculating the standard deviation from a grouped frequency distribution.

(4) Divide both the "*fx*" and the "*fx²*" columns by *n* (the total number of observations). Call these respectively E1 and E2.

(5) Record the value of A (the midpoint of the cell called "0" on the arbitrary scale) and *m* (the difference from midpoint to midpoint of the cells).

(6) Calculate $\bar{X}$ and σ for the grouped frequency distribution by using the equations given at the bottom of Figure 122.

Other methods of calculating the standard deviation can be found in the standard statistical texts.

Standard deviation of a universe (σ')

When we wish to refer to the standard deviation of an underlying universe or parent population, we use the symbol σ'. In an industrial process the true value of σ' is usually unknown. However, it is possible to estimate σ' by using a sample (or series of samples) as follows:

$$\sigma' = \text{(sigma of a sample of given size)} \times \frac{1}{c_2}$$

where c_2 is a factor which varies with sample size as shown in Figure 123. σ' can also be estimated from the centerline on an *R* chart as follows:

If the *R* chart shows control,

$$\sigma' = \frac{\bar{R}}{d_2}$$

where d_2 is a factor which varies with sample size as shown in Figure 123.

Sample Size	d_2	c_2
2	1.128	.5642
3	1.693	.7236
4	2.059	.7979
5	2.326	.8407
6	2.534	.8686
7	2.704	.8882
8	2.847	.9027
9	2.970	.9139
10	3.078	.9227

Fig. 123. Table of factors for estimating σ'.

In cases where the *R* chart is in control but the $\bar{X}$ chart is out of control, the estimate of σ' which is obtained from the *R* chart will be a better estimate of the standard deviation of the underlying universe than the value obtained by calculating the "root mean square" deviation. For example:

The original data of Figure 122 were shown on page 14. $\bar{R}$ for samples of 5 was found to be 1.59. The d_2 factor for samples of 5 is 2.326.

$$\sigma' = \frac{\bar{R}}{d_2} = \frac{1.59}{2.326} = .68$$

This is a truer estimate of the standard deviation of the underlying process than the value of .86 which was calculated on page 130. This is because the distribution shifted its center during the period when the measurements were obtained, and the shift in center has inflated the estimate arrived at on page 130.

Range

The range is denoted by the symbol *R*. It is calculated as follows:

Let M = the largest value in a set of measurements
m = the smallest value
R = $M - m$

The range is used in quality control to detect certain types of assignable causes. Also, the average range of a series of samples which show control may be used as above to estimate σ'.

D-1.3 Shape

The third important characteristic of a distribution is its shape, or profile. Most distributions of actual observed data are irregular in shape, but sometimes distributions are found to be fairly uniform and symmetrical about the mean. Statistical techniques make use of a number of theoretical distribution shapes, which may or may not be approximated by the distributions observed in practice. Among the important theoretical shapes are the following:

(1) Normal distribution.
(2) Distributions which are symmetrical but not normal.
(3) Distributions showing various degrees and types of skewness.
(4) Distributions showing more than one mode or "peak."

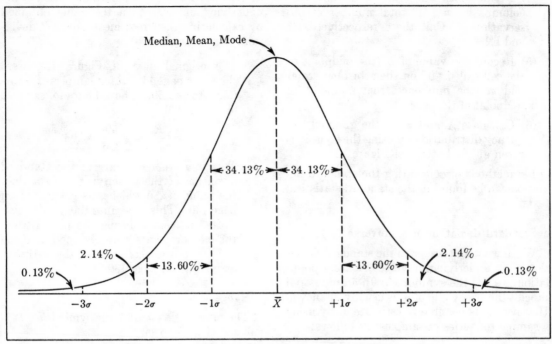

Fig. 124. Normal distribution.

D-1.4 Normal distribution

When statisticians speak of a "normal" distribution they mean one which is specifically defined by a certain mathematical equation. This distribution is perfectly symmetrical about its mean and has the familiar "bell shape" which is illustrated in Figure 124.

The equation for the Normal Distribution can be written in various ways, one of which is the following (Reference No. 6):

$$p(X) = \frac{1}{\sigma_x \sqrt{2\pi}} e^{-\frac{(X - \bar{X})^2}{2\sigma_x^2}}$$

where $p(X)$ is the ordinate to the curve for a given value of X (the measured variable).

This distribution has a number of important characteristics, among which are the following:

a. The areas on either side of the mean are equal.
b. About 68.26% of the total area is included within a distance of $\pm 1\ \sigma$ from the mean.
c. About 95.45% of the total area is included within a distance of $\pm 2\ \sigma$ from the mean.
d. About 99.73% (or virtually all) of the area is included within a distance of $\pm 3\ \sigma$ from the mean.

The table on page 133 gives a more complete listing of the percentages or areas associated with the Normal Curve.

For estimating the *percentage outside of limits* when a distribution is normal, calculate "t" as shown in the table for either the maximum or minimum limit. The percentage is given opposite the value of "t" in the appropriate column, depending on whether the value of "t" is found to be negative or positive.

The normal distribution is important in quality control for two reasons:

(1) Many distributions of quality characteristics of a product are reasonably similar to the normal distribution. This makes it possible to use the normal distribution for estimating percentages of product that are likely to fall within certain limits.

(2) Even when the distribution of product is quite far from normal, many distributions of statistical quantities, such as averages, tend to distribute themselves in accordance with the Normal Curve. For

132

TABLE I
NORMAL DISTRIBUTION

	Percentage Outside of Max. $t = \dfrac{\bar{X} - \text{Max.}}{\sigma'}$			Percentage Outside of Min. $t = \dfrac{\text{Min.} - \bar{X}}{\sigma'}$	
t	If t is negative	If t is positive	t	If t is negative	If t is positive
0.0	50.0%	50.0%	0.0	50.0%	50.0%
0.1	46.0%	54.0%	0.1	46.0%	54.0%
0.2	42.1%	57.9%	0.2	42.1%	57.9%
0.3	38.2%	61.8%	0.3	38.2%	61.8%
0.4	34.5%	65.5%	0.4	34.5%	65.5%
0.5	30.8%	69.2%	9.5	30.8%	69.2%
0.6	27.4%	72.6%	0.6	27.4%	72.6%
0.7	24.2%	75.8%	0.7	24.2%	75.8%
0.8	21.2%	78.8%	0.8	21.2%	78.8%
0.9	18.4%	81.6%	0.9	18.4%	81.6%
1.0	15.9%	84.1%	1.0	15.9%	84.1%
1.1	13.6%	86.4%	1.1	13.6%	86.4%
1.2	11.5%	88.5%	1.2	11.5%	88.5%
1.3	9.7%	90.3%	1.3	9.7%	90.3%
1.4	8.1%	91.9%	1.4	8.1%	91.9%
1.5	6.7%	93.3%	1.5	6.7%	93.3%
1.6	5.5%	94.5%	1.6	5.5%	94.5%
1.7	4.5%	95.5%	1.7	4.5%	95.5%
1.8	3.6%	96.4%	1.8	3.6%	96.4%
1.9	2.9%	97.1%	1.9	2.9%	97.1%
2.0	2.3%	97.7%	2.0	2.3%	97.7%
2.1	1.8%	98.2%	2.1	1.8%	98.2%
2.2	1.4%	98.6%	2.2	1.4%	98.6%
2.3	1.1%	98.9%	2.3	1.1%	98.9%
2.4	0.8%	99.2%	2.4	0.8%	99.2%
2.5	0.6%	99.4%	2.5	0.6%	99.4%
2.6	0.5%	99.5%	2.6	0.5%	99.5%
2.7	0.4%	99.6%	2.7	0.4%	99.6%
2.8	0.3%	99.7%	2.8	0.3%	99.7%
2.9	0.2%	99.8%	2.9	0.2%	99.8%
3.0	0.1%	99.9%	3.0	0.1%	99.9%
3.1	0.1%	99.9%	3.1	0.1%	99.9%
3.2	0.1%	99.9%	3.2	0.1%	99.9%
3.3	0.05%	99.95%	3.3	0.05%	99.95%
3.4	0.03%	99.97%	3.4	0.03%	99.97%
3.5	0.02%	99.98%	3.5	0.02%	99.98%
3.6	0.02%	99.98%	3.6	0.02%	99.98%
3.7	0.01%	99.99%	3.7	0.01%	99.99%
3.8	0.01%	99.99%	3.8	0.01%	99.99%
3.9	0.01%	99.99%	3.9	0.01%	99.99%
4.0	0.00%	100.0 %	4.0	0.00%	100.0 %

this reason the normal distribution has important uses in statistical theory, including some of the theory which underlies control charts.

Tests for normality

The engineer may occasionally wish to test a set of data for normality—that is, to test whether it might reasonably have come from a normal population. Some of the difficulties of doing this are discussed on pages 78–79. Satisfactory tests for normality require fairly large amounts of data.

Three common methods of testing for normality are the following:

(1) Chi-square test. See Reference No. 13.

(2) Normal probability paper. The data

133

are plotted cumulatively on paper having special graduations. If the distribution is perfectly normal, the graph will be a straight line. See Reference No. 13.

(3) Calculation of skewness (lack of symmetry) and kurtosis (degree of flatness). These measures of non-normality may be tested for significance like any other statistical measures. See Reference No. 13.

The engineer should remember that for many quality control purposes it is not necessary to know whether a distribution is normal.

D-1.5 Distributions which are symmetrical but not normal

The engineer should not assume that all symmetrical distributions are normal. Examples of non-normal symmetrical distributions

are shown in Figure 125.

The engineer will note that the areas in different portions of these curves are very different from the "normal" areas. Distribution A, which is flatter than the normal curve, is called a "platykurtic" distribution. Distribution B, which is more peaked than the normal curve, is called a "leptokurtic" distribution. The amount of flatness (or kurtosis) can be measured, if desired, by a measure known as "β_2." See Reference No. 19.

It is rarely necessary to measure flatness in quality control applications, but the engineer should be aware that such a characteristic exists.

D-1.6 Skewed distributions

Distributions are said to have *positive* or *negative* skewness depending on the direction of the longer tail. A distribution is skewed

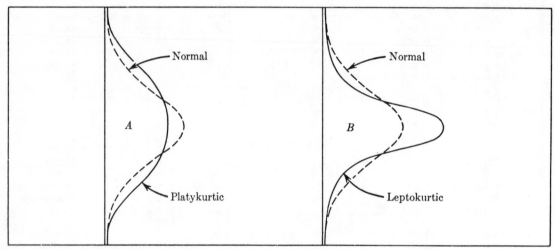

Fig. 125.   Distributions which are symmetrical but not normal.

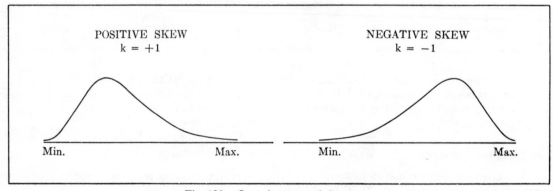

Fig. 126.   Opposite types of skewness.

positively if the long tail is on the maximum side and negatively if the long tail is on the minimum side. These two types of skewness are illustrated in Figure 126.

The degree of skewness is measured by a factor called $\sqrt{\beta_1}$ or "k." See Reference No. 19.

One of the common theoretical distributions involving skewness is known as the "Second Approximation to the Normal Curve." Its equation is

$$p(X) = \frac{1}{\sigma_x \sqrt{2\,\pi}}\, e^{-\frac{(X-\bar{X})^2}{2\sigma_x^2}} \left[1 - \frac{k}{2}\left(\frac{X-\bar{X}}{\sigma} - \frac{(X-\bar{X})^3}{3\,\sigma^3}\right)\right]$$

using the same notation that was employed on page 132.

The distributions shown in Figure 126 are "Second Approximation" curves with $k = +1$

TABLE II
SECOND APPROXIMATION WITH $k = +1$

Percentage Outside of Max. $t = \dfrac{\bar{X} - \text{Max.}}{\sigma'}$			Percentage Outside of Min. $t = \dfrac{\text{Min.} - \bar{X}}{\sigma'}$		
t	If t is negative	If t is positive	t	If t is negative	If t is positive
0.0	43.3%	43.3%	0.0	56.7%	56.7%
0.1	39.4%	47.4%	0.1	52.6%	60.6%
0.2	35.8%	51.6%	0.2	48.4%	64.2%
0.3	32.5%	55.0%	0.3	44.6%	67.5%
0.4	29.3%	60.4%	0.4	39.6%	70.7%
0.5	26.4%	64.7%	0.5	35.3%	73.6%
0.6	23.8%	69.0%	0.6	31.0%	76.2%
0.7	21.5%	73.1%	0.7	26.9%	78.5%
0.8	19.4%	77.0%	0.8	23.0%	80.6%
0.9	17.4%	80.7%	0.9	19.3%	82.6%
1.0	15.8%	84.1%	1.0	15.9%	84.2%
1.1	14.3%	87.2%	1.1	12.8%	85.7%
1.2	12.9%	89.9%	1.2	10.1%	87.1%
1.3	11.6%	92.3%	1.3	7.7%	88.4%
1.4	10.4%	95.4%	1.4	5.6%	89.6%
1.5	9.3%	96.0%	1.5	4.0%	90.7%
1.6	8.3%	97.1%	1.6	2.9%	91.7%
1.7	7.4%	98.5%	1.7	1.5%	92.6%
1.8	6.5%	99.3%	1.8	0.7%	93.5%
1.9	5.7%	99.9%	1.9	0.5%	94.3%
2.0	4.9%	100.0 %	2.0	0.0%	95.1%
2.1	4.2%	—	2.1	—	95.8%
2.2	3.6%	—	2.2	—	96.4%
2.3	3.1%	—	2.3	—	96.9%
2.4	2.6%	—	2.4	—	97.4%
2.5	2.1%	—	2.5	—	97.9%
2.6	1.7%	—	2.6	—	98.3%
2.7	1.4%	—	2.7	—	98.6%
2.8	1.1%	—	2.8	—	98.9%
2.9	0.9%	—	2.9	—	99.1%
3.0	0.7%	—	3.0	—	99.3%
3.1	0.5%	—	3.1	—	99.5%
3.2	0.4%	—	3.2	—	99.6%
3.3	0.3%	—	3.3	—	99.7%
3.4	0.2%	—	3.4	—	99.8%
3.5	0.2%	—	3.5	—	99.8%
3.6	0.1%	—	3.6	—	99.9%
3.7	0.07%	—	3.7	—	99.9%
3.8	0.03%	—	3.8	—	99.9%
3.9	0.01%	—	3.9	—	99.99%
4.0	0.00%	—	4.0	—	99.99%

and $k = -1$ respectively. The tables on pages 135 and 136 show the percentages or areas associated with these two curves. The engineer should compare the percentages with those of the Normal Distribution on page 133.

As in the case of a normal distribution, these tables can be used for estimating the *percentage outside of limits*. Follow the rules on page 132 in calculating the value of "t" and read the percentage in the appropriate column.

Some distributions having higher degrees of skewness are shown on pages 57, 58 and 163.

D-1.7 Distributions having more than one mode or peak

Common distributions of this type are shown on pages 155, 158, 162, 166, 173, 174, 176 and 179. Bimodal or multi-modal distributions

TABLE III
SECOND APPROXIMATION WITH $k = -1$

	Percentage Outside of Max. $t = \dfrac{\bar{\bar{X}} - \text{Max.}}{\sigma'}$			Percentage Outside of Min. $t = \dfrac{\text{Min.} - \bar{\bar{X}}}{\sigma'}$	
t	If t is negative	If t is positive	t	If t is negative	If t is positive
0.0	56.7%	56.7%	0.0	43.3%	43.3%
0.1	52.6%	60.6%	0.1	39.4%	47.4%
0.2	48.4%	64.2%	0.2	35.8%	51.6%
0.3	44.6%	67.5%	0.3	32.5%	55.0%
0.4	39.6%	70.7%	0.4	29.3%	60.4%
0.5	35.3%	73.6%	0.5	26.4%	64.7%
0.6	31.0%	76.2%	0.6	23.8%	69.0%
0.7	26.9%	78.5%	0.7	21.5%	73.1%
0.8	23.0%	80.6%	0.8	19.4%	77.0%
0.9	19.3%	82.6%	0.9	17.4%	80.7%
1.0	15.9%	84.2%	1.0	15.8%	84.1%
1.1	12.8%	85.7%	1.1	14.3%	87.2%
1.2	10.1%	87.1%	1.2	12.9%	89.9%
1.3	7.7%	88.4%	1.3	11.6%	92.3%
1.4	5.6%	89.6%	1.4	10.4%	95.4%
1.5	4.0%	90.7%	1.5	9.3%	96.0%
1.6	2.9%	91.7%	1.6	8.3%	97.1%
1.7	1.5%	92.6%	1.7	7.4%	98.5%
1.8	0.7%	93.5%	1.8	6.5%	99.3%
1.9	0.5%	94.3%	1.9	5.7%	99.9%
2.0	0.0%	95.1%	2.0	4.9%	100.0%
2.1	—	95.8%	2.1	4.2%	—
2.2	—	96.4%	2.2	3.6%	—
2.3	—	96.9%	2.3	3.1%	—
2.4	—	97.4%	2.4	2.6%	—
2.5	—	97.9%	2.5	2.1%	—
2.6	—	98.3%	2.6	1.7%	—
2.7	—	98.6%	2.7	1.4%	—
2.8	—	98.9%	2.8	1.1%	—
2.9	—	99.1%	2.9	0.9%	—
3.0	—	99.3%	3.0	0.7%	—
3.1	—	99.5%	3.1	0.5%	—
3.2	—	99.6%	3.2	0.4%	—
3.3	—	99.7%	3.3	0.3%	—
3.4	—	99.8%	3.4	0.2%	—
3.5	—	99.9%	3.5	0.2%	—
3.6	—	99.9%	3.6	0.1%	—
3.7	—	99.9%	3.7	0.07%	—
3.8	—	99.9%	3.8	0.03%	—
3.9	—	99.99%	3.9	0.01%	—
4.0	—	99.99%	4.0	0.00%	—

usually result from the presence of more than one system of causes.

D-2 DISTRIBUTIONS DERIVED FROM SAMPLES

D-2.1 Sampling distributions

In general, the most convenient and useful way to collect data is in small groups called *samples*. For example we might measure 5 pieces of product occasionally and record them as in Figure 127. The x's represent the individual pieces of product and the large dot is their average.

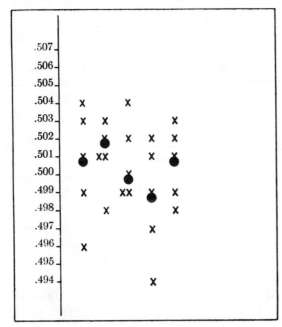

Fig. 127.   Samples of 5 and their averages.

We could group the individual measurements together, if we wished, to form a frequency distribution.

In addition to the individuals, however, we now have a number of *averages*. The averages do not spread as widely as the individual measurements.

If we had enough averages and grouped them together, we would find that they tended to form a frequency distribution of their own, which would be considerably narrower than the distribution of individuals. This can be seen in Figure 128.

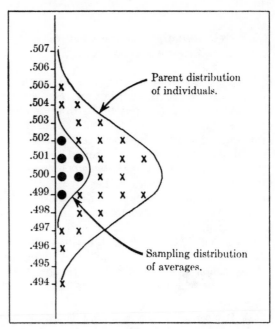

Fig. 128.   Frequency distribution of data similar to Figure 127.   A smooth curve has been drawn around the x's and also around the dots.

The distribution of sample averages is called a *sampling distribution* since, in order to obtain it, we must have a series of samples. In the same way, a series of ranges calculated from samples will form a sampling distribution of ranges. A series of percentages calculated from samples will form a sampling distribution of percentages. A series of counts obtained from samples will form a sampling distribution of counts.

Sampling distributions form the basis of most control charts. The sampling distributions mentioned above form the basis of $\bar{X}$ and R charts, p charts and c charts respectively.

D-2.2 Parent distribution

The underlying distribution of the process from which the samples were taken is referred to as the *parent distribution* in order to distinguish it from the distributions derived from samples. Other names for the parent distribution are:

(1) Universe.

(2) Population.

(3) Distribution of individuals.

D-2.3 Relationships between parent and sampling distributions

Sampling distributions are related mathematically to the parent distribution from which the samples came. The parent distribution determines (a) the standard deviation of the sampling distribution, (b) its center or average, and (c) to a certain extent its shape.

Some of the relationships between parent and sampling distributions are rather involved, but in the case of the *sampling distribution of averages* the relationships are quite simple. For this reason, the sampling distribution of averages has been used in the illustrations which follow.

The sampling distribution of averages has the following relation to the parent:

(1) The center of the sampling distribution of averages is the same as that of the parent.

(2) The shape of the sampling distribution of averages is governed to some extent by the parent, but in general the sampling distribution tends to follow the normal curve quite closely, even when the parent distribution is irregular, skewed, triangular or square. For most practical purposes in engineering work, it can be assumed that the sampling distribution of averages is approximately normal.

The engineer should note, however, that this would not hold for parent distributions having very extreme forms (such as U-shapes or J-shapes), unless the samples are very large. If the engineer should encounter such a case in practice, he may expect to find the shape of the sampling distribution significantly affected by the parent.

(3) The standard deviation of the distribution of sample averages is related to the standard deviation of the parent distribution as follows:

Standard deviation of averages =

$$\frac{\text{standard deviation of parent}}{\sqrt{n}}$$

where n = number of individuals in each sample average.

If $n = 5$, the standard deviation of averages = $\frac{1}{\sqrt{5}}$ times the standard deviation of the parent. This is $\frac{1}{2.236}$, or approximately 45%.

The control limits which appear on an $\bar{X}$ chart are merely the 3 sigma limits for the sampling distribution of averages.

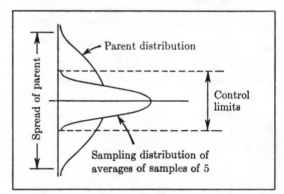

Fig. 129. Control limits for averages: Samples of 5.

In the drawing above, the area of the sampling distribution is shown as approximately equal to that of the parent.

D-3 METHODS OF PLOTTING A FREQUENCY DISTRIBUTION

Consider the measurements shown on page 14 (Gain in Db.). There are 100 measurements in all and they range from 8.3 to 12.8. This is a spread of 4.5 db. When a frequency distribution is to be made from a large number of observations scattered over many different values on the scale of measurement, it is usually convenient to group the data into intervals or cells. Arrange the intervals in such a way that there will be, if possible, from 10 to 30 cells. In the present example it would be convenient to divide the spread into cells of 0.2 db. each. Tally the number of observations that fall into each cell as shown in Figure 130.

The cell boundaries should be arranged in such a way that there is only one cell in which

Gain in Db.	
12.7–12.8	x
12.5–12.6	
12.3–12.4	xxx
12.1–12.2	x
11.9–12.0	xxx
11.7–11.8	xx
11.5–11.6	xxxx
11.3–11.4	xxxxxxxxx
11.1–11.2	xxxxxxxxxx
10.9–11.0	xxxxxxxx
10.7–10.8	xxxxxxxxxxx
10.5–10.6	xxxxxxx
10.3–10.4	xxxx
10.1–10.2	xxxxxxxxxxxxxxx
9.9–10.0	xxxxxx
9.7–9.8	xxxxxx
9.5–9.6	xx
9.3–9.4	xxx
9.1–9.2	
8.9–9.0	
8.7–8.8	
8.5–8.6	x
8.3–8.4	xxx
8.1–8.2	

Fig. 130. Distribution of measurements in Figure 13
(page 14).

a given measurement may be placed. The width of all cells should be the same, and the total number of observations in all cells should not be less than 25.

Histograms

A more formal way of plotting a frequency distribution of observed values is to erect a series of columns, each having a width equal to the cell width. The height of the column represents the number of observations in each cell. Such a representation of data is called a histogram. It is used in the same way as any frequency distribution. See Figure 131 on page 140.

Other methods of plotting a frequency distribution are given in Reference No. 2.

Fitting a curve to data

Engineers are frequently called on to "fit" a theoretical curve to a set of observed data. The most common example is that of comparing actual data with a theoretical Normal Curve. In order to draw a theoretical curve, the engi-neer must first calculate the average and standard deviation of the observed data. Second, he must know the ordinates or areas of the theoretical curve he wishes to reproduce (usually obtainable from tables). Third, he must be able to adjust the plotting scales for the observed data and the theoretical curve so that the areas will be equal.

A simple way to do this is as follows:

(1) Divide the data into a convenient number of cells and compute the average and standard deviation as shown on page 130. Call these $\bar{X}'$ and σ' respectively.

(2) Translate the cell boundaries into ± values of sigma, or standard deviations from the average. Thus, if B = the cell boundary in terms of absolute units, take $\dfrac{B - \bar{X}'}{\sigma'}$ to obtain the cell boundary in terms of sigma.

(3) Look up each pair of cell boundaries in the Table of Percentages or Areas for the theoretical curve you have in mind. The difference between the two percentages (one for each boundary) gives the theoretical percentage that should fall in each cell.

(4) Mark off the cells at the bottom of a piece of graph paper, indicating both absolute units and ± values of sigma. Plot a point at the midpoint of each cell corresponding to the theoretical percentages. Choose any convenient vertical scale.

Draw a smooth curve through the points representing the theoretical distribution.

(5) Taking the observed data which are to be used for comparison, convert the frequencies for each cell into "percentage of total frequencies" by taking $\dfrac{\text{Observed}}{\text{Total}}$. Erect bars for each cell corresponding to the observed percentages. Use the same vertical scale as for the theoretical distribution.

(6) You now have a drawing with (a) a smooth curve for the theoretical distribution and (b) a histogram for the observed data. (See Figure 132 on page 141.) The

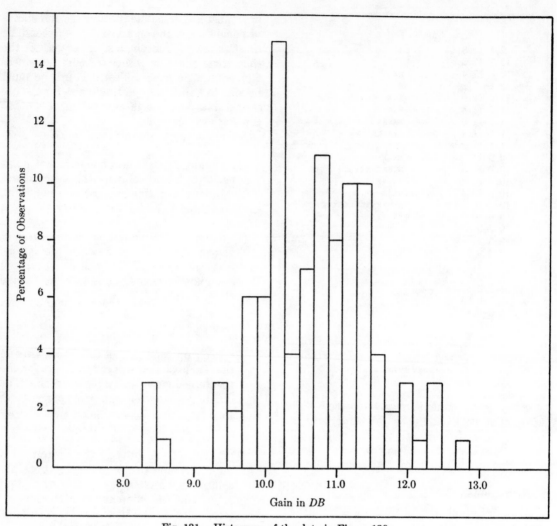

Fig. 131.   Histogram of the data in Figure 130.

distribution and the histogram have the same average and standard deviation, and the same general area.

For presentation it is generally desirable to change the scale markings at the bottom of the drawing to show convenient absolute values: for example, the values corresponding to the midpoints of the cells instead of their boundaries, or any other convenient values.

A chi-square test can be used, if desired, to obtain a numerical measure of the "goodness of fit." See References No. 5 and 13.

D-4 PRACTICAL USES OF FREQUENCY DISTRIBUTIONS

A frequency distribution of individual measurements found in a sample is likely to exhibit some of the characteristics of the parent distribution of product. Such observed distributions are useful for

(1) Comparing a collection of units with the specification.

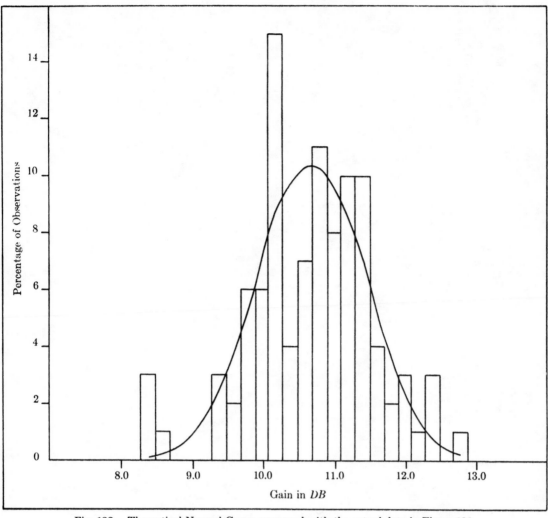

Fig. 132. Theoretical Normal Curve compared with the actual data in Figure 131.

(2) Suggesting the shape of the parent distribution or universe.

(3) Indicating certain discrepancies or peculiarities in the data, such as coarseness, gaps or screening.

Observed distributions should, however, be used with caution, and the engineer should beware of attempting to get more information out of them than a distribution can give. Do not attempt to draw general conclusions from distributions unless the data are in control. This can be determined only by plotting the data on control charts.

PART E
Correlation

————— ✦ —————

E-1 GRAPHICAL METHODS OF STUDYING CORRELATION

E-1.1 Scatter diagrams

The simplest way to study correlation is to plot a scatter diagram. Obtain values for the two variables, x and y, in pairs. That is, measure x on a certain unit and y on the same unit, identifying them as a pair. One point on the scatter diagram represents one pair of x and y values. Figures 133–135 show typical scatter diagrams which indicate (a) positive correlation (b) negative correlation and (c) no correlation.

Correlation is said to be positive if the y values increase as the x values increase. Correlation is said to be negative if the y values decrease as the x values increase. There is absence of correlation if the y values may be either higher or lower as the x values increase.

If the scale markings on Figure 133 and Figure 134 are spaced alike, Figure 133 shows a higher degree of correlation than Figure 134. The more the points scatter, the less is the correlation.

E-1.2 Trend arrangements

Since correlation can be defined as a trend in y with increasing (or decreasing) values of x, it is possible to use a control chart to test for correlation. This technique is similar to the scatter diagram except that it is possible to apply a control chart test to see whether a trend really exists. Proceed as follows:

(1) Arrange the pairs of measurements in ascending order of x. Then, ignoring x, divide the data into convenient subgroups and plot a standard control chart for y. This method can be followed with either variables or attributes data.

(2) If the control chart shows an upward

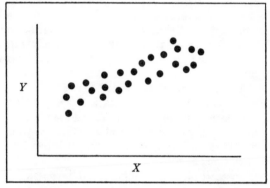

Fig. 133.   Scatter diagram: Positive correlation.

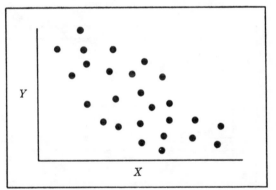

Fig. 134.   Scatter diagram: Negative correlation.

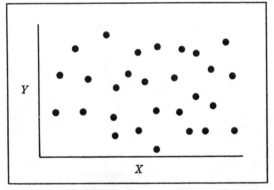

Fig. 135.   Scatter diagram: No correlation.

143

trend, there is positive correlation. If the trend is downward, there is negative correlation. If the chart stays in control, there is no reason to conclude that the two variables are correlated.

The control chart will also show whether there is a change in the variability of y as x increases. There may be a change in variability when there is no change in the average.

In addition, the control chart may indicate that some of the data are "wild" or out of control. It is necessary to make a special allowance for such data in any estimates involving correlation.

For maximum sensitivity use an $\bar{X}$ and R chart, and collect the data in such a manner that there will be 2, 3, 4 or 5 measurements of y at each of several values of x. The subgroups will then be rational subgroups with respect to variations in x.

Instead of using subgroups it is possible to

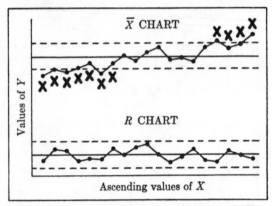

Fig. 136.   Trend arrangement: Positive correlation between x and y.

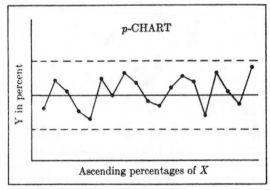

Fig. 137.   Trend arrangement: No correlation between x and y.

plot the individual values of y, basing the control limits on the moving range. This type of chart is not as sensitive as an $\bar{X}$ and R chart.

E-1.3 Determining the slope of the correlation

In many cases it is possible to tell, without calculation, the approximate "trend line" which the data appear to follow. Frequently, however, the engineer wishes to draw a line which will represent the relationship as exactly as possible. If he attempts to do this by eye, he may or may not be successful. The degree of success depends largely on how far the data scatter. See Figures 138 and 139.

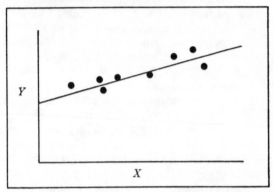

Fig. 138.   Few engineers would disagree on this.

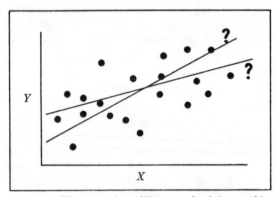

Fig. 139.   There may be a difference of opinion on this.

In doubtful cases the engineer should calculate the "regression line of y on x" (or of x on y) as explained below.

E-2 REGRESSION LINES

A "regression line" or "line of regression" is a line which represents the slope of correlated data as accurately as possible. The "line of best fit" is defined as the line which will make the *sum of the squares* of the deviations from the line a minimum. The method of calculating this line is known as the "method of least squares."

E-2.1 How to calculate the line of regression

Let x = the value of one variable.
y = the value of the other variable.

Draw up a table as shown in Figure 140.

Variables	x	y	xy	x^2
Data				
Totals				
Symbols for Totals	Σx	Σy	Σxy	Σx^2

Fig. 140. Table for calculating a line of regression.

The equation for the straight line regression is

$$y = mx + c$$

where

$$m = \frac{\Sigma xy - \dfrac{(\Sigma x)(\Sigma y)}{n}}{\Sigma x^2 - \dfrac{(\Sigma x)^2}{n}}$$

$$c = \frac{(\Sigma x)(\Sigma xy) - (\Sigma y)(\Sigma x^2)}{(\Sigma x)^2 - n(\Sigma x^2)}$$

n = the number of pairs of x, y values.

Substitute these values into the equation and plot the sloping line. As a check on your calculations, make sure the line passes through the point $\bar{x}$, $\bar{y}$.

Alternative method

If the engineer has already calculated the coefficient of correlation, "r," as shown on page 146, this can be used to calculate the line of regression. The method is shown in Figure 143.

E-2.2 Regression of y on x and x on y

The line of regression described in paragraph E-2.1 is known as the "regression of y on x." This is used to predict or estimate y values when given x. It assumes that x is the "independent variable" whose values can be fixed or which is accurately known. It assumes that y is a "dependent variable" whose values will change with any change in the value of x.

It would also be possible to calculate a line for the "regression of x on y." In that case we would assume that y is the independent variable while x is dependent, and we would predict or estimate x values when given y. To calculate this line, merely reverse x and y in the equations given above.

The two lines of regression, y on x and x on y, will not ordinarily be the same for any actual set of data. The engineer must decide which variable to consider as independent and determine the line accordingly.

If the engineer has no reason for considering either variable to be independent, he may wish to calculate both lines of regression and compare them. For many practical purposes the most useful line will be a line midway between the line of regression of x on y and the line of regression of y on x.

E-2.3 How to put control limits around a line of regression

To put control limits around a line of regression, proceed as follows:

(1) Calculate the coefficient of correlation, "r," as shown in Sub-section E-3.

(2) Calculate the "standard error of estimate," σ_e, as follows:

$$\sigma_e = \sigma_y \sqrt{1 - r^2}$$

(3) Use σ_e to establish regular 3 σ control limits about the regression line as in Figure 141 on page 146.

It is also possible to plot the successive *deviations* from the regression line, using control limits based on the moving range or an $\bar{X}$ and R chart. If the deviations are found to be out of control, we cannot be confident that the regression line really fits the data.

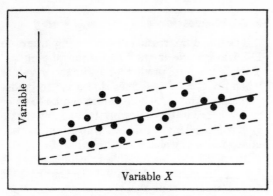

Fig. 141.   Control limits around the line of regression.

E-3 FORMAL CORRELATION ANALYSIS

Whether or not he has calculated a line of regression as in Sub-section E-2, the engineer may wish to obtain a mathematical measure of the degree of correlation between two variables. The degree of correlation is measured by the "correlation coefficient" (designated by the symbol "r").   It is calculated as follows:

$$ r = \frac{\frac{1}{n} \Sigma[(x - \bar{x})(y - \bar{y})]}{\sigma_x \sigma_y} $$

where x and y are the values of the two variables, respectively, and n is the number of pairs.   The terms in the denominator (σ_x and σ_y) can be obtained by taking the "root mean square" deviation of all the values of the variable from their average as on page 130, or alternatively by filling in the form shown in Figure 142.   Figure 143 shows how the correlation coefficient can be used to calculate lines of regression if the engineer has not previously done so.

General meaning of "r"

The value of "r" will be positive if there is positive correlation between the variables and negative if there is negative correlation.   The general meaning of "r" is summarized in Figure 144.

Precautions

In using the coefficient of correlation it is necessary to observe the following rules and precautions:

(1) While "r" is a measure of the linear relationship between x and y as it exists in a given set of numbers, even a high value of r does not imply that x and y are related as cause and effect.   It is possible to have a high degree of mathematical relationship with no causal relationship whatsoever. For example: statistics show that teachers' salaries and the national consumption of liquor tend to go up and down at the same time.   This does not prove that when teachers get higher salaries they spend the additional money on liquor.

It is possible that two variables which are not related to each other may both be related to a third variable.   This will cause the first two variables to show a mathematical relationship when there is no real cause and effect.

The engineer should make sure that there is an engineering reason to account for the correlation before he attempts to draw conclusions from a calculated value of r.

(2) While unrelated sets of numbers should have zero correlation *on the average*, individual samples may, as a result of sampling fluctuation, have values of "r" above or below zero.   Consequently, the fact that "r" is other than zero does not necessarily indicate that two sets of numbers are related.

Do not draw any conclusions based on the correlation coefficient until you have tested it for significance as follows:

   (a) Multiply r by $\sqrt{n}$, where n is the number of pairs of measurements used to determine r.   Call this "t."
   (b) If t is greater than 3, consider that the correlation is significant.   If t is less than 3, the correlation may not be significant.   The lower the value of t. the less likely it is that the correlation is significant.

If the correlation is not definitely significant as determined above, this may be due to (a) real absence of correlation or (b) insufficient data. If the engineer has reason to believe that correlation should exist he may wish to obtain more data, calculate a new value of r, and test the new value for significance.

Cell width for Y.	47000 to ↓51490	51500 to ↓55990	56000 to ↓60490	60500 to ↓64990	65000 to ↓69490	69500 to ↓73990	74000 to ↓78490	78500 to ↓82990	y	f	fy	fy^2	Σfxy
64.0–68.4									+4	0	0	0	0
59.5–63.9								xxx	+3	3	+9	27	+27
55.0–59.4					x		xxx xxxx	xxxx	+2	12	+24	48	+52
50.5–54.9				x	xx		xxx	x	+1	7	+7	7	+8
46.0–50.4				xx	x				0	3	0	0	0
41.5–45.9		xx		x	x				−1	4	−4	4	+7
37.0–41.4	x	xx							−2	3	−6	12	+20
32.5–36.9	x								−3	1	−3	9	+12
28.0–32.4	x	x							−4	2	−8	32	+28
23.5–27.9									−5	0	0	0	0
x	−4	−3	−2	−1	0	+1	+2	+3	Totals	35	+19	139	+154
f	3	5	0	4	5	0	10	8	35	n	(A) +.543	(B) 3.971	(C) +4.400
fx	−12	−15	0	−4	0	0	+20	+24	+13	(D) +.371			
fx^2	48	45	0	4	0	0	40	72	209	(E) 5.971			

To obtain the values in the Σfxy column, calculate fxy separately for each one of the "boxes." Then total all the fxy's for each row and enter in the Σfxy column.

$$\bar{x} = D = +.371 \qquad\qquad \bar{x}^2 = .138 = F$$

$$\bar{y} = A = +.543 \qquad\qquad \bar{y}^2 = .295 = G$$

$$\bar{x}\bar{y} = D \text{ times } A = .2015 = H$$

$$\sigma_x = \sqrt{E - F} = \sqrt{5.833} = 2.415 = J$$

$$\sigma_y = \sqrt{B - G} = \sqrt{3.676} = 1.917 = K$$

$$\sigma_x\sigma_y = J \text{ times } K = 4.630 = L$$

$$\text{Coefficient of correlation} = \frac{C - H}{L} = \frac{+4.1985}{4.630} = +.907 = r$$

To test whether the apparent correlation is significant, make a t-test as follows:

$$t \text{ (no. of sigma)} = r \text{ times } \sqrt{n} = .907 \times \sqrt{35} = 5.38$$

If t is greater than 3 consider that there is significant correlation.

Fig. 142. Calculation of the coefficient of correlation.

Cell width for X values $= 4500 = w$
Cell width for Y values $= 4.5\ = m$

$\sigma_x = J$ times $w = 10868$

$\sigma_y = K$ times $m = 8.626$

$\bar{X}$ = Midpoint of cell $x = 0$, plus (D times w)
$67245 + 1670 = 68915$

$\bar{Y}$ = Midpoint of cell $y = 0$, plus (A times m)
$48.2 + 2.44 = 50.64$

Regression of Y on X:

$$b = \frac{r \text{ times } \sigma_y}{\sigma_x} = \frac{.907 \text{ times } 8.626}{10868} = .0007199$$

$$a = \bar{Y} - (b \text{ times } \bar{X}) = 50.64 - 49.61 = 1.03$$

$$Y = a + bX$$

Regression of X on Y:

$$b = \frac{r \text{ times } \sigma_x}{\sigma_x} = \frac{.907 \text{ times } 10868}{8.626} = 1142.7$$

$$a = \bar{X} - (b \text{ times } \bar{Y}) = 68915 - 57866 = 11049$$

$$X = a + bY$$

Fig. 143. Calculation of lines of regression. The values are obtained from Figure 142.

Relationship Between x and y		
$r = +1.0$	Strong, positive.	As x increases, y always increases.
$r = +0.5$	Weak, positive.	As x increases, y tends in general to increase.
$r = 0$	No correlation.	x and y are independent.
$r = -0.5$	Weak, negative.	As x increases, y tends in general to decrease.
$r = -1.0$	Strong, negative.	As x increases, y always decreases.

Fig. 144. Meaning of the coefficient of correlation.

E-4 OTHER INFORMATION ON CORRELATION

For further information on correlation see References No. 5, 13 and 26. These references give information on multiple correlation, partial correlation and curvilinear correlation, none of which are covered in this Handbook.

PART F
Control Chart Patterns

This part of the Handbook gathers together much of the information needed by the engineer in interpreting control chart patterns for process capability studies or designed experiments. It is assumed that the engineer is already familiar with the elementary theory of control charts as given on pages 5–12 and also with the method of testing control chart patterns for unnaturalness as given on pages 23–30. It is also assumed that the engineer is familiar with the practical analysis of shop charts as discussed in Part C of the Shop Section and of process capability studies as discussed in Engineering Part A. The present material does not duplicate either the elementary theory or the practical analyses. It is intended to be used as supplementary reference material for those interested in a more thorough understanding of control charts.

F-1 CONTROL CHART THEORY

F-1.1 Control charts in general

The control chart in essence is a set of statistical limits applied to a sequence of points representing a process under study. The data comprising each individual point are random, but the points themselves are plotted in some deliberately chosen non-random arrangement selected to represent the most important variable. See Figure 145.

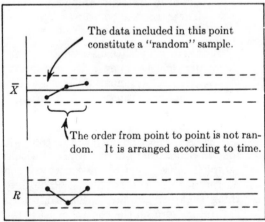

Fig. 145. Theory of the control chart: meaning of random samples.

In a process capability study, the most important variable is usually considered to be time. Consequently, the points are plotted in the order of time; that is, in the order of pro-

duction or (if the test method is one of the factors to be studied) in the order of testing. Where a process capability study is to be broken down by "production paths," the separate paths constitute an important variable, and therefore the points are plotted according to these paths. In a designed experiment the important variables are in turn the different factors included in the experiment. Consequently, the points are arranged and re-arranged according to these factors.

The control chart tests the arbitrary or non-random arrangements of points to determine whether they behave as if they were random. If the plotted points indicate nothing but randomness, this tends to show that the variable which formed the base of the arrangement is not a significant variable.

On the other hand, if the points indicate that non-randomness has entered the data, this tends to show that the variable on which the arrangement was based is actually a significant variable.

F-1.2 Assignable causes

The control chart has a unique ability to detect and identify causes. First the pattern is tested for evidence of unnaturalness as explained on pages 23–30. Unnatural patterns are then associated with appropriate causes. The "causes" are extraneous disturbances or influences which interfere with or change the

Assignable Causes Associated with things which are:	Non-Assignable Causes Associated with things which are:
Unnatural	Normal
Disturbed	Natural
Unstable	Stable
Non-homogeneous	Undisturbed
Mixed	Homogeneous
Erratic	Coming from a single distribution
Abnormal	
Shifting	Not changing
Unpredictable	Steady
Inconsistent	Predictable
Out-of-the ordinary	Same
Different	Consistent
Important	Statistically constant
Significant	Non-significant

Fig. 146. Conditions associated with assignable and non-assignable causes.

ordinary behavior of the process.

The causes which disturb a process are called "assignable causes," because the reasons for them can be identified or "assigned." Assignable causes are always associated with "unnatural" behavior—that is, with something out of the ordinary or some change in the cause system.

The "natural" variation in the process is also the result of causes, but these are known as "non-assignable" causes. Non-assignable causes are relatively small in magnitude. They are also numerous, closely intermingled and statistically in balance. It is not possible to identify or "assign" such causes without going to special effort.

The following is a description of how the control chart detects assignable causes.

(1) When we break a series of measurements into very small samples and plot them, (for example, in the order of time), this forces any disturbing causes to show up in one of two ways.

(a) *Some disturbances come and go in the process periodically (occasional disturbances).*

A machine setter changing a setting will cause a periodic disturbance in the process. Occasional causes like this will not affect observations that are close together, as in a small sample, but they will affect observations that are farther apart or in different samples.

These are called causes operating "between samples."

(b) *Other disturbances do not come and go on an occasional basis but exist in the process for considerable periods (continuous disturbances).*

For example, a regular mixture of product made by several machines or operators may constitute such a disturbance. Continuous causes like this will affect the observations in a single small group or sample as much as they affect observations that are farther apart or in different samples.

These are called causes operating "within samples."

(2) "Between sample" causes tend to produce the effects known as instability, cycles, trends, systematic variation etc. "Within sample" causes tend to produce the effects known as stratification and stable forms of mixture. "Between sample" causes tend to have patterns too wide for the control limits, while "within sample" causes tend to have patterns too narrow for the control limits. The only thing that will produce a long-continued natural pattern on the control chart is the absence of disturbing causes within or between samples.

Not all assignable causes in a process are bad or need to be eliminated. For example, toolwear is an assignable cause, but it is accepted as an essential part of any process which involves tooling. Assignable causes may also be the source of important information, as shown on pages 35 and 54.

As a rule, however, assignable causes need to be either eliminated or restricted in some way in the interests of economical manufacture. In any case, whether we intend to eliminate them or not, we need to be aware of their presence in the process and of their magnitude.

F-1.3 Rational sub-groups

One of the chief sources of the power of the control chart is the manner of planning the samples before data are even collected. The samples are planned in such a way that, to the best of our knowledge, the units in any one sample should be a "rational subgroup." A rational subgroup is one which we believe, for rational or logical reasons, is as free as possible from assignable causes. That is, if we believe that different machine settings may have an effect on the characteristic being plotted, we see that all units in the sample come from the same setting. If we believe that different batches of material may have an effect, we see that all units in one sample come from the same batch, etc. A *series* of samples will then show the effect of *differences* in machine settings, batches etc.

We say that a rational subgroup is one that represents, as nearly as possible, a homogeneous set of conditions. In general, we know that manufacturing conditions tend to change from time to time as a result of variables of which we may not be aware. Consequently, to obtain subgroups which have the best chance of being rational, we attempt to include in one sample units made as nearly as possible at the same time.

A small group of consecutively produced units from a process is likely to be a "rational subgroup." That is, it is likely to be made up of a randomly produced set of units representing the immediate state of the process at the time the sample was selected.

It is possible that, in spite of our precautions, the subgroups we believed were rational may contain assignable causes. In that case the causes tend to show up as the "within sample" causes referred to in paragraph F-1.2. "Within sample" causes are harder to interpret than "between sample" causes. For this reason, the careful collection of data in rational subgroups will greatly simplify the use of the control charts.

F-1.4 Order of production (or testing)

When theory states that the samples for control charts should be taken, whenever possible, in the order of production, keep in mind that this means the order of production as related to a single system of causes. The principle of the rational subgroup (see above) is always assumed when we say "order of production."

If a process checker is taking samples from a machine with multiple spindles, or multiple positions or heads, then a series of consecutive units from the machine as a whole will not give him a sample in the "order of production" as the term is used here. If the machine has six heads, he should take every sixth unit in order to get a sample in the order of production from a single head, etc.

Order of production is important primarily because it aids in obtaining a rational subgroup.

F-1.5 Technical terms associated with control charts

Control limits

Control limits are mathematical or statistical limits used to interpret the pattern on a control chart. Unless otherwise noted, the control limits referred to in this Handbook are 3 sigma control limits. Control limits are derived from a knowledge of distribution theory and apply to the particular statistic ($\bar{X}$, R, p, individual measurement etc.) which is being plotted on the control chart. It is important not to confuse "control limits" with specification limits, or with the so-called "natural limits" of the process, which show the natural spread of individual units.

Natural process limits

Three sigma limits for the individual units produced by a process in control are sometimes called the "natural" limits of the process. The natural limits have no necessary connection with specification limits or any other arbitrary limits. Natural limits may be either broader or narrower than the specifications set by engineers.

"Natural limits" are the limits which the process is able to hold when operating normally under the influence of non-assignable chance causes. The term "natural tolerance" is sometimes used in place of "natural limits." See page 61.

Centerline

The centerline on a control chart is a line which passes through the center of a real or assumed set of fluctuating points from which the centerline was calculated. On any particular control chart the centerline may or may not pass through the points actually plotted. For example, the centerline may have been fixed by engineering decision, or it may have been obtained from a series of past data rather than the data currently plotted.

Level

The level on a control chart is a line which passes through the center of the series of points actually plotted. The line may be drawn on the chart or it may be imaginary. The level may or may not be the same as the centerline, since a level is always related to the actual plotted points while the centerline may have been obtained from some other source. It is possible for the same control chart to show more than one level in its patterns.

F-2 INTERPRETATION OF $\bar{X}$ CHARTS

The $\bar{X}$ chart shows where the process is centered. It represents the average of the distribution which the process is creating. If the center of the distribution shifts, the $\bar{X}$ pattern will shift with it. If the center of the distribution follows a trend up or down, the $\bar{X}$ pattern will follow the same trend. The conditions which the $\bar{X}$ chart is intended to reflect are shown in Figures 147 and 148.

F-2.1 Causes affecting the $\bar{X}$ chart

The most common causes which will affect an $\bar{X}$ chart are the following:

(1) *Direct or "true" $\bar{X}$ causes.* These are causes capable of affecting an $\bar{X}$ chart directly. All such causes have one element in common: that is, when they enter the process they are capable of affecting all the product at once or in the same general way. When the temperature changes in a plating bath, it affects all the parts being plated. When a decision is made to use a thicker stock, all the parts become thicker. This type of cause is able to shift the *center* of a distribution without affecting its spread. It is the most common type of cause which shows up on the $\bar{X}$ chart.

The $\bar{X}$ chart can be affected in this way by

Changes in:
    Material.
    Operator.
    Inspector.
    Machine setting.
    Plating current.
    Temperature.
    Strength of solution.
    Time in oven or tank.
    Dimension of a mold or cavity.

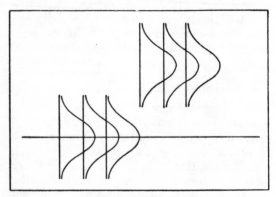

Fig. 147. Shift in level.

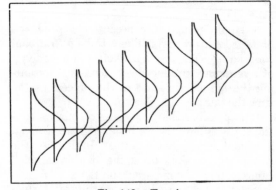

Fig. 148. Trend.

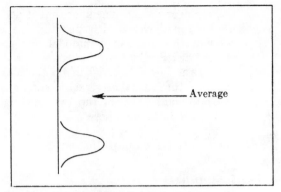

Fig. 149. Original average.

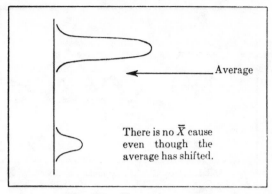

There is no $\bar{X}$ cause even though the average has shifted.

Fig. 150. Change in average.

Winding tension on a reel.
Hardness of stock.
Supplier.
Calibration of a gage or test set.
Wear of tool.
Adjustment of the process or machine.
Expansion or contraction.
Aging.
Drift.
Humidity, moisture content, etc.
Misunderstanding of a drawing, or modification of a requirement.

Disturbances in the $\bar{X}$ chart (not associated with disturbances in the R chart) are almost invariably the result of causes similar to the above.

(2) *Indirect or "false" $\bar{X}$ causes.* There are three types of cause which can affect the $\bar{X}$ chart indirectly but are not true $\bar{X}$ causes. These causes show up on the R chart as well as the $\bar{X}$ chart and are in reality R-type causes. They appear on the $\bar{X}$ chart only as a reflection of the R chart. The engineer should carefully study the following:

A. The $\bar{X}$ chart can be affected by a *change in the proportion of distributions* which constitute a mixture. For example, Figure 149 shows a mixture of distributions and their original average. Figure 150 shows how the average is increased merely because there are fewer units in one of the component distributions. This type of cause can ordinarily be detected on the R chart, and should not be confused with the true $\bar{X}$ causes listed above.

B. Secondly, the presence of freaks in the data, or anything tending to create a pronounced skewness, will cause the $\bar{X}$ chart to follow the R chart and may throw the $\bar{X}$ chart out of control. See Figure 151.

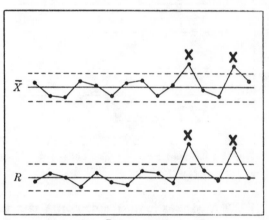

Fig. 151. $\bar{X}$ chart follows R chart.

C. Finally, if the level on the R chart increases or decreases with respect to its previously calculated limits, the control limits for the $\bar{X}$ chart will no longer be accurate, and therefore must not be used to determine whether the $\bar{X}$ points are out of control. See Figures 152 and 153 on the next page.

These three possibilities are the reason for the rules given repeatedly in this Handbook: "Do not attempt to interpret an $\bar{X}$ chart while the R chart is out of control." "Eliminate the R causes first and the chances are that the $\bar{X}$ causes will disappear along with them."

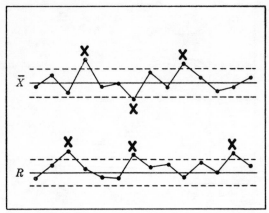

Fig. 152. $\bar{X}$ chart looks out of control but is not. Limits should be recalculated.

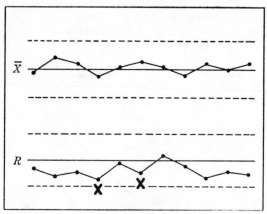

Fig. 153. $\bar{X}$ chart looks stratified but is not. Limits should be recalculated.

F-2.2 Mistakes to be avoided on $\bar{X}$ charts

The most common mistakes made in interpreting $\bar{X}$ charts are these:

(1) *Attempting to interpret an $\bar{X}$ chart when the R chart is not in control.* Examples of this were given above.

(2) *Attempting to relate the $\bar{X}$ chart to a specification without taking account of the distribution's shape.* In particular, be careful not to assume normality in a distribution which may have been truncated or screened.

(3) *Assuming that most of the product is at or near the "average."* Under ordinary circumstances this is a safe assumption, but

the engineer should remember that it does not hold in all cases. It is possible for the product to consist of a bimodal or two-headed distribution with half of the product on the low side and half on the high side. In that case the average would be at the mid-point between the two portions of the product, and there might actually be no product on or around the average. See Figure 149 on page 153.

F-2.3 Summary

$\bar{X}$ charts are used to show trends, to indicate whether there is stability in the distribution's center, and under certain circumstances to indicate the relationship between the process and the specification. $\bar{X}$ charts should always be interpreted in conjunction with R charts, since mixtures or other abnormalities which show up plainly on the R chart are capable of causing apparent changes in level or pattern on the $\bar{X}$ chart.

F-3 INTERPRETATION OF R CHARTS

The R chart is a measure of uniformity or consistency. It reacts to a change in variation or spread. If one process is producing more uniform results than another process, the $\bar{R}$ for the first process will be lower. In general, we want the level on an R chart to be as low as possible.

If all units in the product are receiving the same treatment, the R chart will tend to stay in control. If the R chart does not remain in control or if its level rises, some units are receiving different treatment from the others. This may mean that a separate system of causes has been introduced, or there may be several different systems affecting different portions of the product at the same time. For example, instability of a test set or intermittent contacts on a relay or timer may result in the introduction of more than one system of causes.

If the level on the R chart rises and then stays in control at a higher level, it means that some new element has entered the cause system and has become a regular part of the process. Ordinarily an element which causes the R chart to rise will be an undesirable element. Examples of undesirable causes are: a change to a poorer quality material, increased production pressure, less competent operators or inspectors, less carefully designed tools and machines, a less adequate maintenance program, etc. The R chart will also rise if the component distributions in a mixture become more widely separated. This will tend to show up as stratification or mixture.

If the level of the R chart decreases and the chart then stays in control at the lower level, it means that some element which was treating the units differently has now been eliminated. For example, we have eliminated the poorly trained operators by re-training them; we have eliminated dirty pumps or sockets by a more careful maintenance program; we have eliminated the need for excessive play in the fixtures by getting better piece parts; we have reduced carelessness by installing control charts.

The R chart is far more sensitive to many important types of assignable cause than any other control chart. In particular the R chart is the best method of detecting mixtures, stratification, freaks, erratic conditions, interactions and general statistical instability. Since these conditions will seriously affect the engineer's interpretation of any other chart, the R chart must be considered the most important chart in a process capability study.

The principal conditions which the R chart is intended to reflect are shown in Figures 154, 155 and 156.

F-3.1 Causes affecting the R chart

All causes which affect an R chart have one element in common: that is, they are able to treat part of the product differently from the rest of the product. For example, a poorly trained operator does not do his work the same way every time, so part of the product receives different treatment. Similarly, a careless inspector does not insert his gage the same way every time; a machine in need of repair does not index the same way every time, etc. Causes which affect only a part of the product will change the spread of the distribution. The change in spread may or may not tend also to shift the center.

Among the causes which will affect an R chart are the following:

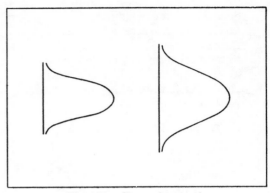

Fig. 154.   Change in spread.

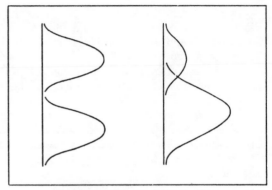

Fig. 155.   Mixture of distributions.

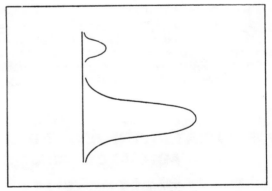

Fig. 156.   Presence of freaks.

Poorly trained operator or inspector.
New operator or inspector.
Tired operator or inspector.
Material which is not uniform.
Fixture which is loose or has excessive play.
Machine in need of repair.

155

Something out of alignment.

Loose threads or screws.

Broken bolts.

Parts stuck together in barrel plating.

Testing equipment which is unstable.

Holders or fixtures which are warped.

Automatic controls which can go out of order.

Parts left at the end of a rod or strip.

Set-up parts.

Damage.

Careless handling.

Selective system of causes; for example, gold plating behaves differently when parts are chamfered than when they are burred.

In addition to the above, the R chart will be affected by mixtures of different "lots." The engineer should remember this in obtaining data for a process capability study, particularly in view of the fact that his control limits and other estimates will be based on the R chart.

Occasional freaks, "wild units," or "mavericks" will show up as isolated high points on the R chart. These are easily recognized because they are so different from the rest of the pattern.

F-3.2 Summary

R charts are used to show the magnitude of the spread of the process being studied, to indicate whether the spread is stable, and to reveal information associated with mixtures, interactions and various forms of instability. R charts should always be interpreted before the corresponding $\bar{X}$ charts are interpreted, in view of the importance of this type of information.

F-4 JOINT INTERPRETATION OF $\bar{X}$ CHARTS AND R CHARTS

Since $\bar{X}$ charts and R charts are concerned with different phases of the distribution being studied, the two charts should finally be interpreted in conjunction with each other. There are two reasons why this is important.

(1) The charts re-inforce each other in giving information about the distribution. It is necessary to consider both center and spread if the information is to be useful.

(2) By considering the charts together it is possible to obtain new information which was not obtainable from either chart considered separately. The additional information has to do with peculiarities or abnormalities in the shape of the distribution from which the samples are being taken.

The basis for obtaining this additional information is as follows:

When samples are taken at random from a normal distribution, there is no correlation between the $\bar{X}$ and R values. That is, the fact that an $\bar{X}$ value is high does not tend to make the R value high or vice versa. There is no necessary relationship between averages and ranges.

Consequently, when a series of samples are plotted on a control chart, if those samples came from a normal population, the $\bar{X}$ points and R points do not tend to follow each other. Both of the patterns appear to be unrelated or truly "random."

If samples are taken from a very skewed population, there will be definite correlation between the $\bar{X}$ points and the R points. If the population is skewed in such a way that the long tail is on the high side (positive skewness) there will be positive correlation between $\bar{X}$ and R. The $\bar{X}$ points will tend to follow the R points, moving in the same direction.

If samples are taken from a population which is skewed with its long tail toward the low side (negative skewness) there will be negative correlation between the $\bar{X}$ points and the R points. The $\bar{X}$ chart will tend to become an "inverted image" of the R chart. The $\bar{X}$ points tend to follow the R points, but in the opposite direction.

The greater the skewness, the more definitely the points will tend to follow each other.

Do not confuse *changes in level* on the $\bar{X}$ chart and R chart with the "tendency to follow" which is being discussed here. The "tendency to follow" means that the *individual points* move up and down together, not the general level. See pages 176–177.

In brief, the engineer should be alert for any indications on the separate charts or on the $\bar{X}$ and R combination which tend to show that the patterns are behaving in anything but a random manner.

F-5 INTERPRETATION OF p-CHARTS AND OTHER ATTRIBUTES CHARTS

A p-chart shows the proportions into which a distribution has been divided. Frequently a p-chart is used to represent "percent defective," and the distribution has been divided into two parts, defective and non-defective, by a simple process of comparing the units of product with a specification and then classifying them in one or the other of these two groups. See Figure 157.

However, p-charts can be used to represent any proportion and need not be associated with product which is defective. For example, a p-chart can be used to show the proportion of units which fall within a certain voltage range as compared with the proportion which fall within other voltage ranges. In all cases, the p-chart represents a division of the distribution on the basis of some previously determined system of classification.

p-Charts can be combined or sub-divided at will; that is, the proportion represented may be the proportion classified on the basis of a single characteristic only, or it may be the proportion with respect to a number of characteristics taken together. The interpretation of a p-chart depends to a considerable extent on knowledge of the number of characteristics which formed the basis for the classification. This is particularly important in the case of a process capability study where early p-charts appear to show fairly good control. If the p-chart results from a combination of many characteristics, the apparent control may be reflecting a "statistical balance" among these characteristics rather than the "singleness of a cause system" which is the real measure of process capability.

The conditions which a p-chart is intended to reflect are shown in Figures 158 and 159.

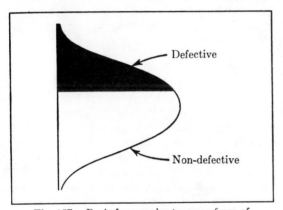

Fig. 157. Basis for a p-chart: some form of classification.

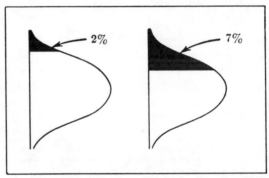

Fig. 158. Change in percent defective (or other basis for classification).

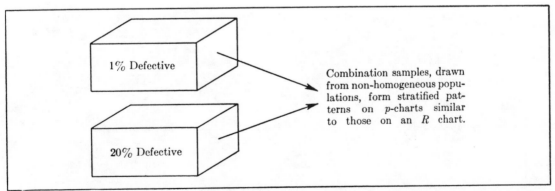

Combination samples, drawn from non-homogeneous populations, form stratified patterns on p-charts similar to those on an R chart.

Fig. 159. Stratified sampling.

F-5.1 Causes affecting the p-chart

The *p*-chart does not reflect any characteristic of the distribution directly. That is, it does not indicate the average, shape or spread. It shows simply the arbitrary classification of the distribution into two or more parts. For this reason it is harder to identify specific causes or types of cause as likely to affect the *p*-chart.

The causes for out-of-control conditions on *p*-charts may include anything which is capable of affecting the center, spread or shape of the product distribution. The *p*-chart is also very sensitive to causes which affect the standards being used as the basis for classification.

In tracing the causes affecting *p*-charts the engineer should rely heavily on job knowledge. He should check the surrounding conditions which are associated with the chart and investigate the process elements which he believes might contribute to those conditions. Among the elements which may be investigated are the following:

(1) Materials (including both processing and inspection).

(2) Machines (including tools, fixtures, gages and other facilities).

(3) Methods (including layouts and other information, deviations from prescribed procedures, changes in motion patterns or changes in the operators' "efficiency").

(4) Men (including their training, attitudes and experience, whether they are properly instructed, whether they are using control charts).

Throughout any investigation into the causes affecting *p*-charts, the engineer should remember that large variables may be operating in the process from time to time without showing up on this chart. For example the distributions in Figure 160 may all look alike on a *p*-chart because they all have the same percent defective.

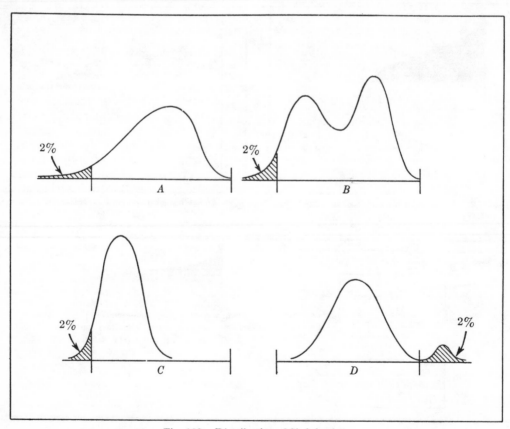

Fig. 160. Distributions 2% defective.

F-5.2 Mistakes to be avoided on p-charts

The most common errors made in interpreting *p*-charts are the following:

(1) *Assuming too quickly that a p-chart is in control.* As mentioned above, a *p*-chart which apparently shows control may only be reflecting a state of balance. Before concluding that an overall *p*-chart is actually in control, break it down into the component characteristics or sources of product and study the sources separately. If the sources are not separately controlled, it is necessary to modify any conclusions based on the overall chart.

(2) *Failing to take account of a change in standards.* One of the first things to look for in a *p*-chart is a possible change in the criteria or in the process checker's method of applying the criteria. If the checker fails to look for certain defects, the level on the *p*-chart may drop. This is much more likely to happen on a *p*-chart than on an $\bar{X}$ and R chart, because of the fact that many characteristics may be combined on a single *p*-chart.

The engineer should also be alert to the fact that slight changes in the line of demarcation between "defective" and "nondefective" may make surprisingly large differences in percentage. Changes in the calibration or maintenance of test equipment may cause large fluctuations on the chart if the dividing line which is used as a basis for classification happens to come at a steep part of the distribution. See Figures 161 and 162.

The *p*-chart contains no mechanism for revealing that the causes in these two cases were really of equal magnitude.

(3) *Concentrating on defects which show a high $\bar{p}$ to the exclusion of defects which show a lack of control.* In analyzing *p*-charts in process capability studies it is common practice to have a number of *p*-charts on various characteristics plotted on similar scales so they can easily be compared. The engineer frequently tends to pay attention to the *p*-charts which show a high level of $\bar{p}$ and to ignore *p*-charts which show a lower level, even though the latter may be seriously out of control.

Since the object of a capability study is to obtain as much information as possible about the process and its variables, the engineer should keep in mind that out-of-control patterns are an excellent source of engineering information. Tracing the causes of unstable patterns on the defects which tend to occur less frequently has often led to reducing the level of other *p*-charts.

F-5.3 Summary

p-Charts are used to show the general level of a process in terms of percent defective or some other proportion, to indicate overall trends, and to permit easy comparison between operators or machines by means of individual charts. When *p*-charts are to be compared it is necessary to make sure that the base for comparison is consistent. The principal difficulties in interpreting *p*-charts arise from including too many characteristics on one chart.

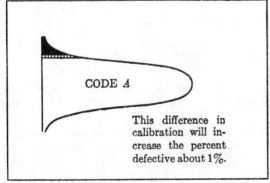

Fig. 161. Effect of recalibrating a test set: Code A.

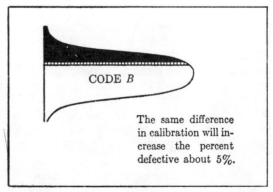

Fig. 162. Effect of the same test set recalibration: Code B.

F-5.4 Special note on attributes control charts

The information given on pages 157–159 applies to all attributes control charts, including np-charts, c-charts and u-charts. All attributes charts are interpreted in the same way as p-charts, and the same precautions should be observed in deciding how many characteristics to include and in drawing conclusions.

F-6 INTERPRETATION OF A CHART FOR INDIVIDUAL MEASUREMENTS

This chart shows the fluctuations of individual measurements in some predetermined order of plotting. The basis for determining the order is frequently time, but in special analyses, including designed experiments, the order may correspond to sources of data, codes, type of product, or some other basis for identification. The chart of individuals is used to show:

a. General trends.
b. Fluctuations of unusual magnitude.
c. Clustering of abnormal measurements at certain points.
d. The relationship between the individual measurements and some previously established standard or specification.

Many of the conditions which show up on an $\bar{X}$ and R chart can also be detected, somewhat less precisely, on the chart of individuals. The tests for unnatural patterns are less reliable than on an $\bar{X}$ and R chart, since the individuals chart may be seriously affected by any change in the shape of the distribution. It is sometimes advisable to check the conclusions drawn from a chart of individuals by obtaining more data and plotting an $\bar{X}$ and R chart.

On the other hand there are certain types of information which may show up more plainly on an individuals chart than on an $\bar{X}$ and R chart. Among these are the following:

(1) Cycles (regular repetition of pattern)

Short cycles, in particular, may not show up for some time on an $\bar{X}$ and R chart.

(2) Trends (continuous movement up or down)

These may show up more rapidly on a chart of individuals. On the other hand it is easy to see many apparent trends which do not actually exist.

(3) Mixtures (presence of more than one distribution)

This shows up on the chart of individuals in much the same way that it shows up on an R chart. That is, there is an absence of points near the middle of the pattern with excessive numbers of points toward either edge. On the chart of individuals this can often be detected by the fact that lines connecting the individual dots tend to be long and rather similar in length instead of showing a random mixture of long and short lines intermingled with each other.

(4) Grouping or bunching (measurements clustering in spots)

If all the freaks on the high side tend to occur at one or two places instead of being scattered randomly throughout the data, this may be detected more promptly on the individuals chart than on an $\bar{X}$ and R chart. The individuals chart may also show other peculiarities in the data—for example, that the measurements tend to occur in pairs.

(5) Relation between the general pattern of individuals and the specification

This chart shows plainly whether the individuals plotted are in or out of limits; whether they are well centered between specifications or close to one side.

F-6.1 Causes affecting the chart for individual measurements

The individuals chart can be affected by any of the causes which affect either $\bar{X}$ and R charts or p-charts. While it is not possible to distinguish between $\bar{X}$ disturbances and R disturbances with anything like the precision which is possible on $\bar{X}$ and R charts, nevertheless the eye can pick up many visual impressions of changes which affect either the center or spread.

F-6.2 Mistakes to be avoided on a chart for individual measurements

On a chart for individuals the sample size is 1, and the control limits are the same as would be used on an $\bar{X}$ chart where $n = 1$. The "$\sqrt{n}$" relationship still holds in comparing the control limits with a specified maximum or minimum limit (see pages 30–31), but in this case (since $n = 1$) the control limits may actually coincide with the specification.

In considering the centerline on a chart for individuals, remember that the shape of the distribution is very important in determining what portion of the product will exceed the specified limits. If the distribution is skewed in the direction away from a certain limit it is safe to run closer to that limit, and vice versa.

F-6.3 Summary

Charts of individual measurements are intended to convey the same general type of information as an $\bar{X}$ and R chart. The control limits are, in general, less sensitive and precise. The chart must be interpreted with considerably more caution. Where necessary check the conclusions on the individuals chart by making an $\bar{X}$ and R chart.

F-7 ANALYSIS OF PATTERNS

The following Sub-section contains descriptions of 15 common control chart patterns, arranged in alphabetical order by name.

1. Cycles.
2. Freaks.
3. Gradual change in level.
4. Grouping or bunching.
5. Instability.
6. Interaction.
7. Mixtures.
8. Natural pattern.
9. Stable forms of mixture.
10. Stratification.
11. Sudden shift in level.
12. Systematic variables.
13. Tendency of one chart to follow another.
14. Trends.
15. Unstable forms of mixture.

Each pattern is explained in a short verbal description and is illustrated by a typical drawing of a control chart. Wherever possible, the underlying distributions represented by the pattern are also shown. Beneath each pattern are listed four types of control chart—$\bar{X}$, R, p and individuals—and a typical list of causes likely to be associated with each chart. This information can be used in interpreting a control chart as follows:

(1) From inspection of the control chart, decide which type of pattern the chart represents.

(2) Look up this pattern in the following pages and compare the chart with the illustrative drawing.

(3) Study the verbal description of the pattern, and relate its description to what is known about your process. Select the appropriate list of causes—$\bar{X}$, R, p or individuals—and attempt to think of similar causes which may be operating in your process.

For an example of the manner in which this information is used, see pages 66–71.

In addition to the information available from patterns, there are many other practical aids in interpreting control charts. Some of these are given in the Engineering Section, pages 53–56 and 61–65. Others can be found in the Shop Section, pages 189–190 and 217–219.

F-8 CYCLES

Cycles are short trends in the data which occur in repeated patterns. Any tendency of the pattern to repeat, by showing a series of high portions or peaks interspersed with low portions or troughs, is an indication of an assignable cause, since the primary characteristic of a random pattern is the fact that it does not repeat. The causes of cycles are processing variables which come and go on a more or less regular basis. In the case of machines they may be associated with a succession of movements, positions or heads. In the case of manually controlled operations, they may be associated with fatigue patterns, shipping schedules, conditions affecting the day and night shifts. In some types of product they may be associated with seasonal effects which come and go more slowly.

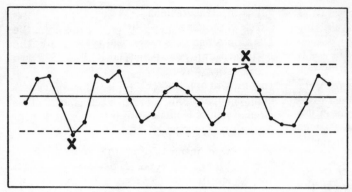

Fig. 163. Cycles.

Fig. 164. Distributions associated with cycles.

The underlying distribution is wider than would be expected from an R chart. It may be bimodal, showing two humps or peaks. Cycles are identified by determining the time interval at which the successive peaks or troughs appear and relating this interval in some manner to the elements in the process. For example:

- An engineer discovered that every seventh measurement was lower than the others. He was able to relate this to a fixture containing 7 holes.
- A supervisor found that every third sample on a continuous piece of wire was suspiciously high. He knew that the samples had been taken 25″ apart. He was able to relate this to a disc over which the wire passed which was 75″ in circumference.
- Cyclical patterns in riveting operations were found to be related to times of the day. The operator's technique varied according to the beginning or end of the week, lunch periods, rest periods, change in shifts, etc.

Other causes which can create this type of pattern are as follows:

$\bar{X}$ Chart
(R chart must be in control.)

Seasonal effects such as temperature and humidity.
Worn positions or threads on locking devices.
Roller eccentricity.
Operator fatigue.
Rotation of people on job.
Difference between gages used by inspectors.
Voltage fluctuation.

Regular difference between day and night shifts.

R Chart

Maintenance schedules.
Operator fatigue.
Rotation of fixtures or gages.
Regular difference between day and night shifts.
Wear of tool or die (causing excessive play).
Tool in need of sharpening (causing burrs, etc.).

p-Chart

Sorting practices.
Sampling practices.
Regular difference between suppliers.

Individuals Chart

Any of the causes affecting $\bar{X}$ charts or R charts.

F-9 FREAKS

Freaks result from the presence of a single unit or a single measurement greatly different from the others. Such units are generally produced by an extraneous system of causes. Occasionally, however, the measurements that look like freaks are in reality a normal part of the process. For example, dielectric breakdowns may actually be the long tails of a distribution of dielectric strength. In this case the "freaks" are a matter of degree.

Another common source of freaks is a mistake in calculation. Failure to subtract properly in obtaining the R point, or failure to divide by the proper number in calculating an $\bar{X}$ or p value, will sometimes have this effect.

Occasionally an apparent freak is the result of a plotting error, as when the person plotting the point has misinterpreted the scale. Accidental damage or mis-handling may also result in freaks.

Freaks are among the easiest of the patterns to recognize, and it is also simple in most cases to identify the cause. The mere fact that the freak is so different from other units in the product makes the identification simpler.

Typical causes which can create this type of pattern are the following:

$\bar{X}$ Charts
(R chart must be in control.)

Freaks do not ordinarily show up on an $\bar{X}$ chart without a corresponding indication on the R chart. A possible exception is the case where a sudden abnormal condition in the process may affect all or most of the units in the sample. Among such conditions may be the following:

Wrong setting, corrected immediately.

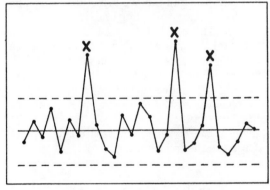

Fig. 165. Freaks.

Error in measurement.

Error in plotting.

Data obtained on a non-linear scale (logarithmic or exponential.) For example, insulation resistance.

Incomplete operation.

Omitted operation.

Breakdown of facilities.

Accidental inclusion of experimental units.

R Chart

Accidental damage in handling.

Incomplete operation.

Omitted operation.

Breakdown of facilities.

Experimental unit.

Set-up parts.

Error in subtraction.

Occasional parts from end of a rod or strip.

Measurement error.

Plotting error.

Some obvious physical abnormality which can be detected by examining the units in the sample that produced the freak point.

p-Chart

Variations in sample size.

Sampling from a distinctly different distribution.

Occasional very good or very bad lot.

Individuals Chart

Same as R chart.

Occasionally freaks result from the fact that the characteristic being plotted has a non-

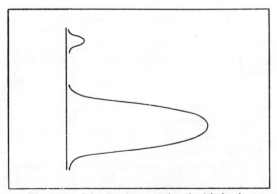

Fig. 166. Distribution associated with freaks (bimodal).

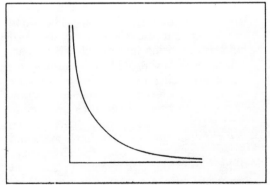

Fig. 167. Distribution associated with freaks (L-shaped).

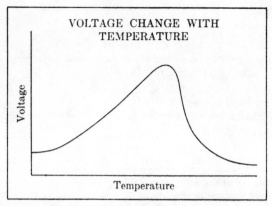

Fig. 168. Source of apparent freaks.

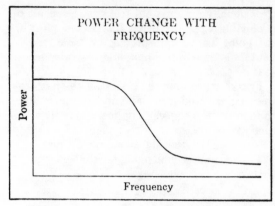

Fig. 169. Another source of apparent freaks.

linear behavior. For example, a characteristic may rise sharply at a certain temperature or pressure: or it may drop off abruptly in a "shoulder" as shown in Figures 168 and 169. If the process is running near the steep slope of such a curve, so that several units in the sample reflect the high part and some other unit or units reflect the drop, this may show up as a freak.

F-10 GRADUAL CHANGE IN LEVEL

A gradual change in level will ordinarily indicate one of two things:

(1) There is some element in the process which is capable of affecting a few units at first and then more and more as time goes on. For example, a group of new operators has been added. As the operators become better trained (which happens at varying rates of speed) more and more of the distribution is affected. The same thing can happen when newly designed fixtures are being introduced one by one, when poorly controlled lots from the storeroom are being replaced by better controlled lots, when a maintenance program is gradually being extended to cover more and more equipment, when operators begin to follow their control charts more and more closely, etc. After the change has taken place the chart tends to settle at some new level.

(2) It may be that some element in the proc-

ess has been changed abruptly, but because of the amount of product "going through the mill" it shows up gradually at the later operations. This could be any one of the causes mentioned under "Sudden Shift in Level."

In either case a gradual change in level produces patterns like the one in Figure 170. The total distribution, including both levels, is wider than would be expected from an R chart.

Gradual changes which do *not* tend to settle down to a new level are spoken of as "trends." Gradual changes in level (with the change occurring in the direction of improvement) are very common in the early stages of a quality control program.

Typical causes which will create this type of pattern are the following:

$\bar{X}$ Chart
(R chart must be in control.)

Gradual introduction of new material, better supervision, greater skill or care on the part of the operator.

Change in maintenance program.

Introduction of process controls in this or other areas.

R Chart

Change to lower level:
  Better fixtures.
  Better methods.
  Greater skill or care on the part of the operator.

Change to higher level:
  Conditions opposite to the above.

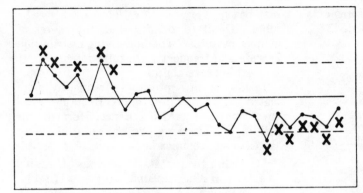

Fig. 170.   Gradual change in level.

Fig. 171.   Distribution associated with gradual change in level.

p-Chart

Any of the causes affecting $\bar{X}$ and R charts.
Addition or removal of requirements.
Relaxation or tightening of standards.

Individuals Chart

Same as $\bar{X}$ chart.

F-11 "GROUPING" OR "BUNCHING"

One of the characteristics of a natural pattern is that measurements of any given magnitude tend to be scattered more or less uniformly throughout the data. It is an indication of unnaturalness if all or most of the similar measurements occur quite close together. When measurements cluster together in such a nonrandom fashion it indicates the sudden introduction of a different system of causes. For example, the low points in Figure 172 came from a pan of rejected parts which were shipped accidentally. A similar pattern was obtained on a disc-spraying job when the mask occasionally slipped and permitted conductive material to leak over the edge of the discs. The underlying distribution is a mixture, frequently showing a few units distinctly separated from the rest of the product.

Indications of this kind are sometimes observed on $\bar{X}$ charts but they tend to occur more frequently on charts for individuals, R charts or p-charts. In many cases a chart of individual measurements will be more sensitive in picking up this type of disturbance than any other chart.

Typical causes for non-random bunching of the measurements are as follows:

$\bar{X}$ Charts
(R chart must be in control.)

Measurement difficulties.
Change in the calibration of a test set or measuring instrument.

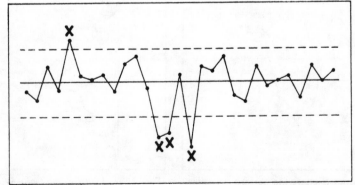

Fig. 172.   Grouping or bunching.

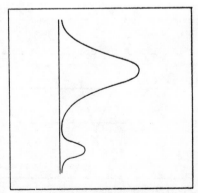

Fig. 173.   Distribution associated with grouping or bunching.

Different person making the measurements.
Shift in distribution for a limited period.

R Chart

Freaks in the data.
Mixture of distributions.

p-Chart

Change in technique of classification.
Shift in one of the underlying distributions of product.
Changes in assortment of product.

Individuals Chart

Extraneous cause resulting in a totally different distribution for a limited period of time.
Errors in plotting.

F-12 INSTABILITY

Instability of the pattern is shown by unnaturally large fluctuations. The pattern is characterized by erratic ups and downs, frequently resulting in x's on both sides of the chart. The fluctuations of the pattern appear to be too wide for the control limits. This type of pattern may arise in either of two ways:

A. A single cause, capable of affecting the center or spread of the distribution, may operate on the process erratically.
B. A group of causes, each capable of shifting the center or spread (or both), may operate on the process in conjunction with one another.

In the latter case the patterns of instability may become very complex. The causes may be more difficult to identify than the causes of simpler patterns. The underlying distribution is wide and frequently irregular in shape. It may exhibit several peaks.

Instability in a process is frequently associated with mixtures, and "Unstable Mixtures" may be regarded as a special form of "Instability." There are two ways of discovering the causes of complex instability:

(1) Check the process for obvious "Unstable Mixtures" as explained on pages 179–180. These are the easiest causes of instability to identify and eliminate. When the unstable mixtures are eliminated, the pattern of instability may become much easier to interpret.
(2) If the pattern is still complex, break the process into smaller segments or operations and plot a separate chart for each. Take the one whose pattern is most similar to the original complex pattern, and break it down still further. Continue in this way until the pattern becomes simple enough to interpret.

In seeking out the causes of complex patterns, remember that the ultimate causes are likely to be very simple. They appear to be complicated only because they exist in complex combinations. Among the common causes for instability are the following:

X̄ Chart
(R chart must be in control.)

Simple causes

Overadjustment of a machine (where the

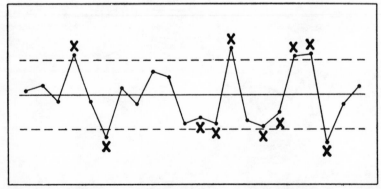

Fig. 174. Instability on an X̄ chart. On an R chart the pattern is similar, but the low points tend to gather just inside the lower limit, since they cannot fall below it.

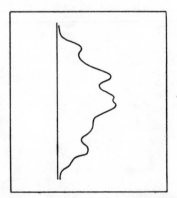

Fig. 175. Distribution associated with instability.

operator resets on the basis of one or two measurements instead of using a chart).

Fixtures or holders not holding the work in position.

Carelessness of operator in setting temperature control or timing device.

Different lots of material mixed in storeroom.

Piece parts mixed on the line (in different bins or pans).

Code differences (which are related to differences in design or in difficulty of assembly).

Differences in test sets or gages.

Shop running deliberately on high or low side of specification (causing other distributions to be run off-center also).

Erratic behavior of automatic controls.

Complex causes

Effect of many process variables on an end characteristic.

Effect of screening and sorting operations at various stages in the process.

Effect of differences in testing or gaging methods after product has been accumulated for shipment.

Effect of experimental or development work being done by engineers.

In general, we attempt to keep complex causes from affecting the $\bar{X}$ chart by locating $\bar{X}$ and R charts as far back in the process as possible.

Note also that apparent instability on the $\bar{X}$ chart frequently accompanies an R chart that is out of control. In such cases the $\bar{X}$ chart may appear to have erratic ups and downs even when the center of the distribution is actually stable. See pages 153–154.

R Chart

Instability on high side

Untrained operator.

Too much play in positioning or holding fixture.

Mixture of material.

Machine in need of repair.

Unstable testing equipment.

Work holder warped.

Lapping plates worn.

Lapping materials not properly used.

Operator carelessness.

Assemblies off-center.

Defective piece parts.

Trouble with test set.

Instability on low side

Better operator.

More uniform piece parts.

Better work habits.

Possibly the effect of control charts installed in other areas.

p-Chart

High side

Operator inexperience.

Operator carelessness.

Poor maintenance.

Defective piece parts or material.

Trouble with test set.

Low Side

Operator improvement.

Better sub-assemblies.

Better equipment or material.

Relaxation of standards.

Improper checking.

Other causes

Instability on the p-chart may also be caused by:

Variations in sample size.

Occasional lots which are very good or very bad.

Sampling from distinctly different distributions.

Non-random sampling.

Individuals Chart

Any of the causes which can affect the $\bar{X}$ chart or R chart.

F-13 INTERACTION

Interaction is the tendency of one variable to alter the behavior of another; the tendency of two or more variables to produce an effect in combination which neither variable would produce if acting alone. Interactions are studied formally by means of designed experiments. They are also detected informally by means of process capability studies.

Interactions may be detected on an $\bar{X}$ chart whenever the data have been identified in two or more ways. See Figure 176 on page 168.

In addition, interactions due to variables not

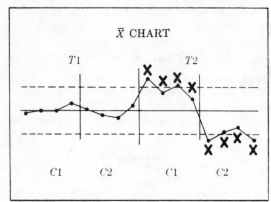

Fig. 176. Interaction on the $\bar{X}$ chart: there is an interaction between T and C.

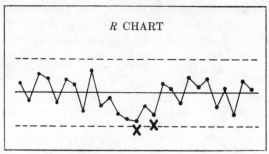

Fig. 177. Interaction on the R chart.

previously identified can often be detected on the R chart. See Figure 177.

The chart in Figure 177 is explained as follows:

All variability in a process can be thought of as the result of interactions. That is, potentially large variables exist in the process and tend to occur at more than one level. The effects of these are modified by other variables which also exist at different levels. Machine effects are modified by type of maintenance or material. Operator effects are modified by amount and kind of training. Effects due to manual skill are modified by differences in tools, tweezers or gages. It is difficult to think of any process variable which is not, in reality, the result of interactions.

In a designed experiment, where certain variables can be deliberately removed for analysis, the effects of all other variables are treated as "unanalyzed interaction." They are included in the residual or "experimental error." In the same way, in a process capability study, the unanalyzed interactions are included in the R chart. If significant variables exist and are present at more than one level, they tend to inflate the R chart. If, by intention or otherwise, one of the significant variables should occur at one level only, this would immediately remove some of the inflation from the R chart.

A low pattern on the R chart, like that in one portion of Figure 177, indicates that some of the inflation usually present in the process has temporarily been removed. We conclude from this that some important interacting variable must have been present at one level only.

The chart in Figure 177 shows that this variable, if kept permanently at one level, could reduce the spread of the process to less than half its usual magnitude.

Low x's on the R chart are one of the most important indications which can occur in a process capability study.

Identifying the interacting variables

Since low x's on the R chart indicate that some important variable was present at only one level, this can be used to identify the important interactions.

- If the samples that produced the low x's were all from one inspector, the inspectors are likely to be an important interacting variable.
- If the samples that produced the low x's were all from one fixture, the fixtures are likely to be an important interacting variable.
- If the samples that produced the low x's were all from newly lapped fixtures, the uneven or warped surfaces of the older fixtures may be the important interacting variable. And so on.

Remember that the spread can usually be reduced if any one of the interacting variables is reduced to a single level. If one of the variables cannot be reduced to a single level economically, try reducing another. Some practical examples of this are the following:

Machines of different ages may constitute an important variable, but only in the presence of different degrees of maintenance. (There is an interaction between machine age and maintenance). Since it would not be economically feasible to run the job with only one machine, we concentrate on eliminating the differences in the effectiveness of the maintenance.

Similar interactions may exist between operator differences and different degrees of training or supervision.

From this point of view, one of the chief objectives of a quality control program is to improve the piece parts, improve the design of the tool, provide better training or closer supervision, so that we can use different operators, machines and batches of material and still get uniform product.

For formal methods of studying interaction in a designed experiment, see pages 94–97 and 99–101.

F-14 MIXTURES

In a mixture pattern the points tend to fall near the high and low edges of the pattern with an absence of normal fluctuations near the middle. This pattern can be recognized by the unnatural length of the lines joining the points,

which tends to create a more or less obvious "seesaw" effect. See Figure 178.

A mixture pattern is actually a combination of two different patterns on the same chart—one at a high level and one at a low level. If we were to take an extreme mixture pattern and reconnect the points in a different manner they would look like Figure 179. If we grouped the plotted points into a frequency distribution they would tend to look like Figure 180.

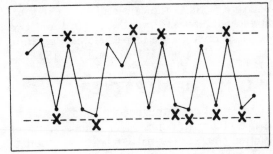

Fig. 178. Mixture.

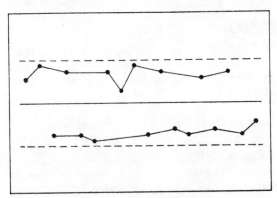

Fig. 179. Separate patterns.

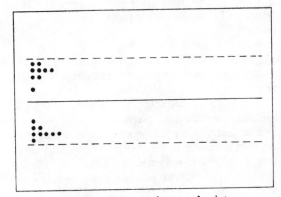

Fig. 180. Separate clusters of points.

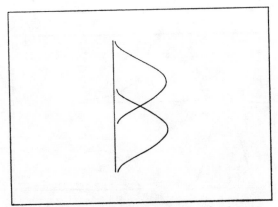

Fig. 181. Distribution associated with mixture (obvious mixture).

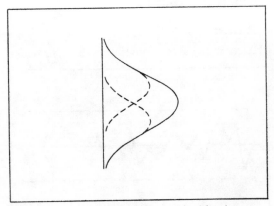

Fig. 182. Distribution associated with mixture (less obvious mixture).

The components in a mixture may be widely separated as in Figure 181 or close enough to blend as in Figure 182. The wider the separation between the component distributions, the more obvious will be the indications of mixture.

When the component distributions maintain the same relative positions and proportions over a period of time, we call it a "Stable Mixture." When the relative positions or proportions are not constant, we call it "Unstable Mixture." Since the causes of stable and unstable mixtures are not the same, these two types of mixture are listed below as separate patterns. See pages 171–172 and 179–180.

F-15 NATURAL PATTERN

A natural pattern is one which gives no evidence of unnaturalness over a long series of plotted points. The pattern is stable; there is no trend; there are no sudden shifts, no erratic ups and downs, no x's. The cause system appears to be in balance and the process is "in control."

Stability alone, however, is not sufficient reason for calling the pattern natural. A stratification pattern may have stability, but it shows definite evidence of assignable causes.

The physical characteristics of a natural pattern are described on page 24.

The distribution associated with a natural pattern is likely to be fairly smooth and unimodal, not extremely flat, not extremely skew. However, a natural pattern does not necessarily indicate a "normal" distribution.

The following is a summary of the principal meanings of a natural pattern:

R chart

A natural pattern on the R chart provides direct evidence of the process uniformity. If the chart covers an operator's work it shows the operator's technique; this can be used to compare different operators. If the chart covers a machine dimension it shows the capability of the machine: that is, how close a tolerance it can hold. This can be used to compare different machines. It is also a direct measure of the spread of the underlying parent distribution. See page 56.

$\bar{X}$ chart and R chart

A natural pattern on both the $\bar{X}$ chart and the R chart gives direct evidence of the average of the parent distribution. It also means that the average did not change during the charted period and that most of the product was actually near the indicated average. When the $\bar{X}$ and R chart are both in control it is possible to make reliable comparisons between the process and the specified limits. See pages 119–122.

p-Chart

A natural pattern on a p-chart indicates that there is a constant fraction defective in the product; also that the sampling is random (not stratified).

Chart for individual measurements

A natural pattern on a chart for individual measurements indicates that the distribution is stable with respect to both average and spread; also that its shape is reasonably symmetrical, since unsymmetrical distributions tend to give indications of unnaturalness on this type of chart.

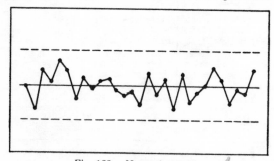

Fig. 183. Natural pattern.

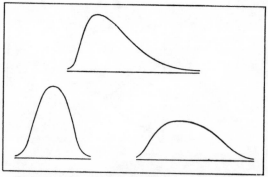

Fig. 184. Distributions associated with a natural pattern.

General

If the pattern on a control chart is in control for considerable periods of time, it means that we have a stable, steadily running process which is not being disturbed by outside causes. In a shop situation all that needs to be done in interpreting such a chart is to compare it with the specification limits or other authorized standards. In a capability study, however, this type of pattern may indicate that the engineering problem has not yet been solved. It is often necessary to disturb a natural pattern or a process running in control in order to bring about improvements, cost reductions, etc.

In dealing with a natural pattern, the engineer should keep in mind that causes not now identified are not necessarily unidentifiable. It is always possible to identify more of them if we are willing to exert the effort to do so. Theoretically it would be possible to keep on identifying and eliminating causes until all variability would be reduced to zero.

Practically, however, the causes become progressively more difficult to isolate or distinguish, so there is no practical possibility of reducing the variability to zero. The causes which are left in a so-called "natural pattern" are so small and balanced that it requires special effort (equivalent to setting up a new process) to reduce these causes further.

See page 150 for a discussion of "natural" or "non-assignable" causes.

F-16 STABLE FORMS OF MIXTURE

These are a special type of mixture, as explained on page 170. Stable mixtures result from the presence of more than one distribution, the distributions being in balance. The mixture is shown by a pattern which may or may not react to the formal tests but which indicates abnormality by the absence of the usual number of points near the center or edge of the chart. Stable mixtures will show up plainly on $\bar{X}$ charts, R charts, p-charts and charts for individual measurements. See Figures 185 and 186 on page 172.

The distribution consists of more or less widely separated components which do not change with respect to each other in either pro-portion or location. The samples may be taken from each distribution separately (in which case the mixture will show up on an $\bar{X}$ chart or p-chart), or they may be taken from the two distributions combined (in which case the mixture will show up on an R chart).

There are two forms of stable mixture which result from a special systematic way of taking the sample: these are called "Systematic Variable" (pages 175–176) and "Stratification" (pages 172–174).

When mixtures are stable, the causes producing the distributions are likely to be settled or permanent in nature: product coming steadily from two different sources, a difference in machine design, a consistent difference between first and second shift. Stable mixtures occur most frequently when measurements are taken on the end product instead of at the early operations. On the whole however, they are less common than unstable mixtures.

Typical causes which may produce stable mixtures are the following:

$\bar{X}$ Chart

Consistent differences in material, operators, etc., where the distributions are subsequently mixed.
Different lots of material in storeroom.
Large quantities of piece parts mixed on the line (in different pans or bins).
Code differences.
Differences in test sets or gages.

R Chart

Different lots of materials in storeroom.
Large quantities of piece parts mixed on the line (in same pan or bin).
Frequent drift or jumps in automatic controls.
Difference in test sets or gages.

p-Chart

Non-random sampling technique.
Lots coming from two or more different sources.
Screening of some lots at a prior operation.
Difference in process checkers.
Difference in test sets, gages etc.

Individuals Chart

Any of the causes which can affect the $\bar{X}$ chart or R chart.

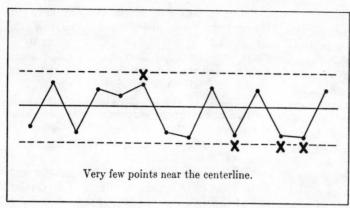

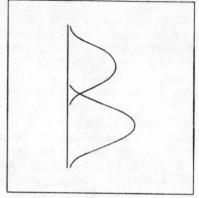

Fig. 185. Stable mixture. See also Figures 187 and 192.

Fig. 186. Distribution associated with stable mixture.

F-17 STRATIFICATION

Stratification is a form of stable mixture which is characterized by an artificial constancy. Instead of fluctuating naturally inside the control limits, with occasional points approaching the upper and lower limits, a stratification pattern appears to hug the centerline with few deviations or excursions at any distance from the centerline. In other words, stratification is shown by unnaturally small fluctuations, or an absence of points near the edge of the chart.

As shown in Figure 188 the underlying distribution is a composite, made up of small distributions which are radically different.

We sometimes describe stratification by pointing out that the pattern is *unnaturally quiet.* Do not make the mistake of thinking that a pattern like this shows "good control." On the contrary, it shows lack of control because distributions that were intended to be the same are very different. The following is an explanation of the way in which a pattern of stratification forms.

Formation of a pattern of stratification

Stratification results when samples are taken consistently from widely different distributions, in such a way that one or more units in every sample will come from each of the distributions. The most common way of getting this effect is to allow the person who selects the sample to take one part from each operator in a group of operators, or one part from each machine, or each position on a machine, etc. Sometimes people do this without realizing the possible implications because they are anxious to make the sample "representative."

When sampling is done in this manner the selection of units is not random, and consequently the pattern will not fluctuate as in the case of randomness. On an R chart, for example, the *level* on the chart will be unnaturally high because of the separation between the distributions. The *fluctuations*, however, will be unnaturally small because the largest and smallest units in each sample are fairly similar. This can be seen in the following example.

Imagine five machines which are turning out distributions very different from each other. See Figure 188. The spread of each individual distribution is ±.001, but the distance between the highest and lowest distributions is nearly .005. A process checker takes one part from each machine in making up a sample of 5.

When the checker takes a sample in this manner and calculates the value of R, this value will consist mostly of the difference between the highest and lowest machines. Successive values of R will differ slightly from each other, but they will all be in the neighborhood of .005. Their pattern of fluctuation will be entirely different from a series of natural R values, which (if they had an average range of approximately .005) would fluctuate all the way from zero to nearly .011. In Figure 188 there is no possibility of getting a range higher than .007 or less than .003. Consequently the

172

pattern will show unnaturally small fluctuations as compared with a natural pattern having the same average range.

Similar reasoning will show how such a pattern forms on other types of chart.

By a careful study of the stratified pattern on an R chart, it is possible to estimate how far the distributions are separated.

Stratification on a p-chart

Stratification patterns may form on a p-chart if there are large differences between various containers of product and if the samples are always selected in such a way as to include some units from each container. An extreme example is the following:

If one container were composed solely of defectives and there were no defectives in any of the other containers, and if the inspector took an equal number of units from each container, all the inspector's samples would contain exactly the same number of defectives. A p-chart on the inspector's data would show nothing but a straight line at the average percent defective. The stratification in this case would be so great that it would remove all sampling fluctuation.

Causes of stratification

The cause of stratification may be any element in the process which is consistently being spread across the samples. It will probably be the machine if you are taking one part from each machine. It will probably be the spindle if you are taking one part from each spindle. It will be the boxes of product if you are taking part of your sample from each box. Among the most common causes for stratification are the following:

$\bar{X}$ Chart

Anything which is capable of causing mixture may also produce stratification. However, stratification shows up less readily on the $\bar{X}$ chart than on the R chart.

Apparently stratified patterns on an $\bar{X}$ chart are frequently the result of incorrect calculation of the control limits.

The misplacing of a decimal point may cause an apparent effect of stratification.

R Chart

Any of the causes listed under Stable Mixture.

p-Chart

Any of the causes listed under Stable Mixture.

Individuals Chart

Since true stratification results from spreading a sample across two or more distributions, this type of pattern cannot occur on a chart for individual measurements.

Sometimes, however, the control limits on a chart for individuals may become inflated by

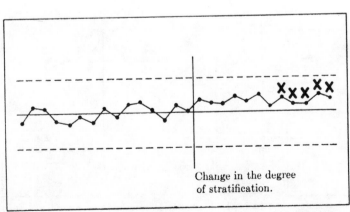

Fig. 187. Stratification.

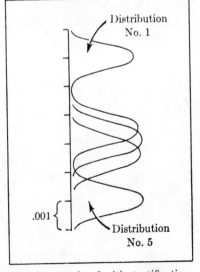

Fig. 188. Distribution associated with stratification.

erratic data or mixtures. This may in certain cases produce an effect similar to stratification.

F-18 SUDDEN SHIFT IN LEVEL

A sudden shift in level is shown by a positive change in one direction. A number of x's appear on one side of the chart only.

If the two periods are plotted separately in a frequency tabulation, the underlying distributions will be separate and distinct. If the two periods are combined, the distribution may be wide or show separate peaks. Sudden shifts may show up on any of the commonly used control charts.

(1) On an $\bar{X}$ chart this type of pattern indicates the sudden introduction into the process of a new element or cause (usually a simple or single cause) which moves the center of the distribution to a new location and then ceases to act on it further. The pattern shifts up or down from the centerline and rapidly establishes itself around the new level.

(2) On an R chart a sudden rise in level

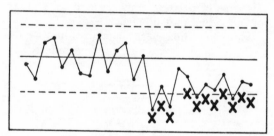

Fig. 189.   Sudden shift in level.

generally indicates the introduction of a new distribution in addition to the distribution previously in the product. A sudden drop in level generally indicates that one or more distributions have been removed.

(3) On a p-chart this type of pattern indicates a major change in the distribution of product or in the method of measuring the product. As indicated below, the p-chart is interpreted differently depending on whether the change is in the high direction or the low.

(4) On a chart for individuals a shift in level is interpreted the same way as a similar shift on the $\bar{X}$ chart.

A sudden shift in level is one of the easiest patterns to interpret on any chart. Typical causes include the following:

$\bar{X}$ Chart
(*R* chart must be in control.)

Change to a different kind of material.
New operator.
New inspector.
New test set.
New machine.
New machine setting.
Change in set-up or method.

R Chart

Change in motivation of operators.
New operators.
New equipment.
Change to different material or different supplier of piece parts.

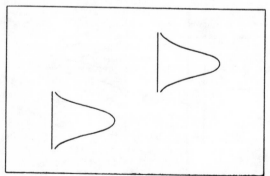

Fig. 190   Distribution associated with sudden shift in level (separate plotting).

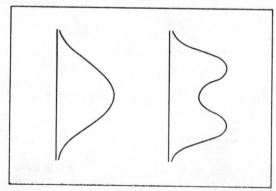

Fig. 191.   Distribution associated with sudden shift in level (combined plotting).

174

The following causes will make the R pattern rise:

Greater carelessness on the part of the operators.

Inadequate maintenance.

Less expensive or less accurately designed machines and facilities.

Positioning or holding device in need of repair.

Anything which tends to make the product less uniform.

The following causes will make the R pattern drop:

Improved workmanship.

Machines or facilities with better capability.

Anything which tends to increase uniformity.

p-Chart

Changes in level are commonly due to:

New lot of material.

Change from one machine or operator to another.

Change in the calibration of a test set.

Change in method.

Change in standards.

Higher level on p-chart indicates:

Worse material.

Poorer machines, tools, fixtures, piece parts etc.

New or less adequately trained operators.

Tightening or addition of requirements.

Lower level on p-chart indicates:

Better operators.

Better machines, tools, piece parts etc.

Better methods or materials.

Loosening or removal of requirements.

Individuals Chart

Any of the causes which affect $\bar{X}$ charts, R charts or p-charts.

F-19 SYSTEMATIC VARIABLES

One of the characteristics of a natural pattern is that the point-to-point fluctuations are unsystematic or unpredictable. If the pattern for any reason becomes predictable (for example, if a low point is always followed by a high one or vice versa) the pattern is not natural and there must be an assignable cause. A systematic pattern of any kind indicates the presence of a systematic variable in either the process or the data. The most common appearance of such a pattern is a regular sawtooth effect like that in Figure 192 on page 176.

The distribution which accompanies this pattern is wide and flat-topped. It may or may not show separate peaks, depending on the distance between the high and low points.

Cycles are one form of systematic or repeating pattern. (See pages 161–162.) Systematic variables may originate in either the process or the data.

Systematic variables in the process

Any of the causes listed under cycles on the $\bar{X}$ chart may act as systematic variables if they alternate on a regular basis. For example, day shift always high, night shift always low.

Systematic variables in the data

These are often introduced by the way in which the data are divided in forming samples. For example, an engineer was testing the same units repeatedly over a period of time in order to study possible deterioration or drifting. Ten such units were being tested but as a matter of convenience he wished to plot samples of 5. He divided the 10 units into two groups of 5 and plotted them alternately on the chart. The result looked very much like the pattern in Figure 192.

The systematic ups and downs in such a case are not due primarily to process changes (which the chart is intended to analyze) but rather to the fact that one group of units happens to have a higher average (or range) than the other. The difference between groups may be so large that it will not be possible to detect other variation. The best way to avoid the systematic effect is to plot two separate charts, one for each group of units.

Among the causes for systematic variation are the following:

$\bar{X}$ Chart

Difference between shifts.

Difference between test sets.

Difference between assembly lines where product is sampled in rotation.

Systematic manner of dividing the data.

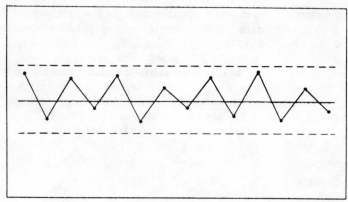

| Fig. 192. Systematic variable. | Fig. 193. Distribution associated with systematic variable. |

R Chart

This effect is generally due to a systematic manner of dividing the data.

Less frequently there may be a large difference in spread between different conveyors, shifts, sources of material, etc., being sampled in rotation.

p-Chart

This effect is almost always due to drawing the samples systematically from different sources.

Individuals Chart

Systematic variation is often due to differences between tools, chucks, positions, assembly fixtures, locating holes, etc.

It shows up particularly when the measurements are being recorded in the order of production, and when the above elements in the process are contributing in succession to the production order.

F-20 TENDENCY OF ONE CHART TO FOLLOW ANOTHER

Part of the meaning of randomness is that the pattern is unpredictable and never repeats. Two control charts which are individually fluctuating at random and which are not in any way connected with each other in a cause and effect relationship will have no tendency to follow each other. Conversely, when two control charts do follow each other it indicates at least the possibility of some relationship between them.

There are two ways in which patterns may tend to follow each other.

(1) There may be a point-to-point correspondence. That is, the individual points may tend to move up and down in unison with respect to other nearby points. See Figure 194. If this happens regularly over a long series of points it indicates some relationship between them.

(2) There may be a level-to-level correspondence. That is, the two patterns may tend to show shifts in level at the same time or to follow trends simultaneously. See Figure 195. This may or may not be accompanied by a point-to-point correspondence also.

Point-to-point correspondence

Point-to-point correspondence generally occurs when the samples plotted on the two corresponding patterns were the same samples. For example, the corresponding $\bar{X}$ and R points on the same control chart are obtained from the same samples. It is also possible for the points on different charts to come from the same samples. For example, we may take a

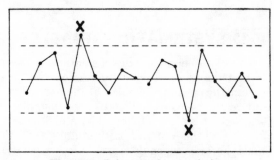

Fig. 194. Point-to-point correlation.

176

sample of 5 parts and measure these parts for several different characteristics which are then plotted on separate control charts but represent the same samples.

When point-to-point correspondence is observed between the two patterns on the same $\bar{X}$ and R chart (that is, when the $\bar{X}$ chart tends to follow the R chart, point by point) this indicates skewness in the underlying parent distribution. See page 156. When point-to-point correspondence is observed between two different characteristics on two different $\bar{X}$ and R charts (for example, when the $\bar{X}$ points for Power Output tend to go up or down with the $\bar{X}$ points for a certain dimension "B") it indicates that there is probably a cause and effect relationship between the two characteristics. The cause and effect relationship may be a direct one (Dimension "B" actually causes a change in Power Output) or it may be indirect through a third variable (Dimension "B" is affected by a certain spacing and this spacing also governs Power Output).

When two characteristics show point-to-point correspondence on their $\bar{X}$ charts over a considerable period of time, the indicated relationship is very close. When the two R charts in addition show point-to-point correspondence, the relationship is even stronger. If two characteristics have practically a 1-to-1 relationship (and the same samples are used for both charts) their patterns will be almost duplicates. $\bar{X}$ and R charts can be used in this manner to study correlation.

Level-to-level correspondence

When a level-to-level correspondence is observed between the two patterns on the same $\bar{X}$ and R chart (that is, the $\bar{X}$ level changes at the same time as the R level), this does not in-dicate any necessary relationship. Except in rare cases, where the standard deviation of a characteristic happens to be proportional to its magnitude, the $\bar{X}$ and R levels are completely independent.

When a level-to-level correspondence is observed between two different characteristics on two different control charts (whether or not they come from the same samples) it may or may not indicate that the two characteristics are related. For example, many p-charts tend to show improvement in the early stages of a process control program. While these are undoubtedly tied together loosely by a common cause—the increased emphasis on process control—there is no reason to suppose that one characteristic causes or governs another.

While it cannot be said that a level-to-level correspondence necessarily indicates a cause and effect relationship, on the other hand it is definitely true that wherever a cause and effect relationship exists the patterns will tend to react together. Consequently, when the engineer observes the levels changing together on various charts, he should at least check to satisfy himself whether a relationship exists. In making such a check he should first examine his theoretical knowledge to see whether such a relationship would be reasonable; remembering, of course, that new knowledge comes from the discovery of relationships which were not suspected before. If it appears reasonable that the two characteristics might be in fact related, the engineer should check them further, following the methods suggested on page 56.

F-21 TRENDS

A trend is defined as continuous movement up or down; x's on one side of the chart followed by x's on the other; a long series of points without a change of direction. Two examples of trends are shown on page 30.

When a trend is present, the total distribution is flat-topped and wider than would be predicted by an R chart. It shifts its location gradually in one direction over a period of time. Trends are in general fairly easy to identify and associate with the process.

Trends may result from any causes which work on the process gradually. The nature of the cause can be determined by the type of

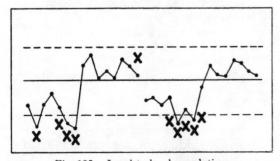

Fig. 195. Level-to-level correlation.

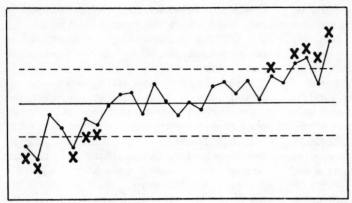

Fig. 196. Trend.

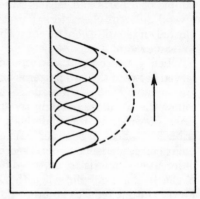

Fig. 197. Distribution associated with a trend.

chart on which the trend appears. If it appears on the $\bar{X}$ chart, the cause is one which moves the center of the distribution rather steadily from high to low or vice versa. If it appears on the R chart, it is gradually increasing or decreasing the spread. If it appears on a p-chart, it is gradually increasing or decreasing the percent defective, etc. Caution needs to be used in the interpretation of trends because it is very easy to think we see trends where none really exist. The irregular up-and-down fluctuations in a natural pattern often appear to the uninitiated to look like trends.

Sometimes the changes which show up as trends on a chart are not really gradual. Sudden changes in the process frequently look like trends either as a result of shop practices which prevent a sharp cut-off or change-over, or merely as a result of chance fluctuations in the data. Some of the most frequent causes of trends are the following:

$\bar{X}$ Chart
(R chart must be in control.)

Tool wear.
Wear of threads, holding devices or gages.
Deterioration of plating or etching solution.
Aging.
Inadequate maintenance on test set.
Seasonal effects, including temperature and humidity.
Human variables. (These may be affected by the amount of supervisory attention, etc.)
Operator fatigue.
Increases or decreases in production schedules.
Gradual change in standards.

Gradual change in proportions of lots.
Poor maintenance or housekeeping procedures.
  For example, accumulation of dirt or shavings, clogging up of fixtures or holes.
Pumps becoming dirty.
Degreaser becoming exhausted.

R Chart

Increasing trend

Something loosening or wearing gradually.
Dulling of a tool.
Change in proportion of lots.
Various types of mixture.

Decreasing trend

Gradual improvement in operator technique.
Effect of better maintenance program.
Effect of process controls in other areas.
Product more homogeneous, or less affected by mixture.

p-Chart

Trend upward.

This means the process is turning out more defectives. The trend may be due to:
  Introduction of poorer material.
  Poorer work by operators.
  Tool wearing too far.
  Drift in a test set.
  Tightening or addition of requirements.

Trend downward.

This means the process is turning out fewer defectives. The trend may be due to:
  Increasing skill or greater care on the part of the operators.

Better material or tools for the operators to work with.

Relaxation of requirements.

Relaxation of standards.

Individuals Chart

Anything which causes trends on the $\bar{X}$ chart, and to a lesser extent the R chart, may affect a chart of individuals. Indications of trends are less reliable, however, on the chart for individuals, and should ordinarily be checked with an $\bar{X}$ and R chart.

F-22 UNSTABLE FORMS OF MIXTURE

These are a special type of mixture, as explained on page 170. Unstable mixtures are one of the most common types of pattern and also one of the most important. This type of mixture is caused by having several distributions in the product which are capable of shifting or changing with respect to each other. The change may be a change in location or merely a change in proportion. For example: one distribution may be just coming into the process or just going out; one of the distributions may be shifting its average or spread with respect to some of the others.

The mixture pattern appears on the $\bar{X}$ chart when samples are taken separately from the different sources of product, and on the R chart when samples are taken at random from the different sources combined. In either case, unstable mixtures tend to show up quite plainly on a p-chart or chart for individual measurements.

Unstable mixtures are closely related to four other types of pattern:

1. Instability.
2. Interaction on the R chart.
3. Grouping or bunching.
4. Freaks.

In general, the detection and elimination of unstable mixtures will tend to make other patterns easier to interpret.

Since the various forms of mixture are largely a matter of degree, any of the unstable patterns may change quite rapidly from one type to another. For example, if freaks or wild readings in the data become fairly numerous, they will be interpreted as unstable mixture. Among the common causes for unstable mixtures are those listed on the following page.

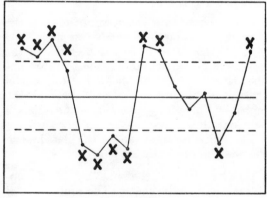

Fig. 198. Unstable mixtures.

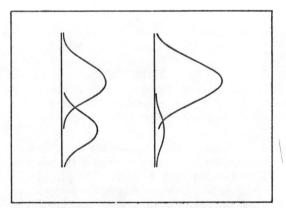

Fig. 199. Distribution associated with unstable mixture (change in proportion).

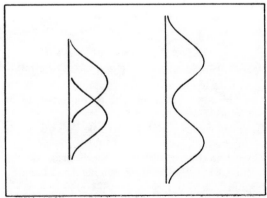

Fig. 200. Distribution associated with unstable mixture (change in location).

179

$\bar{X}$ Chart
(R chart must be in control.)

Distribution changing due to differences in material, operators, test sets, etc.

Breakdown in facilities or automatic controls.

Overadjustment of the process.

Effect of experimental or development work.

Carelessness in setting temperature control, timing device, etc.

Wrong sampling procedures.

Change in the method of measurement.

Errors in plotting.

Incomplete operation.

Setup parts.

R Chart

Two or more materials, machines, operators, machine setters, test sets, gages, etc.

Too much play in a fixture.

Holding or locking devices unreliable.

Mixture of material.

Looseness of a chuck.

Maintenance schedules not adequate.

Operator in need of further training.

Operator fatigue.

Tool in need of sharpening.

Machine in need of repair.

Fixtures or holders not holding the work in position.

Lack of alignment, etc.

Accidental damage.

Operation not completed.

Breakdown of facilities.

Unstable testing equipment.

Experimental units.

Defective piece parts.

Error in calculating or plotting.

p-Chart

Serious lack of control in the process producing a series of lots.

Use of unreliable checking equipment or methods.

Characteristics which tend to be "all good" or "all bad."

Unsystematic screening by shop prior to the time when the product reaches the checking point.

Variations in sample size.

Non-random sampling.

Individuals Chart

Any of the causes capable of affecting the $\bar{X}$ chart or R chart.

F-23 CALCULATION OF TESTS FOR UNNATURAL PATTERNS

Tests for unnatural patterns are obtained by simple probability calculations as shown below. It is necessary to know the probability associated with the portion of the control chart to which the test will apply. For $\bar{X}$ and R charts, use the probabilities given in Figures 201 and 202. For other control charts, use (a) the $\bar{X}$ and R tests or (b) special tests calculated as on page 183.

In all cases, the standard three sigma limit should be included as one of the tests.

Tests for $\bar{X}$ chart

In the case of an $\bar{X}$ chart, we assume that the distribution is approximately normal. The tests are calculated in such a way that if the process is in control, and if the tests are applied simultaneously to one-half of the control chart at a time (upper half or lower half), the probability of getting a reaction to the tests will be about .01.

The following tests can be calculated using the probabilities in Figure 201.

(1) Consider only the outer third in the upper half of the chart. The probability of getting one point at random in this area or beyond is .0227. The probability of getting two points in succession in this area or beyond is .0227 x .0227 or .00052.

Since this is a smaller probability than we wish to use for the test, we increase the probability by letting the test apply to two out of three successive points instead of two points in succession. The probability of "two out of three" is calculated as follows:

The probability of getting two points in succession in the outer third of the chart or beyond is .0227 x .0227. The probability of getting a third point in the sequence in some other portion of the chart (but not in this particular outer third or beyond) is

NORMAL DISTRIBUTION

	Probability = .00135	
	— — — — — — — — — — — — —	3 σ Control Limit
Outer third	Probability = .02135	
Middle third	Probability = .1360	
Inner third	Probability = .3413	
	———————————————	Centerline
Inner third	Probability = .3413	
Middle third	Probability = .1360	
Outer third	Probability = .02135	
	— — — — — — — — — — — — —	3 σ Control Limit
	Probability = .00135	

Fig. 201.   Probabilities used in tests for unnatural patterns: $\bar{X}$ charts.

DISTRIBUTION OF RANGES WHEN THE PARENT POPULATION IS NORMAL

		Samples of 5	Samples of 2	
	Probability =	.0046	.0094	
	— — — — — — — — — — — — —			3 σ Control Limit
Outer third	Probability =	.0294	.0360	
Middle third	Probability =	.1231	.1162	
Inner third	Probability =	.3120	.2622	
	———————————————			Centerline
Inner third	Probability =	.3396	.1724	
Middle third	Probability =	.1735	.1910	
Outer third	Probability =	.0178	.2128	
	— — — — — — — — — — — — —			3 σ Control Limit
	Probability =	.0000	.0000	

Fig. 202.   Probabilities used in tests for unnatural patterns: R charts.

1 − .0227 or .9773. The probability of getting a run of three points, two of which are in this particular outer third (or beyond) and one of which is not, is .0227 x .0227 x .9773 x 3 = .0015. The probabilities are multiplied by 3 because the odd point in the series—the one which does not count in the test—might be either the first, the middle or the last in the series.

(2) Consider now all points in the middle third or beyond. The probability of getting a single point at random in this area is .0227 + .1360, or .1587. The probability of getting four points in a series in this area and one point in some other area is .1587 x .1587 x .1587 x .1587 x .8413 x 5 = .0027.

(3) Consider now all the points on one side of the centerline. The probability of getting one such point at random is .3413 + .1360 + .0227, or .50. The probability of getting eight points in succession on one side of the centerline is .50 x .50 x .50 x .50 x .50 x .50 x .50 x .50 = .0039.

These three probabilities, when added to the probability of exceeding the regular three sigma limit, give a total of .0094, as shown on page 183.

The actual probability associated with the combined tests is somewhat less than this total since there is a certain probability that the same point may react to more than one test.

All the above tests are "one-sided" tests. That is, they are calculated from the probabilities on one side of the centerline only. Tests for stratification and mixture, on the other hand, are usually calculated from the "two-sided" probabilities. It is possible to calculate any desired number of tests by using the principles illustrated above. Examples of this will be found in Reference No. 20.

Tests for R chart

The distribution of ranges is not normal even when the parent population is normal. It varies according to the size of the sample from which the range is computed. The probabilities associated with ranges of samples of 5 and ranges of samples of 2 are shown in Figure 202. Note that these probabilities are quite different from those of the normal distribution.

For ranges of samples of 5, however, it is possible to use the same tests as for a normal distribution without producing a large difference in the total reaction to the tests. This is shown on page 183. Note that the probability of reaction may be quite different in the case of individual tests, but the sum of these probabilities is not far from .01.

The $\bar{X}$ tests may therefore be adopted as "standard" tests and used not only for the $\bar{X}$ chart but also for the R chart when the sample size is 4 or 5. This is a practical advantage in many routine applications of control charts, since it is not necessary to learn more than one set of tests.

Samples of 2

For ranges of samples of 2, the probabilities are sufficiently different to make it advisable to use a separate set of tests. Suitable tests are shown in Figure 203.

If the parent population is normal, the probabilities associated with the tests in Figure 203 are as follows:

Upper Half of Chart	*Ranges of Samples of 2*
Single point out	.0094
2 successive points	.0021
3 successive points	.0042
7 successive points	.0025
Total	.0182

Lower Half of Chart	*Ranges of Samples of 2*
10 successive points	.0040
6 successive points	.0043
4 successive points	.0020
Single point out	—
Total	.0103

Even with the special tests, note that the total of all tests for the upper half of the chart approaches the .02 probability rather than .01. This is because of the large probability of getting a single point outside of the standard three sigma limit. The latter probability itself is nearly .01.

Ranges of samples of 2 are used mainly in Designed Experiments, where there is no need

	Upper Half		*Lower Half*
	Single point out		
A	2 succ. points in Zone A or above		
B	3 succ. points in Zone B or above		
C	7 succ. points in Zone C or above		
		C	10 succ. points in Zone C or below
		B	6 succ. points in Zone B or below
		A	4 succ. points in Zone A or below
		—	Point out is not possible

Fig. 203. Tests applied to the R chart when $n = 2$.

to avoid the complication of using a second set of tests.

Tests for p-charts and various other control charts

On most charts where control limits are reasonably symmetrical, it is sufficiently accurate to use the standard tests. However, by making use of the principles described above, it is possible to calculate special tests for *p*-charts or other charts whose control limits may at times be unsymmetrical. First find the probabilities associated theoretically with each third of the control band, and calculate tests which will result in the desired total probability of getting a reaction to the tests.

For a *p*-chart use either Binomial or Poisson probabilities: for a *c*-chart use the Poisson, etc.

The tests in the following column are roughly equivalent to each other when applied to areas having the indicated probabilities, and can be used as a general guide. The probability of reaction to each test is approximately .0014 ± .0002.

Total Probability Derived from Distribution (in a particular zone and beyond)	Suitable Test
.02	2 out of 3
.04	2 successive points
.11	3 successive points
.13	4 out of 5
.20	4 successive points
.27	5 successive points
.33	6 successive points
.40	7 successive points
.44	8 successive points
.48	9 successive points
.52	10 successive points

Practical shop applications

In most cases, when doing practical work in the shop, it is sufficient to use the tests explained on pages 23–28. If special tests are wanted to fit a particular situation, the tests should be calculated and checked by the responsible Quality Control Team.

Standard Control Chart Tests (as given on pages 23–28)		
	Probability of Getting a Reaction to the Tests	
Upper Half of Chart	Normal ($\bar{X}$)	*Ranges of Samples of 5*
Single point out	.0013	.0046
2 out of 3	.0015	.0033
4 out of 5	.0027	.0026
8 in a row	.0039	.0023
Total	.0094	.0128
Lower Half of Chart	Normal ($\bar{X}$)	*Ranges of Samples of 5*
8 in a row	.0039	.0063
4 out of 5	.0027	.0054
2 out of 3	.0015	.0009
Single point out	.0013	—
Total	.0094	.0126

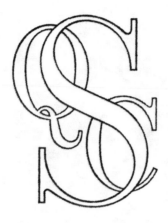

Section III

Shop
Applications

PART A
Process Control Charts

This part of the Handbook covers the planning, installation and use of Operating process control charts. Process control charts are the hub around which the whole program in the Shop revolves.

Designed Experiments are an aid in making process capability studies. Process Capability Studies are helpful in obtaining information about the process. Sampling Plans, as used by Inspection, are a useful means of checking on the adequacy of the process controls.

However, unless the Designed Experiments are translated into process capabilities, and the process capabilities are in turn translated into tangible results in the Shop, all the improvements brought about by experiments and capability studies will be just so much paper. In the same way, unless the shop is controlling its processes, it is not possible to realize the economies and advantages of sampling inspection.

For this reason the Shop Section is in many respects the most important part of the Handbook.

Shop objectives

In starting process control charts in a given area, or on a given job, it is necessary to have in mind some tangible objective. This objective may be:

    a. To improve quality.
    b. To reduce losses or re-work.
    c. To make the process more stable—that is, less subject to unpredictable trouble.
    d. To find the cause of some difficulty which is currently being experienced.
    e. To discover which operations or characteristics are capable of changing or influencing other operations.
    f. To check on the importance or suitability of specifications, etc.

All of these are in line with the general quality control objective of improving quality and at the same time reducing costs.

The details of planning, installing and using the shop control charts should be handled jointly by a Quality Control Team.

A-1 PLANNING THE CONTROL CHARTS

A-1.1 Where to put the first charts

Almost any shop will need a certain number of shop control charts. The charts should be set up in such a way that they will show the significant "causes of variation" affecting the particular job. There are three ways of discovering these causes of variation.

(1) *Process capability studies.* These studies frequently end by showing the proper places for shop charts. See pages 47–63 for the method of making such a study, and pages 63–65 for the method of using the information to set up a chart in the shop. Process capability studies are the best foundation for process control charts.

(2) *Performance studies.* It is possible to use performance studies in place of process capability studies in any of the following cases:

a. Where the shop is having difficulty in meeting a requirement.

b. Where there are large amounts of re-work.

c. Where it is necessary to adjust, re-adjust or do selective assembly.

d. Where someone is performing 100% inspection.

Follow the directions for performance studies on page 74. Work gradually backward into the earlier operations until you discover the most important sources of trouble.

(3) *Nature of operation or characteristic to be studied.* The following situations will almost always benefit from charts, whether or not there is any apparent indication of trouble:

a. Cases where the individual operator directly controls important results.

b. Cases where the machine setter has to keep the machine centered within narrow limits.

c. Cases where it is desirable, for economic reasons, to hold the distribution in some specific place.

d. Cases where it is desired to study or question the specifications.

In certain cases the engineer may set up charts in the shop for the purpose of gathering engineering information. These charts should be marked "experimental chart" or "engineering study" to distinguish them from the regular shop control charts.

A-1.2 How to decide on the proper type of chart

Three types of control chart are commonly used in the shop:

a. $\bar{X}$ and R charts.

b. p-Charts (or other attributes charts such as np-charts, c-charts, and u-charts).

c. Charts for individual measurements with control limits based on the moving range.

The following are appropriate situations in which to use each type of chart.

$\bar{X}$ and R charts

Use these charts for:

(1) New jobs, or jobs where there are unsolved engineering problems.

(2) Jobs that have been in production for some time but are chronically in trouble.

(3) Cases where it is difficult or expensive to obtain data, as in destructive testing.

(4) Cases where there are difficult assembly problems, including overlapping tolerances, small clearances and interference fits.

(5) Cases where the chart is needed for diagnostic purposes: the job is in trouble and we have not discovered why.

(6) Cases where it is desired to obtain changes in specifications.

(7) Cases where it is desired to reduce acceptance inspection to a minimum and where the job is in good control.

(8) Cases where the shop must determine when to adjust a machine or process and when to let it alone. This includes cases where the shop must determine whether a set-up is satisfactory.

(9) Cases where attributes control charts have been in use but the shop has been unable to bring the charts into control.

$\bar{X}$ and R charts may be plotted on (a) a critical quality characteristic, (b) a characteristic which is important for economic reasons, or (c) a characteristic which is frequently in trouble.

p-Charts (or other attributes charts)

Use these charts for:

(1) Cases where a chart can help the operators to do better work.

(2) Cases where it is desired to reduce repairs, re-work and scrap, and the causes for these are known to, or controlled by, the individual operators or the Operating group.

(3) Cases where it is desired to obtain a historical picture or summary of the job. p-Charts can be more useful for this

purpose than $\bar{X}$ and R charts, since it is possible to combine many characteristics into a single p-chart.

(4) Cases where it is desired to study trends in individual defects or groups of defects.

(5) Cases where some means of detecting assignable causes is needed and it is not economically feasible to obtain variables data for $\bar{X}$ and R charts.

p-Charts may be plotted on (a) the percent defective, (b) the percent good, or (c) the percent lost or spoiled at the operation. On complex types of apparatus or equipment, where it is possible for many defects to occur on the same unit, it is customary to use c-charts as a substitute for p-charts.

Charts for individual measurements with control limits based on the moving range

Use these charts for:

(1) Operations where it is not possible or convenient to obtain more than one measurement per sample: for example, furnace temperatures, gas pressures, chemical analyses of a quantity of powder or liquid.

(2) Cases where the data must be obtained from accounting figures, etc., which are not available until the end of a week or month.

(3) Any case where it would not be possible or practical to use the regular variables or attributes charts.

A-1.3 How to determine the correct number of charts

It is seldom possible to determine, at the beginning, how many charts will be needed. However, this can be determined over a period of time as follows:

(1) At the beginning, put charts on any characteristics or operations which you believe to be important. The charts themselves will give information as to whether they are actually needed.

(2) As time goes on, take off charts that are found to be unnecessary. Add others that are found to be necessary. More charts will usually be required at the beginning than after the job has become more stable.

(3) Keep up-to-date records of the number of charts on the job. It is best to keep separate records of the variables and attributes charts. In general, for a number of months after the charts are first installed, you should find that the number of charts tends to increase rather steadily until it reaches a maximum. After that it may stabilize at the maximum point or it may even decrease. After the job stabilizes it is quite common to find that it has the same number of charts from one year to the next. However, they are not necessarily the same charts.

(4) If the charts are being used effectively and if new knowledge is being gained about the controlling variables, you should find the proportion of $\bar{X}$ and R charts gradually increasing as compared with p-charts.

(5) All decisions having to do with the removal or addition of charts should be joint decisions of the Quality Control Team.

A-1.4 How to make sure that the charts are set up correctly

Shop charts are not designed to be interpreted in the same manner as process capability studies. When a chart used in a process capability study is out of control it means, "Here is additional information." It may even be essential for the chart to go out of control in order to solve the problem.

Process control charts, however, are deliberately set up in such a way that "out-of-control" is synonymous with trouble. On a process control chart an out-of-control condition should mean:

a. Part of the product will be outside of specifications.

b. There will be an increase in assembly difficulties.

c. Some later operation will suffer.

d. Yields will go down.

e. There will be too many repairs,

or some other undesirable and uneconomical result. If a chart can go out of control without meaning trouble, the chart is not set up properly for shop use.

Among the conditions which may result in having charts set up incorrectly are the following:

(1) The cause of trouble may be too far removed from the point where the chart is located. In that case it will be too difficult for the shop to trace the trouble causing the out-of-control condition.

(2) The product may have been screened or 100% inspected prior to the place where the samples are taken. In that case the information needed for control is probably being thrown out along with the defectives.

(3) The chart may attempt to cover too many characteristics at once. This is often true of p-charts. When the chart shows trouble the shop may have no way of knowing which characteristic is out of control.

(4) Even when the chart covers a single characteristic, there may be too many causes which can affect that characteristic. For example, one engineer was very impatient with the shop for failing to take action on a chart. When the engineer was asked to make a list of all the causes which could throw that characteristic out of control, he found there were 47!

No one in the shop should be expected to investigate an unreasonable number of causes. The Quality Control Team should provide charts on some of the causes back in the process where it will be practical to check them.

The Team should make sure that all charts are statistically correct as well as correctly planned and used.

Scales are important on process control charts, since unsuitable scales may diminish the readability or usefulness of the charts. If fluctuations are made to look very large as a result of the choice of scale, a machine setter may have a tendency to over-adjust the machine. On the other hand, if the scale is such that the fluctuations are very small, shop people may delay in taking action because they have an impression that the fluctuations are unimportant.

As processes come into better control, the fluctuations on the control charts may tend to become smaller. In such cases, it may be necessary to expand the plotting scales from time to time, in order to obtain more readable patterns.

If specification limits are to be indicated on the chart, it is necessary to set up the scales with this in mind. Specified limits should be indicated only as arrows in the margin, so they will not be mistaken for the centerlines or control limits.

A-1.5 Operations which may not need to be charted

It is not necessary to plan control charts on every operation. Some operations may not need to be checked at all. On other operations it may be sufficient to have the operator check one or two parts informally at specified intervals during the run. Informal checks of this kind, which are not plotted or subjected to statistical tests, are called "casual checking."

Too much reliance on casual checking should be avoided. Small samples without statistical limits can only distinguish between conditions which are about 100% good and those which are about 100% bad. If the shop is expected to discover moderately defective conditions, or to tell whether the product is meeting a dimensional limit, this will ordinarily require a control chart.

A-2 DETAILED PROCEDURES IN SETTING UP THE CHARTS

A-2.1 General

The following steps should be taken in setting up charts for shop use.

(1) *Decide where the process should be checked, and how and where the samples should be selected.* Checking for process control should be performed as soon as possible after the operation which is to be controlled. The sample should be selected in such a way as to detect changes in the process as rapidly and economically as

Chart	Recommended Sample Size	Remarks
$\bar{X}$ & R	(a) For the usual shop charts, or engineering studies of a going process, use samples of 4 or 5. (b) For experimental work, or for any kind of chart for which the data are extremely limited, use samples of 2 or 3.	(a) Samples for $\bar{X}$ and R charts should be small rather than large, and should rarely exceed 10. (b) For samples of 2 and 3, the control limits on the R chart are noticeably unsymmetrical. This makes the R pattern more difficult to interpret. See pages 182–183.
p	(a) Where the size of the sample can be specified in advance, try to use samples of 25, 50 or 100. It is advisable to keep the sample size constant for the entire series of samples. (b) p-Charts are easiest to interpret where the product of $n \times p$ is approximately 4 or 5. However, if the fraction defective is small, this would frequently call for uneconomically large samples. (c) In some cases it is convenient to plot the results of 100% sorting, considering each lot or quantity as a "sample."	(a) If the sample size varies from sample to sample, the chart will require special interpretation as shown on pages 18–19. (b) If the sample size is very small and $\bar{p}$ is also small, the control limits will be unsymmetrical. Special tests for such charts are given on page 183. (c) If the sample size is very large (hundreds or thousands) it may be advisable to use "moving range" control limits for the p-chart as explained on pages 196–197.
np	Same as for p-chart except that the sample size must be constant throughout the series of samples.	(a) If the product of $n \times p$ is small, the control limits will be unsymmetrical. See page 183. (b) If n is very large (hundreds or thousands), interpret the chart as explained on pages 196–197.
c	The sample should consist of some constant unit or quantity such as (a) A piece of wired equipment of a particular type. (b) A square foot of rubber or cloth. (c) A certain number of feet of wire, etc.	(a) The sample for a c-chart may consist of a number of separate units, provided the group of units are handled as if they were one. For example, we might count the number of loose connections in groups of wired panels containing 8 panels in each group. The sample in this case would be "a group of 8 panels." (b) For further information, see remarks under "np-charts."
u	The sample may consist of any convenient number of units or quantities of product, each unit or quantity being of the type that would be used for a c-chart. It is not necessary for the number of units to be constant. For example, the sample may consist of ten radar systems the first month, eight radar systems the second month, etc. However, the term "radar system" should have essentially the same meaning from month to month.	(a) If the number of units varies much from point to point, calculate separate control limits as explained on page 18. (b) If the number of units does not vary from point to point, this type of chart should be converted to a c-chart. (c) For further information, see remarks under "p-charts."
Individual measurements with control limits based on moving range.	Since individual measurements only are plotted, the sample size is 1.	Care should be taken that the meaning of "individual" is essentially the same from point to point. For example, if accounting figures are being plotted, the point should represent a week's data consistently or a month's data consistently, etc. If monthly points are used, five-week months should ordinarily be converted to a four-week basis.

possible. Care should be taken to make sure that the samples are truly representative of the process. Ordinarily, the best kind of sample for process control purposes is the "instantaneous" sample obtained by taking a small group of successive units at regular intervals from the process.

In planning the selection of samples, it is often helpful to list the various known changes in the process which may be able to affect the characteristic or characteristics being plotted. The samples should be selected in such a way as to detect those changes. It is possible that more than one control chart will be needed to control a particular operation.

(2) *Decide on the sampling interval (or checking frequency).* This depends on (a) the cost of making checks and (b) the rapidity with which the process is likely to change. The necessary frequency of check may be every few minutes, every few hours, once a shift, once a day, once a week or once a month. At the beginning it is usually necessary to take more frequent samples than after the process begins to settle and the charts come into control. One of the important responsibilities of the Quality Control Team is to keep reviewing the checking frequencies on all control charts with the object of increasing the interval between checks wherever possible.

(3) *Decide on the sample size to be used.* Ordinarily, this is determined by the type of chart. The table on page 191 will be helpful. It contains a summary of the information given in Section I of the Handbook.

Do not hesitate to use sample sizes other than those recommended here if there is a good practical reason. However, the possible implications of the chosen sample size should be carefully discussed by the Quality Control Team.

(4) *Decide on the centerline and control limits for the chart.* In a process capability study these are merely calculated from the data. In a process control chart they require an engineering decision. Detailed information on making these decisions is given on pages 64–65 and 193–197.

(5) *Provide what is necessary for obtaining data and plotting and handling the control charts.* This includes the following:

a. Provide gages and other devices for making the checks.

b. Appoint someone in the shop to take the samples, make the checks and plot the charts.

c. Train the process checker in carrying out these duties properly, including the marking of x's on the chart when the pattern is out of control. Make sure that the process checker knows what to do about abnormal data or "freaks."

d. Provide suitable forms for recording the data and other forms for plotting the charts.

e. Also provide suitable chart holders and facilities for mounting the holders. For the sake of appearance as well as usability, these should be standard throughout the plant.

Holders can be designed for mounting on benches, pipes, pillars, walls or whatever is available in the area. The fixtures that hold the charts should be such that the charts can be readily removed and replaced. For durability, the charts should be mounted on a backing in such a way that the shop can easily turn to previous sheets. It should be possible to insert fresh copies of the chart on top of the old ones so that a chronological history of the job is made available by turning a few pages.

(6) *Write a layout giving the shop specific instructions on how to use each chart.* The writing of the layout is the responsibility of the product engineer. It should include instructions on obtaining the samples, making the checks, calculating, plotting, marking the patterns and deciding what to look for when the chart goes out of control. The product engineer is usually assisted in this by the other members of the Quality Control Team. As experience accumulates through the quality control meetings, the layout may be modified to include additional information.

A-2.2 Centerlines

On a process control chart the centerline is located by engineering decision. It should represent the place (or places) where the Team has found it is desirable and possible for the process to run. The considerations on which this decision should be based are discussed on pages 64–65.

Three techniques are possible in setting the centerline on a shop chart.

(A) The centerline may be chosen to represent the *desired average* for the process—that is, some single place where the distribution ought to be held most of the time in order to get the best results. The "best results" may refer to the best quality, the highest yields, the lowest cost or the best balance between any or all of these. The decision to use this type of centerline should preferably be based on a process capability study. In some cases the "one best place" for the distribution has been specified in advance as an engineering requirement.

While this type of centerline is sometimes used on R charts or p-charts, it is used more commonly on $\bar{X}$ charts or charts for individual measurements with control limits based on the moving range.

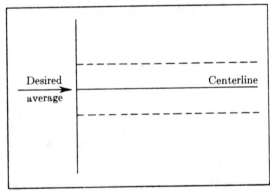

Fig. 204.   First method of setting the centerline on a shop control chart: desired average.

(B) In case there is no specific point which represents a desired average, there may still be a high or low limit which the engineer does not want the distribution to exceed. In that case the centerline on the process control chart is made to represent the *highest or lowest permissible average* for

$\bar{X}$, R, p or individuals, as the case may be.

This type of centerline can be used for any type of control chart. In the case of a p-chart or R chart it often represents the best the process has been able to do so far. The engineer does not want it to get worse, but he may intend to lower the centerline as soon as the process can be improved. Ordinarily, $\bar{R}$ or $\bar{p}$ should be as close to zero as possible for economic reasons.

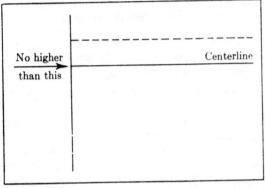

Fig. 205.   Second method of setting the centerline on a shop control chart: highest or lowest permissible average.

(C) In many cases there is an area or "band" of acceptable levels within which the engineer is willing to let the process run. For example, we may wish to allow a shift of several thousandths of an inch to take care of toolwear, or unavoidable differences between machine settings or batches of material. We may not care how much the process fluctuates, as long as the distribution does not move outside this permissible band.

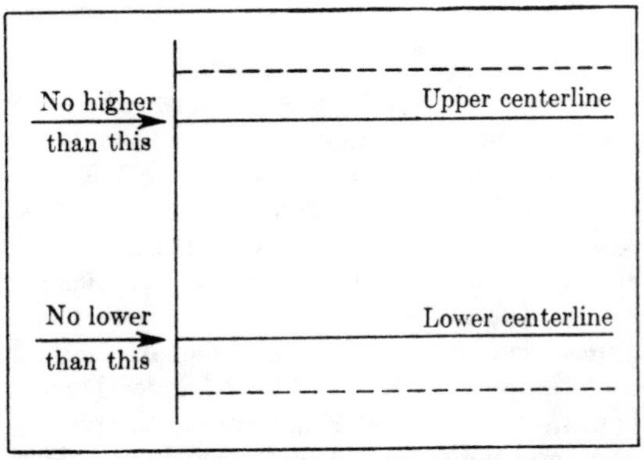

Fig. 206.   Third method of setting the centerline on a shop control chart: a band of acceptable averages.

193

In such cases show two centerlines on the shop chart, one on the high side and one on the low side. This double centerline is used only on $\bar{X}$ charts or charts for individual measurements, never on R charts or p-charts.

Centerlines located by any of the above methods are called "economic centerlines" because they are chosen on an economic or engineering basis. The control limits placed around such centerlines are called "economic control limits."

Precautions to be taken in locating centerlines on shop charts

Never locate a centerline on a shop control chart at a point where it is impossible or impractical for the process to run. Centerlines may, however, be located in such a way as to encourage the process to improve. Sufficient data should be available to show that the improvement is possible. An example is given in Figure 207.

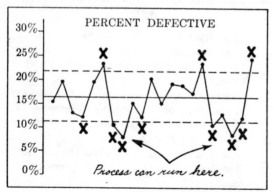

Fig. 207. Shop chart used as the basis for an economic decision.

This chart says it is possible to run the process at about 10% defective even though the current level is about 15% defective. A shop chart on this process could properly be set up with its centerline at 10%. On the other hand, *do not put the centerline on a p-chart at some low percent defective just because you think that such a level would be desirable.* If the chart predicts that the process can run at 10% defective and you want it to run at 2%, improve the process first and then move the centerline down. Also, if you intend to move the centerline down as the process improves, explain this to the opera-

tors at the beginning and tell them where it will stop. In the same way, do not put the centerline on an $\bar{X}$ chart, R chart or chart for individual measurements in a place where you have no evidence that the shop would be able to run.

A-2.3 Control limits

In all cases, control limits for process control charts should be located the proper statistical distance from the selected centerline. Once the centerline has been fixed, the control limits follow automatically. The location of the limits is determined by the formulas given on pages 12–21.

The following, however, is one essential difference between the control limits on process control charts and the control limits on process capability studies:

All process capability studies employ two control limits, one on either side of the centerline. For shop charts it is permissible to omit one of the control limits (on $\bar{X}$ charts or charts for individual measurements) in any of the following cases:

a. Where a double centerline is used on an $\bar{X}$ chart or chart for individual measurements, show only the outer control limit for each of the centerlines. This is because the shop is not required to take action on process shifts that take place between the centerlines.
b. Where the centerline on an $\bar{X}$ chart or chart for individual measurements is fixed at the highest permissible level, show only the high control limit. This is because the shop is not required to take action when the process is below that level.
c. For similar reasons, when the centerline is fixed at the lowest permissible level, show only the low control limit.

The lower control limit may be omitted on a p-chart after the process has become stabilized at an economically low level. When this is done it indicates that the shop is not expected to strive for further improvement.

In all cases where a control limit is shown, the shop should be expected to apply tests for unnatural patterns and mark x's where indi-

cated. The presence of x's should always call
for some kind of action. If action is not
wanted when the distribution moves in a certain direction, this is sufficient reason for omit-
ting the control limit on that side.

A point of special importance on the R chart
is that the lower control limit *should never be
omitted*. This is because of the great economic
importance of the information contained in x's
on the low side of an R chart. See pages 168–
169.

A-2.4 "Modified" control limits for $\bar{X}$ and R charts

"Modified" control limits are based on a
special form of economic centerline, which is
designed to let the process run just high enough
or just low enough to keep out of trouble with a
specification. The restrictions for using modified control limits are as follows:

It is first necessary to make a process capability study and obtain a controlled pattern of
R. From this it is possible to calculate the
"process spread of individuals," as indicated on
page 56. If the process spread of individuals
is much narrower than the specification limits,
and if product anywhere within specification
limits is satisfactory, it is possible to use modified control limits on an $\bar{X}$ and R chart. Do not
attempt to use modified limits if any of the
above conditions are not met.

Theory of modified limits

When the specified limits are wide and the
distribution is narrow, as shown in Figure
208, the distribution can be allowed to move up
or down a considerable distance.

It is possible to make simple calculations,
based on distribution theory, to determine
how far the distribution can be permitted to
move. The calculations apply to the $\bar{X}$
chart only.

Normal distribution

(1) First locate a pair of centerlines on the
$\bar{X}$ chart at the highest and lowest permissible point for the center of the distribution. This is done as follows:

    a. Find the value of d_2 associated with the
sample size to be used on the chart.
(See page 131.)

    b. Locate the two centerlines for the $\bar{X}$
chart as follows:

Upper Centerline for $\bar{X} =$
$$\text{Upper Specification Limit} - \frac{3\bar{R}}{d_2}$$

Lower Centerline for $\bar{X} =$
$$\text{Lower Specification Limit} + \frac{3\bar{R}}{d_2}$$

These two centerlines are shown in Figure
209.

(2) If only one limit is specified (upper or
lower), use only the appropriate centerline.

(3) Calculate control limits in the standard
way for the size of sample used, by adding
$\pm A_2\bar{R}$ to each of the centerline values.
The A_2 factors are given on page 12.
Show only the outer control limit for each
centerline, as indicated in Figure 209.
An example of a chart with modified control limits is shown on page 65.

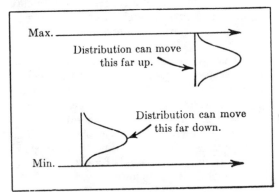

Fig. 208. Conditions for the use of modified
control limits.

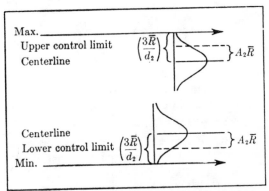

Fig. 209. Determining the location of modified
control limits.

(4) Check the location of the modified limits by eye to make sure your calculations are not in error. For samples of 5 the dotted control limit should be about halfway between the centerline and the specified limit (more accurately speaking, about 45% of the distance). This rule is obtained as follows:

Percentage of distance from

$$\text{centerline outward} = \frac{100 \times A_2}{E_2}$$

where A_2 and E_2 vary with the sample size and are obtained from the tables given on pages 12 and 131. ($E_2 = 3/d_2$.)

For samples of 5, $A_2 = .577$ and $E_2 = 1.29$.

$$\frac{100 \times .577}{1.29} = 45\%.$$

Similar calculations can be made for other sample sizes.

Non-normal distributions

Distributions which are not normal may spread more or less than 3 sigma from the average. Consequently it may be necessary to modify the factor "3" in the equations for centerlines in paragraph (1) above. If the distribution is skewed, it may be necessary to use one factor for the side with the long tail and another factor for the side with the short tail. These factors should be estimated on the basis of engineering judgment. A further discussion of non-normal distributions is given in the Engineering Section, pages 56–58.

Corresponding modifications must also be made in the E_2 factors referred to in paragraph (4).

Summary of conditions for using modified limits

(1) If the spread of the process is wider than the distance between specified limits, it is not possible to use modified limits on the $\bar{X}$ chart.

(2) If the spread of the process is just equal to the distance between specified limits, the upper and lower centerlines on the $\bar{X}$ chart will coincide. There is, therefore, no advantage in using modified limits.

(3) It should always be possible to use modified limits on the $\bar{X}$ chart if there is only one specified limit (maximum only or minimum only).

(4) Since the modified limits are derived on the basis of a controlled R chart as determined by a process capability study, it is necessary to maintain a standard R chart at all times wherever modified limits are applied to the $\bar{X}$ chart. If the R chart goes out of control it is no longer safe to use the modified limits on the $\bar{X}$ chart.

(5) No modified limits of any kind are ever applied to an R chart.

A-2.5 Modified limits on charts for individual measurements

Modified limits are sometimes used on charts for individual measurements provided there is adequate knowledge about the shape of the distribution of individuals.

A-2.6 Modified limits for p-charts or c-charts

There is no counterpart for modified control limits which can be used on a p-chart or c-chart. However, when p-charts are used at the end of a production process and where the sample sizes are very large, we sometimes use a special type of control limit on the p-chart which has much the same effect as the modified limits discussed above. The following are the conditions under which the special limits may be used:

When large amounts of data are combined on an overall p-chart, these data may include many different variations in raw material, part numbers, code numbers, processing batches or inspection lots. These are assignable causes which cannot be studied properly except with individual p-charts at various operations. Superimposed on these ordinary types of causes, however, may be large general shifts or trends which affect the whole shop. The overall p-chart can be used to study these broad shifts and trends by calculating its control limits as follows:

(1) Consider the sample percentages as

individual pieces of data similar to records that might be obtained from accounting.

(2) Calculate control limits for these values using the moving range.

(3) Select as the period on which to base the calculations a time when the shop situation is considered "normal" or free from unusual trouble.

Such control limits will tend to ignore the assignable causes present during the "normal" period but will tend to show up any large general trends. Do not attempt to use these special limits for p-charts if the charts are intended for direct process control.

A-3 OTHER METHODS OF CHARTING

Use of "t"-charts and charts for other statistics

In cases where varying sample size is a problem, any of the standard control charts can be plotted as "t" charts. The "t" chart merely uses a standardized scale for plotting in which "t" stands for the number of sigma away from the centerline on the chart. The control limits for the "t" chart are drawn at ±3 sigma and the centerline at 0 sigma. If a point on the original control chart would be halfway between the centerline and the control limit, it is plotted on the "t" chart at 1.5 sigma. If a point on the original chart would be two-thirds of the way between the centerline and the control limit, it is plotted on the "t" chart at 2.0 sigma, and so on. A "t" chart always has its control limits the same distance from the centerline, regardless of how the sample size may vary.

The "t" chart is useful for certain summary purposes, but is much less useful for process capability studies or process control. The chart is more difficult to interpret correctly than other types of chart. Much information is lost by converting the absolute information into values of "t." Out-of-control points, or patterns which are not balanced around the centerline, are likely to be misleading. A "t" chart is often more sensitive to the changes in sample size (which are buried in the chart) than it is to the changes in the process which we are trying to detect. A Quality Control Team should therefore use the ordinary types of control chart wherever possible.

The above objections do not apply to control charts for sample maximum values, sample minimum values, sample totals, sample medians or other statistics calculated from samples. It is quite permissible to use control charts for any of these statistics, provided equations are available for calculating the necessary control limits.

Use of the Quality Measurement Plan (QMP) Chart

Quality Assurance (see reference 36) recently changed from the "t" chart form of rating to a Quality Measurement Plan based on Bayesian statistics (see reference 37).

Substitutes for $\bar{X}$ and R charts

Engineers sometimes prefer to plot, or have the shop plot, the *total* of a sample of measurements rather than the *average* ($\bar{X}$). This is permissible in the case of constant sample sizes, since the average is derived from the total by dividing through by a constant. Plotting the total instead of the average merely amounts to changing the plotting scale on the $\bar{X}$ chart and has no effect whatever on the statistical analysis. Charts on which totals are plotted instead of averages are known as "total and range charts" or "sum and range charts."

Occasionally some other statistic may be substituted in place of $\bar{X}$. In life testing it is sometimes convenient to use the median of a sample instead of its average. If a sample of 5 units are put on life test the median is known as soon as the third unit has failed. If we were to use the average of the measurements we would have to wait until all 5 units had failed before the point could be plotted. As a rule, however, a Quality Control Team should plan on using $\bar{X}$ unless it has a good reason for doing otherwise.

There are also possible substitutes for the range chart. The most common is the standard deviation of the sample, often designated as "s." In general, a Quality Control Team will prefer to use ranges for two reasons:

First, because of the simplicity of calculation.

Second, because the range is a more sensitive indicator of certain types of assignable causes.

Other possible measures of dispersion are the mean deviation, quartile or semi-inter-quartile range, etc. but these are seldom useful for quality control purposes. Other substitutes for the $\bar{X}$ and R chart include charts for "median range" and midranges. See Reference No. 14.

Substitutes for p-charts and c-charts

One possible substitute for the standard p-chart or c-chart is a chart for percentages or counts with control limits based on the moving range. See pages 196–197. Another is the use of standard $\bar{X}$ and R charts for the study of attributes data. While attributes charts are used more commonly for this purpose, it is possible to use $\bar{X}$ and R charts for the analysis of any data, including percentages and other attributes measurements. Merely use the percentages as if they were any other series of numbers.

Charts showing demerits (or other forms of weighted defects) are sometimes used as a substitute for the more usual attributes charts. Demerit charts are much less useful than p-charts or c-charts for detecting and identifying assignable causes. Demerit charts should be used with great care and only where the Team is certain that there is no other practical solution.

Ordinarily, instead of using demerits, the same objective can be achieved by dividing the defects into two groups (major and minor) of if necessary into three groups (critical, major and minor). For purposes of control, plot separate charts for major and minor defects. In some cases it may be sufficient to plot the major defects only.

Major and minor defects are sometimes combined at the end of a process where only a broad general summary is required. The shop, however, usually needs more detailed information, and defects of different seriousness should be kept separate at the point where the process is being controlled.

Substitute forms of the "chart for individual measurements"

Individual measurements are sometimes plotted on a "dot" chart. The process checker merely records a dot or x for each unit in the sample without connecting the points. Individual measurements may also be plotted on a "multi-vari" chart in the form of both maximum and minimum readings on each part. The two readings are connected by a line whose length is proportional to the variability within pieces. If each sample consists of 5 parts, there are 5 lines for each sample. This chart may also be used to record out-of-roundness, eccentricity or out-of-parallel conditions.

The above charts are often used without control limits, and thus can not properly be called "control charts." When control limits are used, they are sometimes located one sigma inside the specification limit. Sigma is obtained from some previous estimate of the process standard deviation.

General comment on non-standard control charts

There is no question that the charts most generally useful for process capability studies and process control are the standard types of control chart. Almost invariably, when an engineer or supervisor feels the need for departing from the standard methods, it is because he does not have a full understanding of what can be accomplished by the regular charts.

In particular, if you constantly find reason to use something other than $\bar{X}$ and R charts or p-charts, it is desirable to deepen your understanding of these two basic tools. This does not mean that non-standard charts should never be used; only that when a decision is reached to do so, one should be certain that he has an adequate reason.

A-4 MAKING CHANGES IN SHOP CONTROL CHARTS

Process control charts are dynamic rather than static, and need to be studied and changed continually. The form of the chart may change with any changes in process, schedules, requirements, product design, etc. The charts in use should be re-evaluated repeatedly in the light of demonstrated results or in accordance with added knowledge. It may be necessary to change the charts from time to time for any of the following reasons:

For ease in interpretation.

For greater readability or usefulness of the scale.

To take advantage of current economic decisions.

To remove charts that are no longer necessary or are not economical.

To consolidate a number of charts into a single chart for economy.

To split a single chart into a number of charts for better analysis.

To reduce or increase the intervals between samples.

To take advantage of improvements.

To incorporate new knowledge gained from process capability studies.

In general, process control charts should change with any changes in the state of knowledge about the job. The charts themselves tend to create the conditions which cause them to be changed.

The need for frequent changes is one of the reasons for having Quality Control Teams. It is also one of the reasons why process control information should be written, if possible, in separate process control layouts.

PART B

Introduction of Charts in the Shop

Most responsibilities in quality control are joint responsibilities, and the introduction of control charts in the shop is no exception. The Quality Control Team, as a whole, is responsible for introducing the charts properly and making sure that they work. However, the supervisor has a special responsibility in this connection, since he is the member of the Team who deals directly with the people. Among the specific responsibilities of the supervisor are the following:

(1) To inform himself on the general principles of quality control as covered in the Fundamental Section of this Handbook.

(2) To understand the workings of all charts in his area.

(3) To explain to all his people who are associated with the charts the following points:

    (a) The importance of the charts.

    (b) How they work.

    (c) The benefits to them of the proper use of the charts.

    (d) The fact that the supervisor, himself, intends to use the charts in running the job.

(4) To make sure that the people who are plotting and reading the charts know how to do it correctly.

(5) To watch the charts, and other process controls, and see that they are functioning as intended.

The following is based on the experience of many shop supervisors in (a) introducing the charts, (b) explaining their benefits and (c) guiding the work of process checkers. Also included for reference is a set of General Instructions for Process Control, and a brief description of a Process Control Layout.

———————— ✦ ————————

B-1 EXPLAINING THE CHARTS TO THE PEOPLE

It is possible to introduce control charts in the shop without any special explanation. As time goes on and the operators or machine setters begin to ask questions, the supervisor can answer the questions in as much detail as seems necessary. In a short time, the people will become accustomed to the charts and accept them.

In general, however, it is better to prepare the people carefully and in advance for the introduction of charts. Many supervisors do this by holding a meeting with the operators approximately two weeks before they intend to introduce the charts.

All members of the Quality Control Team should take part in this meeting. The discussion should cover the following:

(1) A talk by the supervisor (perhaps 10 minutes in length) explaining that charts are soon to be started on the job. He should give a description of what the charts are for and explain how they have benefited the operators on other jobs. He should also explain how the charts will be made; who will be the process checker; how the samples will be taken and calculated and plotted. He should emphasize that the main idea is to make the product right the first time rather than have to repair it or have it sorted by Inspection.

(2) A demonstration by the quality control engineer (perhaps 20 minutes in length) to explain how control charts work. The quincunx should be used if the first charts to be introduced are $\bar{X}$ and R charts; a box of sampling beads if the first charts are to be p-charts. The quality control engineer should explain the meaning of control limits, the meaning of x's and what should be done when x's occur on the chart.

(3) A talk by the product engineer, in simple terms and at the operator level, explaining how their product is made, why it is important and what are the characteristics that need to be controlled.

(4) A question period (perhaps 20 minutes in length) during which the operators are encouraged to ask questions. The questions may cover the charting, the work of the process checker or the possible effect of the charts on the operators and their jobs.

This meeting should be followed by other meetings after the charts are put into use. At the subsequent meetings, the supervisor should emphasize the charts which are showing improvement and discuss the possible reasons for any which are in difficulty. As the job improves and begins to settle into a state of control, he should see that the operators have the satisfaction of knowing that this is happening. All those connected with the job should feel proud of their share in this achievement.

Importance of these meetings

Much of the success of the control charts in a given area will depend on the way in which these meetings are conducted. Many Quality Control Teams invite not only the operators but also union representatives, maintenance people and members of the wage incentive organization. This leads to a better understanding of the operators' problems.

The key to successful use of control charts in the shop is that the charts must always be used (a) to help the operator or (b) to obtain process information. Control charts must never be used to check up on people.

B-2 SIMPLE EXAMPLES OF THE ADVANTAGES OF CONTROL CHARTS

The following points should be considered by the supervisor in talking with his people about their control charts.

B-2.1 Advantages for machine setters, layout operators, group chiefs and other technical people

The principal benefits for key technical people are likely to be the following:

(1) Quality control involves a new way of running the job. It is possible to determine scientifically just where the process should run.

(2) The charts tend to make the jobs of technical people easier. They can determine the best combinations of operator and machine. They have definite knowledge of the capability of the machine or process. This means that they have better answers to the questions which arise when something goes wrong.

(3) The charts make it possible to work with distributions instead of only with "plus or minus" tolerances. With control charts there are fewer bottle-necks and fewer periods of serious trouble. The beginnings of trouble are picked up promptly so that the whole line does not become filled with bad parts.

(4) When changes are made in a particular operation, the charts will indicate what effect this has on the end product. The chart tells the machine setter which way to adjust the process and also by how much. The charts can be used to separate machine trouble from operator trouble, or to tell when a machine is in need of repair as distinct from when it has a wrong setting.

(5) It is easier to get help promptly from Engineering, and easier to settle difficulties with Inspection, when the job is covered with control charts.

B-2.2 Advantages for operators

The principal benefits for operators are likely to be the following:

(1) The charts show up unsuitable tools, fixtures, gages, piece rates, etc., and this makes it easier to get the conditions corrected.

(2) The operators no longer need to feel responsible for normal process fluctuations or for difficulties which they cannot control.

(3) The charts help the operators turn out more good product in the same amount of time. This tends to increase the operators' earnings.

(4) The charts make the job more interesting. The people can see the progress of the work and follow trends. They also know where the process is running all the time and do not need to be fearful that the product will be rejected by Inspection.

(5) The charts show up the good work which the people are doing. Most operators become very proud of their control charts.

B-2.3 General advantages

Some of the general advantages of control charts are shown in Figures 210–213. The illustrations cover (a) a machine-controlled operation, (b) a manually controlled operation, (c) a case of real specification trouble and (d) a case which appeared to be specification trouble but wasn't. The following is a brief description of the use made of each chart.

Figure 210. Machine operation.

Here the machine setter was able to improve the process by actually doing less work. The machine was originally "over-adjusted." This happens when changes are made on the basis

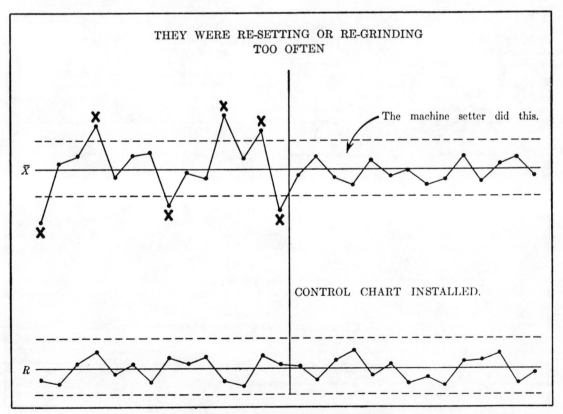

Fig. 210. First example of shop control chart.

of a few isolated measurements. Later the machine setter was given a control chart.

The control chart told him when to re-set and, equally important, when to leave the setting alone. The setting is shown on the $\bar{X}$ chart, the machine capability on the R chart.

Figure 211. Manual operation.

This is an example of a control chart used for operator training. The control limits are based on the work of several experienced operators. Both of the operators shown here were recently hired.

The chart showed that Operator 1 needed further training in the fundamentals of this job (erratic pattern on R chart). Operator 2 was properly trained in the fundamentals (controlled R chart) but there was evidently some bias in her method of working which caused her to work consistently on the low side of nominal ($\bar{X}$ chart).

Both operators were re-trained, but the type of training given in the two cases was very different.

Figure 212. Specification trouble.

In this case the process was running normally (controlled $\bar{X}$ chart, controlled R chart). Still there was product outside of the specification limits. This indicated that the problem might be due to Engineering rather than the Shop.

Figure 213. Process trouble.

This case looked at first like specification trouble, since large quantities of product were found to be out of limits. The patterns, however, were unnatural. Consequently this was not specification trouble but process trouble. Note the change brought about by better maintenance of equipment.

The foregoing examples were based on $\bar{X}$ and R charts. Similar cases could be shown using p-charts or c-charts.

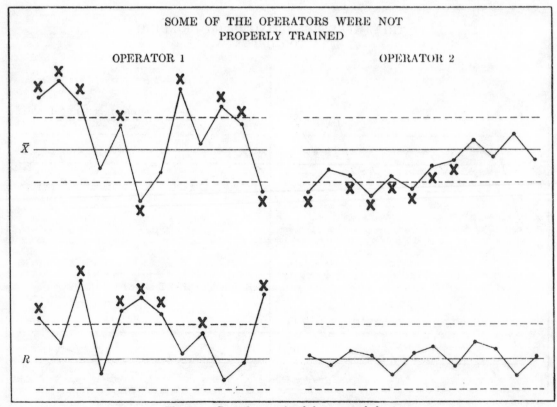

Fig. 211. Second example of shop control chart.

B-3 GENERAL INSTRUCTION FOR PROCESS CONTROL

The following is a general instruction for the use of charts in the shop. The supervisor should make sure that these instructions are understood by all his people who are expected to work with charts.

Instructions for Process Control

1.0 GENERAL

1.1 Purpose

1.11 The purpose of this instruction is to provide general information on process control procedures and to supplement the process control information given in the Manufacturing and Process Control Layouts.

1.12 All process control activities should be carried out in accordance with this instruction unless otherwise stated in the Process Control Layout.

1.2 Definitions and symbols

1.21 Average ($\bar{X}$)
The average is a value obtained by adding up all the individual measurements in a sample and dividing by the number of individual measurements.

1.22 Range (R)
The range is a value obtained by subtracting the smallest measurement in a sample from the largest measurement in the sample.

1.23 Percent Defective (p)
The percent defective is a value ob-

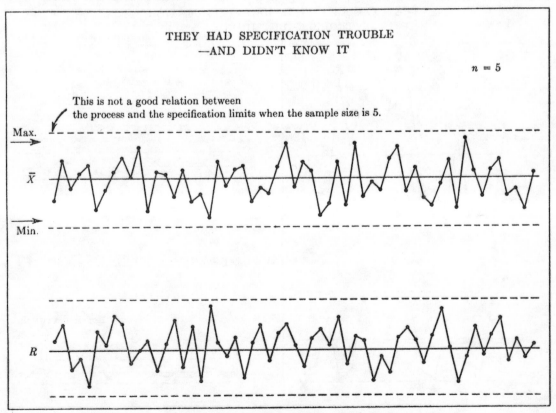

THEY HAD SPECIFICATION TROUBLE
—AND DIDN'T KNOW IT

$n = 5$

This is not a good relation between the process and the specification limits when the sample size is 5.

Max.

$\bar{X}$

Min.

R

Fig. 212. Third example of shop control chart.

tained by taking the number of defective units found in a sample and dividing it by the total number of units in the sample, and then multiplying the result by 100.

1.24 $\bar{X}$ Chart
A control chart on which a series of averages are plotted.

1.25 R Chart
A control chart on which a series of ranges are plotted.

1.26 p-Chart
A control chart on which a series of percent defective values are plotted.

1.27 np-Chart
A control chart on which is plotted the actual number of defective units in the sample, rather than the percent defective.

1.28 c-Chart
A control chart on which is plotted the total number of defects in a sample rather than the number of defective units.

1.29 Control Chart
A chart consisting of one or more solid centerlines and one or more dotted control limits, which is used to evaluate the state of control of a process.

1.210 Chart with "Moving Range" Limits.
This name is applied to a control chart of individual values for which control limits have been calculated using the moving range technique.

1.211 Sample Size (n)
The sample size is the number of units to be selected and checked in the sample.

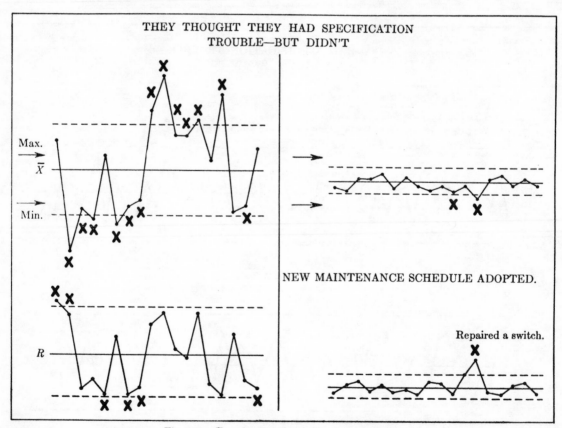

Fig. 213.   Fourth example of shop control chart.

1.212 Sampling Interval or Sampling Frequency.

The sampling interval or sampling frequency is the normal spacing between samples. The spacing may be expressed as so many minutes, hours or days, or it may be expressed as so many pieces produced.

2.0 RECORDS, CHARTS AND FORMS

The records required for process control consist of (a) data sheets for recording the findings in each sample and making calculations; and (b) control chart forms on which the results are plotted. The data sheets and chart forms are set up specifically for each type of chart.

The process checker should maintain a file of old data sheets for a period of time specified by the product engineer or quality control engineer. This file should also include old copies of shop control charts.

The process checker should obtain blank chart forms and data forms, as required, from the quality control engineering organization or other authorized source.

3.0 COLLECTING, RECORDING, CALCULATING AND PLOTTING DATA

3.1 Selecting the samples

3.11 Samples should be selected in the specified manner from the process or product.

3.12 If the sample is to be taken directly from a machine or operator, it should consist of the specified number of pieces taken in consecutive order as produced.

3.13 If the layout states that the sample should represent product made over a certain period of time, the sample should be selected at random from all product made during that period.

3.14 The layout should give specific instructions for any cases where a machine has several positions or heads, an operator is using several fixtures or tools, etc.

3.15 The instructions of the layout with respect to checking intervals should be carefully followed. However, care should be taken to avoid regularity in obtaining the sample at exactly the same time each hour or each day.

3.2 Recording the data

3.21 Units should be checked as soon as possible after the sample is taken.

3.22 The results of the checking should be recorded on the appropriate data form called for in the Process Control Layout.

3.23 In the case of variables data, a separate data sheet should be kept for each quality characteristic. In the case of attributes data, the information recorded should include sample size, number of defectives and type of defect.

3.24 In recording data for a process control check, it is important to record any supplementary information which will identify the data. For example: machine number, operator's name, shift number, time and date. Also, the process checker should record any known change in the equipment or piece parts as soon as it takes place. For example: new cutting tool introduced, or parts from a new supplier.

3.3 Making calculations

The process checker should make all the

necessary calculations called for by the layout. The values of $\bar{X}$, R, p, etc. should be recorded along with the original data.

3.4 *Plotting the data*

The data should be plotted on the appropriate control chart as soon as possible after the calculations are made. All notes identifying the data should be added to the control chart.

4.0 *TESTS FOR UNNATURAL PATTERNS*

4.1 *When to check the pattern*

If the pattern on any control chart no longer appears to be balanced around the centerline, check the pattern for out-of-control indications by making the following tests. The tests should be made as soon as a new point is plotted.

4.2 *How to check the pattern*

In making these tests, consider only one half of the control band at one time.

4.21 Mentally divide the control band into three equal zones. See diagram below.

4.22 Consider the pattern unnatural if it shows any of the combinations listed in the various zones. (If in doubt as to the proper manner of applying these tests, refer to the handbook, pages 23–28.)

4.23 Mark an "x" at the point which contributes the final evidence of unnaturalness. (See page 26.) Mark the "x" above the point if it is on the high side of the centerline. Mark the "x" below the point if it is on the low side of the centerline. Mark all x's about $1/8$ inch from the point being marked.

4.24 Judge the amount of unnaturalness in the pattern according to the number of x's.

4.25 Check whether the background information and notes recorded on the chart seem to be related in any way to the x's.

5.0 *WHAT TO DO WHEN A CHART GOES OUT OF CONTROL*

If out-of-control conditions are observed on any chart, notify the supervisor or his delegate at once.

The reasons for the out-of-control conditions and the action taken should be noted on the control chart at any convenient place near the out-of-control points.

If many such comments are to be recorded, use a code number near the out-of-control points and write the explanations on a separate sheet mounted beneath the control chart, or on the back of the chart.

	Upper Half	*Lower Half*
	Single point out	
A	2 out of 3 in Zone A or above	
B	4 out of 5 in Zone B or above	
C	8 in a row in Zone C or above	
		C 8 in a row in Zone C or below
		B 4 out of 5 in Zone B or below
		A 2 out of 3 in Zone A or below
		Single point out

If a chart persists in staying out of control, or if it keeps going out of control at frequent intervals, this should be called to the attention of the supervisor.

6.0 FREAKS AND OBVIOUS DEFECTS

Follow the directions of the layout in disposing of shorts, opens and other obvious freaks.

Layouts

In addition to the general instructions given above, all process control activities should be covered by Process Control Layouts. The layout should include:

(1) Identification data describing the product, operation, characteristic to be controlled, etc.

(2) Points in the sequence of operation where samples are to be taken.

(3) Sample size, frequency of check and method of selecting the sample.

(4) Characteristics to be checked.

(5) Method of measurement or classification.

(6) Information to be recorded and plotted.

(7) Criteria for determining when action is needed.

(8) Action to be taken.

The following are examples of:

(a) A Process Control Layout.
(b) A Data Sheet for $\bar{X}$ and R charts.
(c) A Data Sheet for p-charts.
(d) A Standard Control Chart Form.

Also included (pages 212 and 213) are examples of shop control charts which have the proper marking, notes and comments.

PROCESS CONTROL LAYOUT		
Title	Assoc. Dwgs. P 483518	
FRONT CONTACT ASSEMBLY	Used on 218-A Mercury Switch	
OPERATIONS AND METHODS		FACILITIES

The normal sample shall be 5 units every two hours from the front contact welder.

1. *Contact Height* shall be .0185 shop min. to .0199 shop max.   Record readings on form AP 510F.   Plot a point on the $\bar{X}$, R chart for every 5 units checked.　　　　　　　　　　　　　　　　Comparator

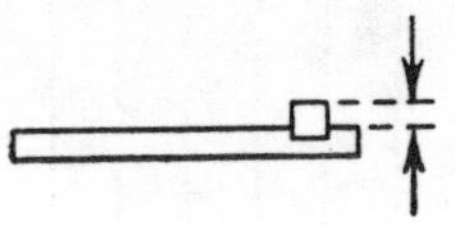

2. *Contact Positioning* shall be .077 min. to .083 max., measured from the midpoint of the height of the contact to the end of the lead wire.   Record readings on form AP 510F.   Plot a point on the $\bar{X}$, R chart for every 5 units checked.　　　　Comparator

3. *Contact Weld.*   Check to see whether the contact is firmly bonded to the wire by pushing against it with a tweezer.   Check for weld splashes which result in a pile-up of metal at the weld.   Record the number of defective units for poor welds and weld splashes on form AP333-y.   Plot a point on the number-of-defectives chart for (a) poor welds and (b) splashes, plotting one point for every 20 units checked.　Tweezer Visual

Note: The process checker shall discuss the pattern or method of checking with the machine setter, supervisor, or engineer if he is in any doubt as to the method of carrying out these instructions.   The process checker shall mark the pattern in accordance with the General Instruction for Process Control and shall notify the supervisor of any out-of-control conditions.   Charts which continue out of control for more than 4 hours shall be hung on the "trouble board" for the supervisor's attention. All points shall be plotted immediately after the sample has been checked.

Fig. 214.   Example of process control information in a process control layout.

AP 510-F (7-52)

DATA SHEET FOR X̄ AND R CHART

PRODUCT _____ **DATE** _____

CHARACTERISTIC _____ **DEPT.** _____

1	2	3	4	5	6	7	8	9	10	11	12
TOTAL											
X̄											
R											

13	14	15	16	17	18	19	20	21	22	23	24
TOTAL											
X̄											
R											

Fig. 215.   Data sheet for $\bar{X}$ and R chart.

DATA SHEET FOR PERCENT DEFECTIVE CHART

FORM NO. _____

PART NO. _____   LIST OF CHARACTERISTICS

PRODUCT _____

NO.

NO.					TOTAL DEFECTIVE	% DEFECTIVE	INITIALS
1							
2							
3							
4							
5							
6							
7							
8							
9							
10							

Fig. 216.   Data sheet for p-chart.

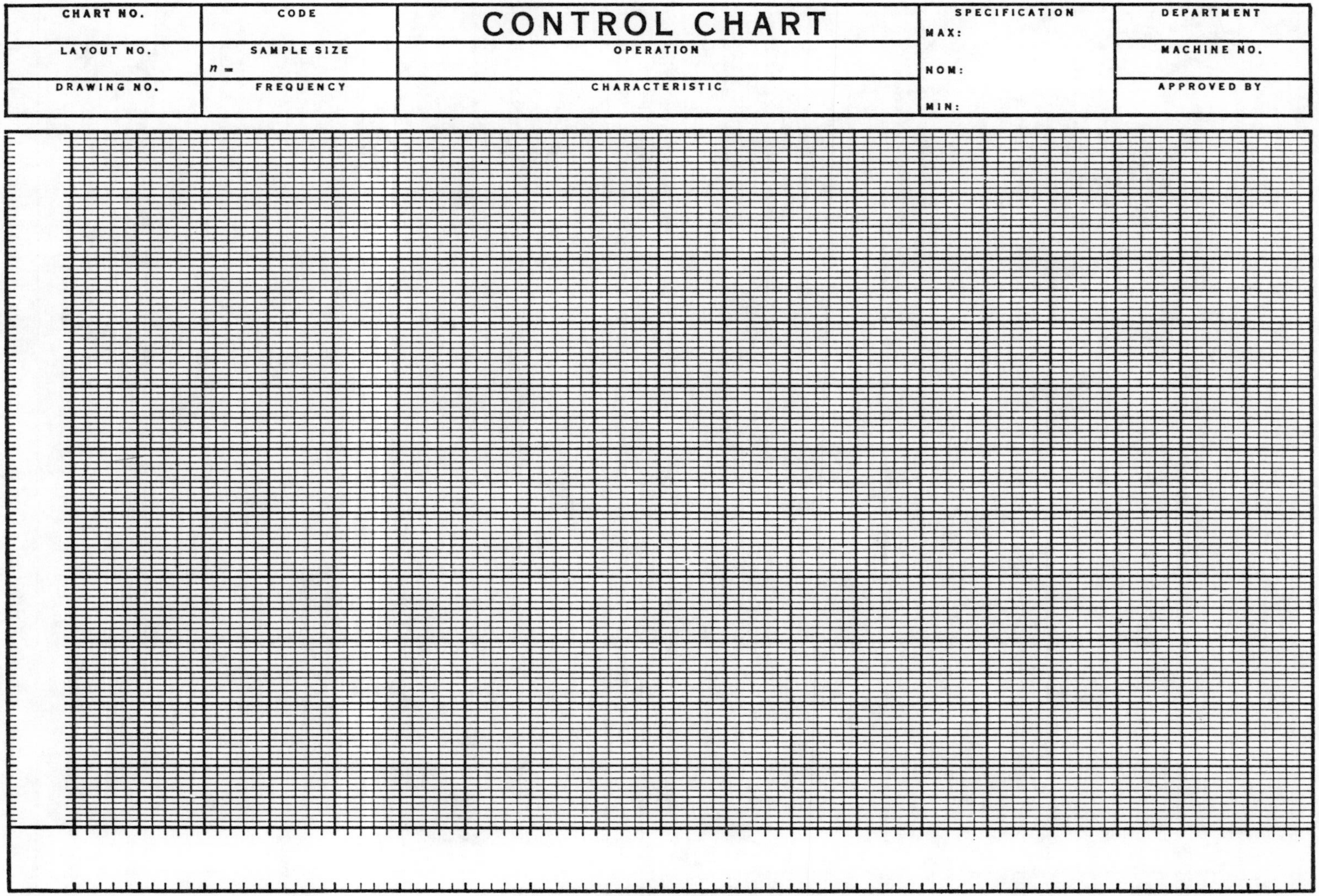

Fig. 217. Standard control chart form.

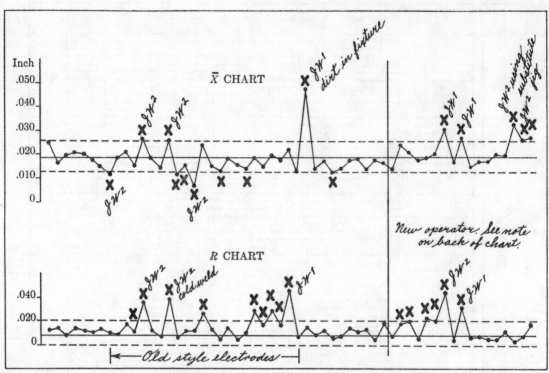

Fig. 218. Example of notes on a shop control chart. The number following the signature is a code number indicating the type of action taken: for example, "1" means the machine was adjusted; "2" means the operator was given instructions, etc. The initials are those of the machine setter or other person making immediate use of the chart.

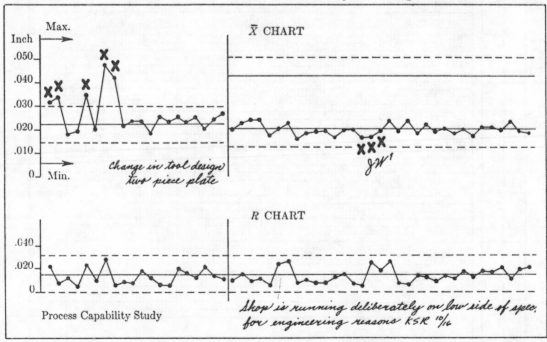

Fig. 219. Engineering comments written on a shop control chart. If the chart is being used primarily for engineering information, it should be labeled "engineering study."

B-4 INSTRUCTIONS FOR PROCESS CHECKERS

The following information is intended to be used by Operating process checkers. The term "process checker" means anyone in the Operating organization who is responsible for taking samples and plotting charts. This person may be a "checker" who is specially set aside to do this type of work for the group; he may be the operator himself, the operator's helper, the machine setter, a layout operator, a group leader, etc. The process checker is expected to know and do the following things in connection with shop control charts.

B-4.1 What the process checker should know

A process checker needs to know how to select samples properly; how to check the necessary characteristics; how to make calculations such as averages, ranges or percentages; how to plot the charts and recognize unnatural patterns.

The Quality Control Team is responsible for seeing that the process checker is adequately trained for this job. The training should include careful practice and drill in the interpretation of the patterns, including the marking of x's as described in the "General Instruction for Process Control." Each process checker should have a copy of this instruction and should be familiar with its provisions, as well as with the provisions of all specific process control layouts which the checker is expected to use.

A new process checker should work with some member of the Quality Control Team (generally the quality control engineer) long enough to make sure that the job routines are thoroughly understood. Much of the success of the control charts depends on the promptness and reliability of the process checker.

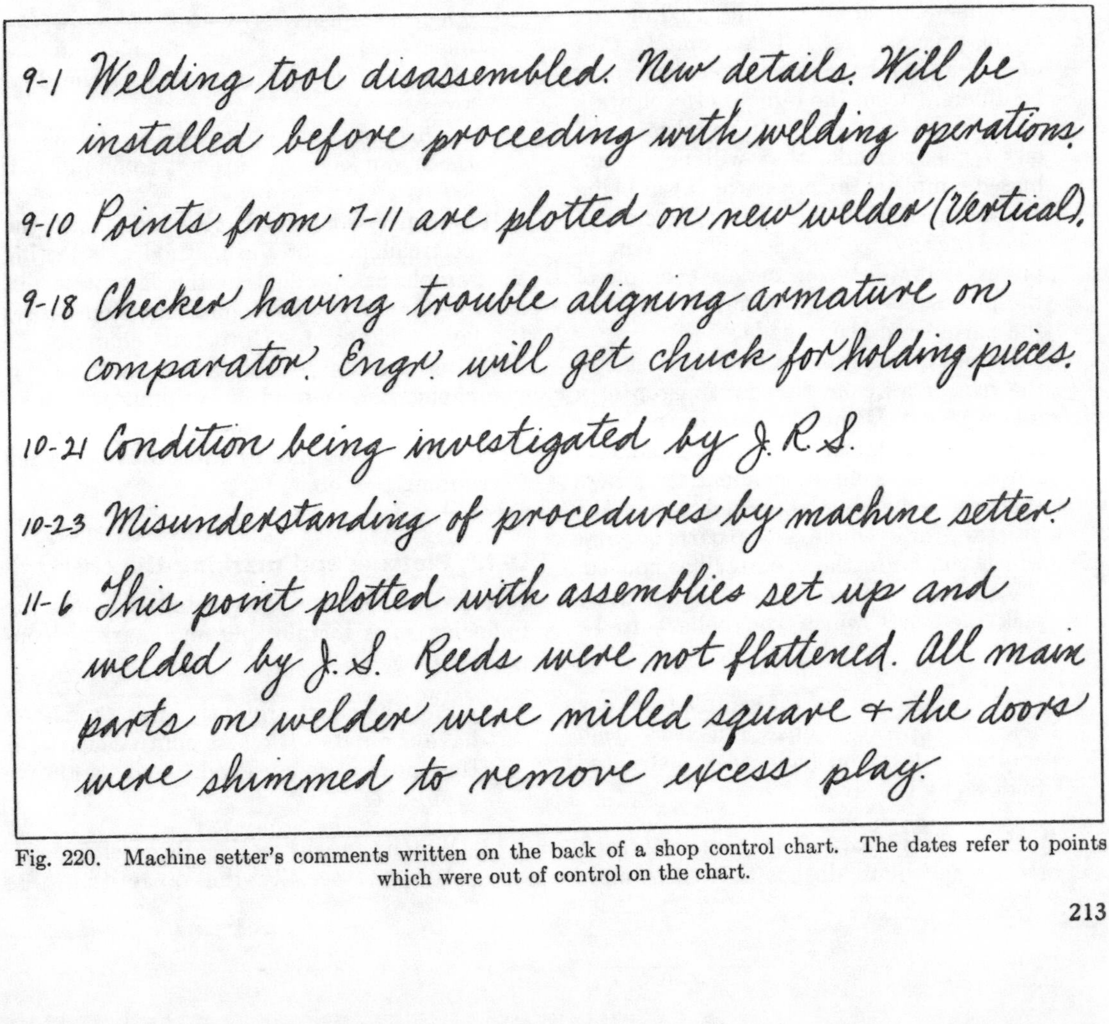

9-1 Welding tool disassembled. New details. Will be installed before proceeding with welding operations.

9-10 Points from 7-11 are plotted on new welder (Vertical).

9-18 Checker having trouble aligning armature on comparator. Engr. will get chuck for holding pieces.

10-21 Condition being investigated by J. R. S.

10-23 Misunderstanding of procedures by machine setter.

11-6 This point plotted with assemblies set up and welded by J. S. Reeds were not flattened. All main parts on welder were milled square & the doors were shimmed to remove excess play.

Fig. 220. Machine setter's comments written on the back of a shop control chart. The dates refer to points which were out of control on the chart.

B-4.2 Taking samples

Since all the information on the control charts will come from samples, it is important to see that the samples are selected properly. The proper taking of samples is governed by statistical laws. If the one who selects the samples breaks the statistical laws, the samples can easily give false or misleading results.

Some of the things a process checker needs to know in taking samples are spelled out in the layout. The layout ordinarily states the sample size, the normal interval between checks, and what product the sample should represent. For example, it may be required to check the last few pieces made; or to take the sample from a pan containing all the parts made since the last check; or to take some parts from each of four operators, etc. All such provisions in the layout must be carefully and strictly carried out. In addition the process checker is responsible for the following:

(1) Samples should give an unbiased picture of the process. Do not deliberately take units that you have reason to believe may be different from the others. If you walk up to a machine or operator and take the last 5 pieces made, that will be an unbiased sample of the process as it was being run at that moment. If you select 5 pieces purely by chance from a pan of pieces, that will be an unbiased sample of the process as it was run during the time the parts were being made.

Do not take samples all from one side of the pan or all from the tray on top of a pile of trays. Do not deliberately pick out the units which look oversize, dented, etc. Do not take samples deliberately where there is something abnormal about the process—for example, set-up parts or work which you know the operator has spoiled. On the other hand, do not deliberately pick the parts which you believe to be good.

(2) Do not take part of the sample from one machine, operator, etc., and part from another unless you have been instructed to do so by the layout.

(3) If checking is to be done at intervals such as one-half hour, do not take the sample always exactly at 10:00, 10:30, etc. If you did this, people would be able to anticipate the sampling and might do their work differently.

(4) Always use the sample originally selected. Do not re-sample. That is, if you do not like what you find in one sample, do not decide to ignore that sample and take another. This would prevent the control chart from giving the proper information.

(5) If you find a "freak" in the sample, handle this as instructed in the layout. If the layout does not cover this point, get special instructions from your supervisor.

(6) The sampling intervals in the layout are supposed to be sufficient for normal conditions when the job is not in unusual trouble. In an emergency the supervisor may ask you to take more frequent samples. If you take more frequent samples, be sure to plot *all* the samples. Do not throw any of the data away.

This does not apply to set-up checks if the layout says they are not to be plotted.

If the supervisor finds that the sample size, the sample frequency, or the method of selecting the sample as specified in the layout is not suitable for the job, he should take steps to get the layout changed. Until it is changed, do not alter the method of taking samples. If you change the method of sampling, you may unconsciously violate the statistical rules. Then you will lose information that is needed for running the job.

B-4.3 Plotting and marking the charts

A process checker is expected to know the following rules for plotting and marking control charts.

(1) Plot the chart promptly, as soon as you have the data. Process control charts, if they are to do any good, must be always up-to-date.

(2) Watch the arithmetic. Be careful in calculating, especially the range (R). Be

sure you really have the highest and lowest measurement when you subtract. Watch the decimal point if there is one. Avoid plus and minus numbers if possible, because it is very easy to make mistakes on these.

To avoid errors, use numbers as simple as possible. For example, if the measurements are .1276, .1249, etc. (all the numbers starting with .12) it would be sufficient to work with 76 and 49. Call it to the attention of the supervisor if you think you see a chance to simplify numbers.

Above all, if the chart looks unusual or "queer" after it is plotted, check the arithmetic before you do anything else. The following is a useful list of checks:

a. If you use mental arithmetic most of the time, check a point occasionally by doing it with pencil and paper.
b. If you habitually obtain averages by taking a total and then dividing by 5, check yourself occasionally by multiplying the total by .2.
c. Glance over the individual values occasionally, and guess what $\bar{X}$ would be.
d. Occasionally add your R value to the lowest individual value in the sample, and see how the sum agrees with the highest individual value.
e. Check percentages occasionally by multiplying the percentage and the sample size, and see how the result agrees with the number of defective units.

(3) Watch the scale of the chart. Be sure you understand it and can plot the points in the proper place. In particular, note that the scale on the R chart may be different from the scale on the $\bar{X}$ chart. This makes the R chart a little more difficult to plot until you become accustomed to the change in scale, but it increases the readability and usefulness of the chart for the people who need to use it.

It is a good idea to check the plotting on any chart occasionally by finding the $\bar{X}$, R or p values (or other values to be plotted) on the vertical scale at the left-hand side of the sheet and then using a straight-edge to check the proper location of the point.

Tell your supervisor if you find that the scale is difficult to use.

(4) Plot all the points on the chart, including the points which go out of control. The chart would be of little or no value if it showed only the best points. If the layout states that when a point goes out of control you should have the process corrected immediately and then take another sample, both samples should be plotted. The chart will show that the process was corrected and brought back into control.

(5) Carefully follow the frequency of checks as specified in the layout.

(6) Identify all points by date, machine number, shift, etc.

(7) As soon as each point is plotted, check to determine whether it should be marked with an "x." Follow the directions in the General Instruction for Process Control. Mark the point if (a) the point itself goes outside of the dotted control limit, or (b) the point is part of an unnatural pattern when considered with the immediately preceding points. The General Instruction for Process Control tells how many preceding points should be considered and how the check should be made. Do not consider the plotting finished until you have marked all the x's that are called for.

(8) Be sure to put notes on the chart to record any change in the process which the supervisor, from his experience, feels could affect the pattern. For example:

- New lot of piece parts.
- Solder with higher proportion of tin.
- Different soldering tip.
- Fixture repaired.
- New operator or inspector.
- Different machine.

These notes will be needed if trouble should develop later in the process.

Finally, the person who takes the data needs to have a good understanding of the requirements. He should know where to check the parts (at edge, center, etc.) He should know how many checks to make on each part. He should know how to use the gage and record the measurements accurately. In the case of visual checks he must have a clear understanding of the criteria or visual standards. If in doubt about any of these things, he should check with the supervisor immediately. A chart is of little use unless it is based on accurate data.

B-4.4 Appearance of control charts

Process checkers occasionally tend to worry about the appearance of their control charts. It is difficult in the shop to keep the charts looking neat and clean. Neatness of course is an asset, and the process checker, in plotting the points and marking x's, should be careful to do a tidy and accurate job. Careless plotting of points and drawing of lines, or smudged erasures, only make the charts more difficult to read.

If the control charts can be neat and clean as well as useful, so much the better.

On the other hand, charts that are actually being used are likely to become well-thumbed, spattered with grease and oil, and scribbled up with marks and notes. Charts that show this evidence of being discussed and used are much more likely to be doing their intended job.

B-4.5 Why should the Operating people plot their own charts?

In a quality control program of the type described in this Handbook, it is essential for the Operating people to plot their own charts. Quality control programs tend to be short-lived and ineffective when people outside of the Operating organization take over the job of plotting and maintaining the charts. The reasons for this are the following:

(1) Process control charts when properly used are part of the "make" operations. They are one of the essential tools for doing the Operating job. They are similar to screw drivers, fixtures, jigs and other essential equipment.

(2) The Operating people should do everything necessary to make the product and make it right. This includes the process control charts.

In the earliest stages of a quality control program, the Operating people sometimes need help in starting the first charts. The earliest charts may be plotted by inspectors, statistical clerks, quality control engineers, etc. However, all such charts should be turned over to the Operating department to plot at the earliest possible moment.

Operating people need their own charts in the same way that the driver of a car needs his own eyes when driving along a crowded highway. No driver would wish to drive blindfolded while someone else watched the traffic and road conditions and instructed the driver when to turn, speed up, stop for traffic signals or attempt to pass another vehicle.

When the Operating department obtains data for its own benefit and plots and uses its own charts, the process controls are functioning in the way they were intended to function. The Operating people are (a) sure of what action to take, (b) able to take it with the least possible delay, and (c) completely responsible for running their own job.

PART C
Action on Control Charts

C-1 IMPORTANCE OF PROMPTNESS IN ACTING ON SHOP CHARTS

In all cases the planning of shop control charts assumes that the checks will be made on schedule, that the diagnosis will be made promptly, and that the remedy will be immediately effective. Any delay in action may have the following adverse effects:

(1) Delay may mean that unnecessary amounts of undesirable product are produced. This will reduce yields, increase scrap and increase the amount of product rejected by Inspection.

(2) Delay may mean that the cause of trouble is harder to identify, and in many cases can not be identified at all. It is an axiom in quality control that the time to identify assignable causes is while those causes are active.

C-2 FIRST TYPE OF ACTION:
To be taken by the Process Checker

As soon as the process checker observes that a chart is out of control, he should immediately initiate the action called for in the process control layout. The chart is "out of control" when any of the recent points are marked with x's in accordance with the standard tests (pages 23–28), or when such other indications are obtained as are described in the pertinent layout. The action to be taken by the process checker ordinarily consists of notifying some responsible person that an out-of-control condition exists. This person may be the machine setter, layout operator, supervisor, or in some cases the individual operator.

In addition to notifying this person that action needs to be taken, the process checker may be asked to take other steps to make sure that the action is not delayed. Some supervisors provide a special hook or board on which the process checker can place the charts which are not brought back into control immediately. In other cases the process checker merely notifies the supervisor or adds a note to the chart when action has not been taken. The principal requirement is that something must be done about every chart that shows a need for action. It must not be possible for charts to be neglected.

C-3 SECOND TYPE OF ACTION:
To be taken by the Operator, Machine Setter, Layout Operator or other responsible person

Depending on the nature of the process and the condition of the chart which is out of control, the machine setter should check the process, machine, equipment, parts, operator or methods. If possible, he should correct the out-of-control condition immediately. If immediate action is not possible he should promptly initiate the proper action and also inform the supervisor. If action is to be delayed for any reason, the responsible person should write a note on what has been done. Notes that are brief enough can be written on the face of the chart. Longer notes or explanations should be written on a separate sheet of paper attached to the back of the chart. See Figure 220 on page 213.

If the machine setter or other responsible person is unable to tell what action should be taken, he should promptly notify the supervisor and get special help. The supervisor should in all cases hold his people responsible for either (a) taking action themselves, or (b) initiating action on the part of someone else.

C-4 THIRD TYPE OF ACTION:
To be taken by the Supervisor

The supervisor should investigate immediately any cases where his people need help in using the charts. In addition to this, he should watch the "trouble board" or other provision made for singling out the charts which have not been brought back into control. He should also spot check all charts on the job occasionally to make sure that the provisions for taking action are being carried out. In general, the cases which are brought to the supervisor's attention will be one of two types.

(1) *Where the necessary action is known but cannot be taken immediately.* In this case the supervisor should write an explanation on the control chart and should discuss the matter fully at the next meeting of the Quality Control Team.

(2) *Where the necessary action is not known and the supervisor must determine it.* This requires ability on the part of the supervisor to investigate and interpret. Since every chart which calls for investigation is a valuable medium for training, the supervisor's investigation should be carried out with the help of the machine setter or other responsible person.

Investigation to determine what action is necessary should proceed as follows:

a. Make certain that x's are properly marked on all charts in accordance with the standard tests. The charts are far easier to interpret after the x's are marked.
b. Relate the chart patterns, if possible, to things you know about the operation or the process. The longer you have had control charts on the job, the easier this will be.
c. If the reasons for the behavior of the chart cannot be discovered immediately, take the following steps:

1. Identify any bad or unusual product as specifically as you can. For example:

- Which operator made these units?
- Which machine?
- Which lot of material did they come from?
- At what bench were they processed?
- At what time of day?
- From which beaker did the etching solution come that was used for etching these units?
- What had the beaker been used for before these units were etched?

Remember also that inspection and testing can be a variable as well as the product. The likeliest cause might be a new gage or test set, or a new process checker. Careful identification of the product associated with unusual patterns will often give clues to unsuspected changes in the process or the method of testing.

2. Beware of assuming too readily that "we are doing everything the same way" or that "nothing has changed." There must be a change in the process if the control chart is showing a different pattern.

3. Charts that are difficult to interpret by themselves often become clear when they are seen in conjunction with other charts. Form the habit of looking at all the charts on your job in a regular order, starting with the earliest operations and going through to the end. Watch for charts that react together, or a chart at a later operation which lags behind another chart by about the time interval that is required for processing. Occasionally you may need to start a new chart to throw light on a chart you already have.

If there is difficulty in interpreting a p-chart, try substituting an $\bar{X}$ and R chart.

4. For special help in interpreting patterns see pages 161–180. The examples of causes given there will help to stimulate your own ideas. They should make you think of similar causes which might apply to your own job.

5. Most causes are associated with ele-

ments in the process which do not involve "singleness"; that is, more than one operator, more than one machine, more than one chuck on the machine, more than one surface condition, etc. A single machine or operator may behave like more than one under certain conditions: for example, looseness of a bearing, excessive play in a fixture, fatigue on the part of a human being.

As causes are discovered which are capable of affecting the control charts on your job, jot them down on the chart so you will have a permanent record. The things you discover about causes on one product will often prove to be helpful in studying other products.

6. If necessary, discuss the pattern with others who have expert knowledge of the job. This should include design engineers, product engineers, maintenance personnel and inspectors as well as your own people. Unusual patterns, or patterns with unusual causes, should be discussed promptly with the other members of the Quality Control Team.

7. If the causes are deeply hidden, it may be necessary to set up a "designed experiment" to isolate the source of the trouble. This is explained in the Engineering Section, Part B.

In interpreting control charts remember that only a small part of the information necessary to solve the problem will come from the control charts. Most of the information must come from job knowledge. Nevertheless, in spite of the fact that statistical analysis will not solve the whole problem, the supervisor should be careful not to underestimate its importance. Without the statistical help furnished by the control charts, the job knowledge of the supervisor will not have maximum effectiveness. The same can be said of the knowledge of the engineer.

As soon as the reasons for any unusual behavior of the chart are known or suspected, do what is indicated to bring the chart back into control. Remember that shop charts must be brought into control as quickly as possible in order to restore or maintain an economical situation.

C-5 FOURTH TYPE OF ACTION:
To be taken by the Quality Control Team

While shop people are expected to take immediate action as indicated above, the Quality Control Team is fundamentally responsible for making sure that the shop control charts work. If the shop is not reaping benefits in the form of fewer troubles, or if the shop people have difficulty in determining what action to take, the Team should immediately check the following list of possible reasons and correct any of these conditions which they find to be responsible:

(1) It may be that the shop is maintaining charts which are not needed, or, on the other hand, the Team may have failed to set up all the charts that are needed.
(2) The shop may be using incorrect methods of selecting samples, incorrect frequency of samples, incorrect control limits, etc.
(3) The measurements, calculations or plotting may be in error so that the chart is not showing a valid picture of the process.
(4) The shop may be failing to take the indicated action when charts go out of control.
(5) The Quality Control Team may not be taking an active enough interest in the causes for out-of-control conditions.

Among the things which the Team may need to do directly in connection with shop charts are the following:

a. Reinstruct the operator or process checker.
b. Provide a better method of checking the machine setting.
c. Provide a way of getting better piece parts.
d. Issue an order for overhauling a machine.
e. Get better maintenance on fixtures, test sets, soldering tips, etc.
f. Have a gage checked.
g. Confer with a supplier.
h. Change a method.
i. Modify a tool.
j. Modify the layout.
k. Modify the specification.
l. Conduct a designed experiment.

C-6 USING SHOP CHARTS TO EXPERIMENT WITH THE PROCESS

When properly guided by the decisions of a Quality Control Team, process control charts can be used to experiment with a going process. Changes in the process are introduced deliberately and preferably one at a time. The effect of the change is observed by noting the pattern on the control charts. It is important to allow sufficient time for the change to affect the pattern (that is, an adequate series of points). The effect of the change will not necessarily be evident from the first one or two points.

The following are forms of experimentation which may be carried on with control charts:

(1) *Engineering studies.* All engineering studies in the shop should be tied in closely with the process control charts. The engineer needs the information on the charts in planning his studies. The supervisor needs the charts to enable him to cooperate effectively with the engineer's activities. Some of the most valuable engineering experiments are carried out during production, and these need to be checked constantly by reference to the shop charts.

Furthermore, it is important for large shop-type variables to be under control, or at least to be properly evaluated and allowed for, if the engineering experiments are to be successful. Once the Quality Control Team is set up and functioning, it tends to assume a more and more important role in the planning and conducting of production experiments.

(2) *Running near the high or low side of a specification.* Supervisors often find it necessary to have parts on the high or low side of nominal in order to compensate for other conditions in the process. With control charts it is possible to say just where the distribution of parts should run, and maintain it there consistently without danger of its shifting too far. Because of the charts, the supervisor, the engineer and the person responsible for making the piece parts are all fully aware of what is being done. Other elements in the process can be adjusted to fit the off-center distribution. This avoids the danger of getting into trouble because of an unforeseen combination of distributions.

The distribution may be run off-center on either a permanent or temporary basis. A few words of caution are necessary.

(a) Whenever you find it advisable to run toward one side of a specification, be sure to discuss this thoroughly at your quality control meetings. It may be that the specification can be changed to coincide with the most desirable operating level.

(b) It is not always wise to shift a distribution to compensate for a temporary trouble. In most cases it is better to attack the main trouble directly and correct it at its source.

(c) Running a distribution temporarily on one side may affect other characteristics in ways you have not foreseen. This can be the source of many supposedly "mysterious" troubles.

In general, try to decide on the best place for the process to run and then keep the process there as consistently as possible. This does not apply to cases involving tool wear where we deliberately let the distribution drift from one side to the other for economic reasons.

Experimenting with a process is quite permissible and even desirable under the guidance of a Quality Control Team. However, it is seldom advisable for the shop to attempt such experimenting alone. The shop needs the advantage of the product engineer's technical knowledge and the quality control engineer's statistical experience for this type of experimentation to be successful. In many cases it is necessary to run formal "designed experiments" as discussed in the Engineering Section.

C-7 MEANING OF AN "ECONOMICAL STATE OF CONTROL"

A perfect state of control is never attainable in a production process. The goal of the process control charts is not perfection, but a reasonable and economical state of control. The problems of defect prevention are similar in many ways to those of accident prevention. We know that it is impossible to eliminate accidents entirely; but we also know that accidents can be driven to greater and greater infrequency by vigorously tracking down assignable causes and then considering all practical means of minimizing or eliminating those causes. The same thing is true of the prevention of defects and other shop troubles.

For practical purposes, therefore, a controlled process is not one where the chart never goes out of control. If a chart never went out of control we would seriously question whether that operation should be charted. For shop purposes a controlled process is considered to be one where only a small percentage of the points go out of control and where out-of-control points are followed by proper action.

In cases where the assignable cause is beyond the operator's control and there is no practical remedy which can be applied immediately, the chart may continue out of control for a number of points until new material or facilities become available or suitable countermeasures are developed. It is necessary to distinguish between such cases and cases where action is merely being neglected. One way of doing this is to put proper notes on the chart.

Charts on the work of new operators are not expected to show control; the charts themselves are being used as a medium for training. Also, on new products or products that are still under development, many of the shop charts are doubling as process capability studies. Out-of-control patterns on such charts may be contributing important information on the cause and effect relationships between the major variables.

While action should always be taken promptly when a shop chart goes out of control, the action itself is more important than the actual degree of control. Operators should understand that they will not be subject to criticism when a point goes out of control.

C-8 SUMMARY CONTROL CHARTS

As an aid to maintaining an economical state of control, the Quality Control Team may wish to set up a "summary control chart" to picture the degree of control of all charts being used on the job. Summary control charts are particularly useful where there is a large number of individual charts (for example, one or more charts for each of a number of operators; or a large number of separate charts on individual operations). The summary control chart is constructed as follows:

(1) Group together all the control charts which are to be summarized. If a particular operation has many similar charts because there are many individual operators or machines, group together all the charts at that operation. It is also possible to combine charts at different operations: for example, all the charts for a particular

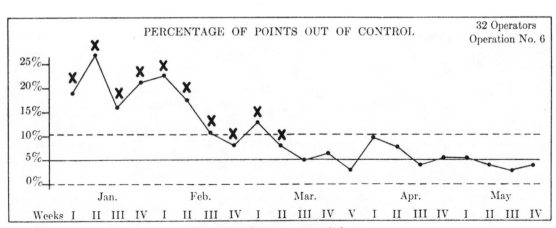

Fig. 221. Summary control chart.

Operating section or pay group, or all the charts for an entire product line or shop. Group the charts in any way that will be useful in studying the state of control.

(2) Choose a time interval for plotting the summary points. The usual choice is one week, but daily or monthly points may be plotted if desired.

(3) Count the total number of points plotted on all charts during the chosen interval, and also the number of points marked with x's when applying the standard control chart tests. Divide the number of "points marked" by the number of "points plotted" to obtain the percentage of points out of control. Obtain control limits for this chart by using the moving range.

This type of chart serves as an indicator of progress in addition to making it easier to study and manage a large number of charts.

Figure 221 shows a summary control chart covering 32 individual control charts. The steady improvement on this job is more easily seen on the summary chart than by looking at the 32 charts individually.

PART D
Quality Control Teams

The importance of the Quality Control Team has been emphasized throughout the Shop Section. It appears in the planning and installation of the charts (Part A), the training of the process checker (Part B), and the use of the charts as a guide to action (Part C). The following are further details on the activities of this Team.

D-1 REGULAR MEETINGS OF THE TEAM

As outlined in the Fundamental Section, the Quality Control Team consists of the product engineer, the Operating supervisor and the quality control engineer assigned to a given area. The primary purpose of the team is to make sure that there will be direct and constant co-operation between Operating and Engineering in all problems having to do with quality control, and also that the statistical methods will be used properly and consistently. The first step in forming a Quality Control Team is to arrange a meeting between the supervisor and the engineers, to consider the job from the point of view of process control and to plan the first capability studies or charts. Thereafter, the team should meet regularly once a week, or every other week, or once a month, depending upon conditions on the job. Meetings should be more frequent in the early stages of the program than after the process has begun to come into control. It is seldom necessary to meet more often than once a week. It is not advisable, even on a well controlled job, to have meetings less often than once a month.

The principal business of a quality control meeting should be to look at control charts. One member of the team should gather up all the charts that are currently in use and bring them to the meeting.

The following action is normally taken at each meeting:

(1) Check up on the action that was promised at the last meeting.

(2) Go over all charts in order (by operation) and note any progress. Note also any characteristics that are giving trouble and any charts that seem to be reacting together. Discuss and tie down the causes for unnatural patterns. If this is not possible immediately, plan the next step to take.

(3) Remove any charts that are no longer needed. Agree on changes for any charts that need to be changed. Plan new charts or new capability studies if required. See that someone is provided to collect the data and do the plotting.

(4) Decide on new action as indicated by the current state of the job. This may be action which can be taken by the Team members themselves or it may involve other organizations or departments. Agree on the person who will take this action and set a time for it.

Among the other things done, but not necessarily at every meeting, are the following:

(1) The group may plan or write those portions of the layout which cover the taking of samples, recording of data and plotting or marking of charts.

(2) They may decide on the best way to train a new process checker.

(3) They may plan special meetings with the operators or machine setters either to keep them informed of progress or to introduce new sampling plans or charts.

(4) They may discuss the results reported by

Final Inspection or study the effect of a proposed new Final Inspection sampling plan.

(5) They may plan and carry out formal Designed Experiments or Cost Reduction Cases.

(6) They may plan and write periodic progress reports to keep other people informed of what they are doing and how the job stands.

In any case, the meetings should be conducted on a systematic basis and should be covered by a set of minutes or notes. Among other things, the minutes should include a summary of current cost reduction cases, planned or completed, involving the use of statistical quality control.

Among the problems brought up by a discussion of the charts are likely to be the following:

Tools, fixtures, gages, test sets.
Specifications, layouts, cases of tight tolerances.
Questions on the capability of machines, materials, methods.
New designs and engineering experiments.

Problems involving wage incentives, schedules, efficiency, capacity, inspection, work done by other departments and other matters of joint interest to Operating and Engineering.

The control charts provide a logical and impersonal approach to these problems. Both supervisors and engineers find that it is easier to get together and easier to get things done.

D-2 QUALITY CONTROL COVERAGE

The ideal amount of quality control coverage on the job is arrived at by studying all operations systematically (starting with the most troublesome as indicated on pages 187–189) in order to determine

(a) their capabilities, and
(b) whether permanent controls are needed.

It is not possible to keep track of quality control coverage by merely watching the number of control charts, since many of the operations may not require any charts. It is necessary, however, for all operations to be *studied*.

SUMMARY OF 2100 ORGANIZATION
STATISTICAL QUALITY CONTROL APPLICATIONS TO SHOP OPERATIONS

| Product Line | NO. OF OPERATIONS (See note below) | | | | |
	"A"	"B"	"C"	"D"	Total
Rectifiers	26	8		149	183
General Purpose	93	6		60	159
Ballast Lamps			91	102	193
Small Runners	40		157	371	568
Miniatures	18	71	78	98	265
Carriers	22	35	149	173	379
Resistance Lamps	25	39	8	11	83
Repeaters	111	12		65	188
Glow Lamps	79	39	42	65	225
Chemicals	1	25	24	54	104
Grids		6	5	14	25
Glass	3	1	3	32	39
Total (2100 org.)	418	242	557	1194	2411

Note:
"A"—The operation has been thoroughly studied and charted. All that is required in the future is routine maintenance of the present controls.
"B"—The operation has been studied or charted, but there is further work to be done.
"C"—The operation has not been studied or charted from the point of view of quality control.
"D"—The operation has been studied, but no permanent controls are required.

Fig. 222. Report on number of operations studied.

Progress can therefore be measured by the number of operations that have been studied.

The term "operations" is used here in the same sense as in studies for Wage Incentive purposes. That is, it is the total number of distinct activities, or sets of closely related activities, required to produce the product. The Quality Control Team, in checking on quality control coverage, should use the list of operations which has already been made up for Wage Incentives.

At intervals of approximately six months, the Team should place each of the operations in one of the categories shown in Figure 222. One of the objectives of the Team should be to reduce the number of operations in category "C," and eventually to have all operations in categories "A" or "D."

At the time when the report in Figure 222 was issued, the quality control programs in this shop were about three years old.

Report on number of charts

In addition to keeping a record of the number of operations covered, it is helpful to keep records of the number of charts installed, by types. Figure 223 shows the record of control charts which accompanied the report on operations in Figure 222. Note that a separate record is kept of $\bar{X}$ and R charts, p-charts used to protect quality, p-charts used to reduce

dropouts, and other miscellaneous charts. Note also that the teams have given an estimate of the total number of charts which they think may be required when the job is completely covered.

It is not possible to give a good estimate of the ultimate number of charts until a large number of operations have been studied.

D-3 REPORTS ON PROGRESS

Since management has a vital interest in the progress of the quality control program, one of the important duties of the Quality Control Team should be to keep management informed at regular intervals. Not later than one year after the start of quality control activities the team should issue a formal Progress Report. Thereafter, reports should be issued at intervals of approximately six months. The reports may cover quality improvement, cost reduction, reduction in the amount of inspection or any other of the goals of a quality control program. The following have been used successfully as indicators of progress.

Yields.
Scrap.
Percent defective.
Amount of re-work.
Repairs (or time spent on repair, in minutes).

		NO. OF CHARTS			
Product Line	$\bar{X}, R$	*p* Qual.	*p* Drop.	Misc.	Total
Rectifiers	28	1	11	4	44
General Purpose	67	31	22	1	121
Ballast Lamps					22
Small Runners	8	14			22
Miniatures	37	233	3		273
Carriers	63	64	6		133
Resistance Lamps	120	18		1	139
Repeaters	59	9	12		80
Glow Lamps	92	53	48		193
Chemicals	170	12		87	269
Grids	30				30
Glass	53	21		31	105
Total (2100 Org.)	727	456	102	124	1409
Total (Inspection)		19		124	143
GRAND TOTAL	727	475	102	248	1552
ESTIMATE OF ULTIMATE NUMBER OF CHARTS	900	500	400	200	2000

Fig. 223. Report on number of charts in use in the shop.

Shop efficiency.
Informal cost reduction.
Formal cost reduction cases.
Number of inspectors.
Size of inspection samples.
Number of operators.
Amount of product rejected by Inspection.
Amount of product requiring detailing.
Number of complaints.
Improvement in Quality Assurance quality ratings (see page 270).
Number of control charts in use.
Number of operations studied and charted.
Number of operators working on jobs covered by process control.
Percentage of points out of control on control charts (see pages 221–222).
Number of jobs on sampling inspection.
Down-time on machines.
Changes obtained in specifications.
Amount of production.
Reduction of back schedules.
Estimates of savings.

Estimates of savings may be based on both tangible and intangible results.

Suitable material for Progress Reports can be obtained from

- Minutes of quality control meetings.
- Records of quality control coverage.
- Quality Assurance rates (see page 270).
- Records of the Inspection department.
- Records of Accounting.
- Cost reduction cases.

The reports should be concise and factual, should be expressed numerically and in the form of charts wherever possible, and should include a brief statement of quality control plans for the immediate future.

D-4 COST REDUCTION

It often develops during the meetings of the Quality Control Team that large cost reduction savings can be realized by applying quality control methods to the job. These savings may result from

A. A reduction in Final Inspection.
B. A reduction in the amount of sorting performed by Operating.
C. The use of process control charts to keep distributions centered and to keep processes in control.
D. The use of engineering studies to improve existing processes or to develop new processes.

Frequently the taking out of formal Cost Reduction Cases is one of the primary objectives of the Quality Control Team.

Many advantages are gained when Cost Reduction Cases are taken out jointly in the name of all members of the team. Progress on the case is reviewed periodically at the quality control meetings. The case and its aims are explained to the machine setters and operators so as to get their fullest co-operation. When the case is closed, a meeting is held to explain the accomplishment to the operators and others. Members of management often sit in as interested listeners at this meeting.

The cost reduction which results from the use of quality control methods, or which is evaluated and made permanent by the use of these methods, should be summarized periodically like any other report on progress. As the quality control program develops, an increased proportion of the effort should be applied to direct cost reduction.

Case No. and Org.	Estimated Expenditures			Estimated Annual Savings	
	Develop. Expense	New Plant	Other Expense	Capacity Level	Current Prod. Est.
– – – –	Reduce (.....) shrinkage and salvage operations by changing the method of assembly and by controlling the manufacturing process through the use of Statistical Quality Control methods.				
	$300	$0	$0	$15100.00	$31400.00
	Conducted by:.(..........................)			1260 Product Engineer	
	(..........................)			2286 Shop Supervisor	
	(..........................)			5220 Q. C. Engineer	

Fig. 224. Excerpt from a joint cost reduction case conducted by a Quality Control Team.

D-5 CONTROL CHART AUDITS

Quality Control Teams maintain a constant check on all process control layouts and process control charts. In addition, it is usually desirable to have a formal periodic review conducted by someone who is not a regular member of the Team. This is to make sure that quality control practices are uniform or consistent throughout the plant and are kept up-to-date. It also ensures that personnel changes, work load pressures, special investigations or human frailties are not permitting the process controls to be misunderstood or neglected.

A formal control chart audit should include a check on all of the following items:

Control charts

How many charts are of the $\bar{X}$ and R type?

How many charts are of the percent defective type?

(Include in this both p-charts and other attributes control charts.)

How many charts are of the percent dropout type?

(That is, charts showing dropouts rather than quality going to next operation.)

Is the chart setup correct?

Is the plotting correct?

Is the plotting being performed as specified?

Is the plotting up-to-date?

Are obsolete charts removed from the job?

Are out-of-control points marked with x's?

Are all specified tests being used for marking out-of-control patterns?

(The tests should include the checking of points inside the control limits as well as outside, as explained in the instructions to process checkers.)

Are the causes for out-of-control conditions noted on the control charts?

Are new performance studies needed?

Is the frequency of checks economic with respect to current performance?

Is action being taken properly on the basis of the charts?

Data

Are the data recorded as specified?

Is the specified form being used?

Are the records up-to-date?

Are the calculations correct?

Gages and test sets

Are the specified gages or test sets used?

Are the facilities properly maintained and inspected?

Inspection plans

(Because of their influence on the Operating process controls, these should be checked whether or not the audit of process controls is combined with a formal inspection audit.)

Is the specified sampling plan being used?

Are the correct methods of inspection used?

Is the specified lot size used?

Is the specified sample size used?

Is full inspection of the sample being performed?

Is the disposition of lots handled correctly?

Are rejected lots reinspected as specified?

Layout information

Are the latest issues in files and in use?

Are inspection criteria specified in the Inspection Layouts?

Are process control criteria specified in the Process Control Layouts?

Are the Inspection Layouts and Process Control Layouts cross-referenced in the Manufacturing Layouts?

Samples for process control

Are they selected by the process checker?

Are they measured by the process checker?

Are they selected at specified intervals and at the specified points in the process?

Since the intent of this audit is to bring the job up to date rather than to find fault, the members of the Team are notified well in advance of the audit.

When the audit is completed, recommendations for corrective action are sent to the Team members and this is followed by a more or less formal discussion. After the discussion a complete formal report is written showing audit items found, action to be taken, and the person or persons responsible. Follow-up on open items is made periodically to ensure closure of all items. A quarterly summary of open items is given to management.

D-6 ROUTINE DUTIES IN CONNECTION WITH PROCESS CONTROL CHARTS

Process control charts require a certain amount of maintenance and upkeep. These duties are divided among the Quality Control Team, the quality control engineering department and the process checker in the shop. If possible, there should be a statistical clerk to work with the quality control engineer and relieve him of details associated with calculating, plotting, filing and keeping records. The activities connected with the proper upkeep of charts are outlined as follows.

(1) *Original master chart.* This is prepared from data furnished by the Quality Control Team. The quality control engineer supervises the actual preparation of the chart. Calculating, plotting and lettering of headings and scales may be done by a statistical clerk. The master chart should be approved by the Quality Control Team before it is used in the shop.

(2) *Copies for the shop.* These should be reproduced from the master chart by the statistical clerk and furnished to the shop as needed. When changes are made in the master, unused copies of the original should be promptly destroyed. The statistical clerk ordinarily furnishes a holder or backing for the chart along with the shop copies.

(3) *Changes in the master chart.* These may include revising the scale, shifting the centerline (or centerlines) to a different point, adding new information, etc. Changes are authorized by the Quality Control Team and carried out by the quality control engineer with the help of the statistical clerk.

(4) *Permanent file of master charts.* This should be maintained by the statistical clerk under the direction of the quality control engineer. The master file should contain copies of all charts which have been used on the job.

(5) *New capability studies (growing out of charts already in use).* These are initiated by the Quality Control Team, which also makes provision for obtaining the necessary data. The data may be collected by the product engineer, the quality control engineer or, in many cases, the process checker. The quality control engineer supervises the collection of data and the calculations and plotting required for the study. The detailed work of calculating and plotting is done by the statistical clerk. The quality control engineer discusses the study with the other members of the Team and the Team decides jointly what action should be taken.

(6) *New performance studies to keep the charts up to date.* These are authorized by the Quality Control Team after a study of current charts. New performance studies are usually made when R charts or p-charts show significantly lower patterns. This indicates the advisability of calculating new control limits. Less frequently performance studies may be required as a result of a shift in $\bar{X}$ which is expected to become a permanent part of the process. The Team decides which period should be used as a basis for new calculations. The statistical clerk makes the calculations and plots a new master chart. The chart is approved by the quality control engineer before being used in the shop.

(7) *Storage.* As successive sheets are obtained and filled by the shop, the current sheet is mounted on top of the previous sheets in the same holder. When the sheets become too numerous, some provision is made for storing. The file of old charts should be kept in the shop area, if possible, and supervised by the process checker. Otherwise, the file is kept in the quality control department and is supervised by the statistical clerk.

From time to time, it may be desirable to reduce the bulk of these records. This is usually done by the quality control engineer after consultation with the product engineer and the Shop. In reducing the bulk of records, care should be taken to avoid throwing away information that will be valuable later. Records may be reduced by (a) making a suitable selection of representative charts from various periods, or (b) compiling a condensed history or summary by plotting representative periods side by side on a new chart. Condensed summaries consisting of brief selected periods, possibly several months apart, are sometimes used to convey to management a picture of the process improvement.

D-7 MANUAL FOR STATISTICAL CLERKS

Statistical clerks should be furnished with a brief manual covering the following information.

a. An explanation of technical terms and abbreviations in connection with the charts. For example, that the abbreviation I_b stands for Plate Current.

b. Simple tables showing frequently used values. For example, square root of 2 square root of 5.

c. Tables showing upper control limits for p-charts or np-charts, given the sample size and number of defects.

d. Directions for calculating control limits for the common kinds of control charts. This should include examples of actual calculations.

e. Sample charts properly plotted with the correct designations and with correctly proportioned scales.

f. Sample data sheets showing the form in which data are ordinarily submitted by the process checker and showing what the statistical clerk is expected to do with the data.

g. Definitions of common terms used in process control. For example, variable, process, lot, sample, etc.

h. Instructions for marking out-of-control patterns.

i. Any special instructions which may be needed on the job, such as directions for plotting charts in a designed experiment.

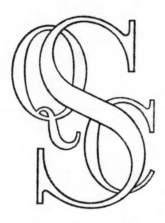

Section IV

Inspection
Procedures

PART A
Principles of Inspection

This part of the Handbook covers the general philosophy of inspection as applied at Western Electric locations, where the term "inspection" relates strictly to the activities of personnel reporting to the formal Inspection organization and does not include either process checking or sorting of the product when performed by the Operating organization. The purpose of this Section is to explain the relationship between inspection and process control, and to emphasize the difference between the acceptance-and-rejection procedures used by Inspection and the "operational sorting" which may be done by the shop.

While inspection is not the primary purpose of a quality control program, there are important benefits to be derived from the application of quality control principles to inspection planning. One important by-product is a reduction in the necessary amount of inspection. Another is the fact that, with properly planned inspection, the Operating organization becomes in fact responsible for the quality of its products.

A-1 PLACE OF INSPECTION IN THE QUALITY CONTROL PROGRAM

A quality control program tries to prevent defects by improvement and control of the process. Checks are made by Operating at regular intervals and are used as a basis for action regarding the process; that is, to tell whether the process should be left alone or whether action should be taken to correct undesirable conditions. This action on the process almost invariably results in a steady improvement in quality and at the same time a steady reduction in cost.

However, an overall quality control program requires more than a check on the process. To achieve the objective of satisfactory quality at minimum cost it is necessary to include proper inspection also. The term "inspection" as used here means *"acceptance inspection,"* which consists of examining a specific quantity of product to provide a basis for action with regard to that particular product; that is, to decide whether the product should be accepted and passed on to the user, or whether some other action should be taken, such as scrap, repair, etc.

Acceptance inspection provides, in effect, a check on the adequacy of the process controls. If the process has been controlled satisfactorily by Operating and Engineering, the product should slip past the acceptance inspection without trouble or delay. On the other hand, if the process controls have broken down, Inspection must step in and provide emergency protection by setting up a "screen" and attempting, as effectively as possible, to keep the bad product from getting out.

Emergency inspection is almost never economical. Part of the science of inspection planning consists in keeping inspection at a low economical level during normal conditions and minimizing the amount of time when inspection must furnish emergency protection. The better the control of the process, the less frequent and shorter will be the periods when emergency protection is needed. Thus there is a definite connection between inspection economy and process control.

There is one other way in which Inspection may contribute to the quality control program.

In the early stages of the program, inspection results are frequently used to pinpoint the trouble areas and to determine where process controls are needed. Inspection personnel sometimes take an active part in making the initial measurements or setting up the earliest charts.

It is important, however, that the actual operation of the program in the shop should be left as soon as possible in the hands of Operating and Engineering. Inspection should be a completely separate function which is concerned with evaluating the end result.

A-2 WHY INSPECTION CAN BE REDUCED BUT NEVER COMPLETELY ELIMINATED

One of the aims of a quality control program is to reduce or minimize the amount of inspection performed. However, it is never possible to eliminate inspection entirely. The Inspection organization has certain responsibilities which cannot be delegated to any other organization. One of these is the responsibility of certifying the quantity and quality of the product for Operating payment purposes. This should be done by an organization separate from the one responsible for making the product.

In addition to this, Inspection represents the user. The user may be another Operating organization or it may be the ultimate customer. Acceptance or rejection of the product before it leaves the Operating group can eliminate extensive handling and negotiation which might result later if the user performed his own inspection.

Inspection, therefore, must (1) assure that the Operating organization has performed its functions properly, and (2) provide adequate safeguards against the shipment of defective product. This may be accomplished by examining each unit of product in detail. This is called 100% or "detail" inspection. The same purposes may also be accomplished by reaching a decision to accept or reject the product after examining only part of it. This is called sampling inspection. Sampling inspection is, as a rule, the more economical procedure.

A-3 USES OF SORTING AND SAMPLING INSPECTION

Prior to the start of a quality control program it is quite common for 100% inspection to be performed by the Inspection organization under any of the following conditions:

(1) Where a job is just going into production, or production is extremely limited. In this case it may not be practical to set up sampling.

(2) Where a requirement is so critical that it is felt that every unit must be checked. For example, a defective may be able to cause personal injury.

(3) Where the product is such that continual sorting of defects from the process is necessary to bring the product to an acceptable level of quality. That is, sorting is necessary for quality improvement.

Most of the 100% inspection performed in industry has been done for the third reason.

In a quality control program it is considered proper for the Inspection organization to do 100% inspection for either of the first two reasons. In the third case, however, where sorting is done to improve quality, the Operating organization should do the sorting, while Inspection takes only a sample. This makes the Operating organization responsible for quality, which is an essential element in a quality control program. It also opens the door to much more rapid improvement of the process, by providing an incentive to do away with the operator sorting.

A-3.1 Operational sorting vs. corrective sorting

When sorting is done by the Operating organization, a distinction is made between necessary or unavoidable sorting, resulting from the nature or capability of the operation, and the unnecessary or avoidable sorting which results from failure to do the job properly. Process capability studies are used to determine how much sorting is to be considered unavoidable.

When a process capability study shows that the process is not capable of turning out product of an acceptable quality, even when the processing is properly done, sorting must be provided to weed out the defectives. This type of sorting is known as "operational sorting" because it has been shown to be an essential part of the "make operations."

On the other hand, if the process is capable of turning out product of acceptable quality, but defectives are produced as a result of poor workmanship or failure to run the process properly, sorting to remove these defectives is called "avoidable sorting" or "corrective sorting." If the capability of the process is such that only 2% would be defective normally, but as a result of carelessness or inattention the product has been running 12% defective, then sorting to remove the unnecessary 10% is "corrective sorting."

The following steps may be taken to determine the need for operational sorting:

A. Make process capability studies to find the normal behavior of the process. Eliminate, as far as possible, the assignable causes which are due to failure to run the process properly. If the resultant capability is good enough to meet the required quality standards, no operational sorting is needed.

B. If the normal capability is not good enough to meet the required quality standards, determine what must be done to bring about the necessary improve-ment. Sometimes the required changes can be introduced by very simple means: For example, putting a chamfer on a fixture, reducing the amount of play in a jig, installing a magnet to hold the parts in position during assembly, changing the operation to a different machine, installing an automatic timer, modifying a requirement, etc. Any of these can result in a significant and rapid improvement. Also, putting control charts in the shop will improve the performance of almost any process that depends largely on the operator's technique. In any case where sufficient improvement can be obtained in a very short space of time, it will not be necessary to make provision for operational sorting.

C. If the capability of the present process is not good enough to meet the quality standards and it is not possible to improve it immediately, operational sorting should be provided as a temporary measure until the process can be improved. The "capability" percentage of defects is obtained from the process capability study.

Except for the rare cases where Inspection may be required to do 100% inspection (new or limited production, or an occasional extremely critical requirement), the relationship between Operating and Inspection in a quality control program should be one of those shown below.

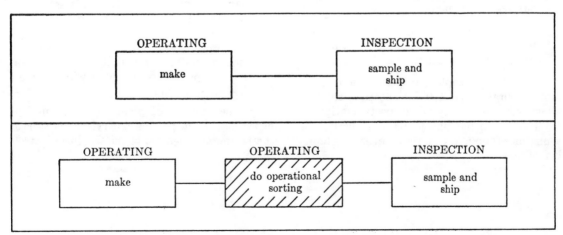

Fig. 225. Permissible relationships between Operating and Inspection.

235

In any case where the second alternative is used, one of the duties of the Quality Control Team should be to eliminate the operational sorting as soon as possible by process improvement.

A-3.2 Total amount of effort expended in checking the product

In cases where Inspection has been performing 100% inspection and this activity is now to be transferred to the Operating organization as "operational sorting," while Inspection takes a subsequent sample, this will result in a temporary increase in the total amount of checking. There will now be 100% checking by one organization plus an additional sample by another.

However, experience shows that when sorting is transferred to the Operating organization, it is much more likely to be reduced promptly. In a short time the sorting by Operating should be reduced sufficiently to make the total effort of Operating and Inspection considerably less than the original 100% inspection.

A-3.3 Summary of the advantages of sampling inspection

For acceptance purposes, sampling has three advantages over 100% inspection:

(1) It puts the responsiblity for quality in the hands of the Operating organization where it belongs.

(2) It is more economical as far as inspection costs are concerned.

(3) It tends to encourage more rapid improvement of the process than is the case under 100% inspection.

In addition, sampling inspection is usually more accurate than 100% inspection, since it allows less opportunity for "inspection fatigue." Product which has passed 100% inspection is sometimes found to contain a surprising number of defects.

A-4 INSPECTION PLANNING

The cost of inspection is usually small in comparison with the total cost of a product. Nevertheless, inspection procedures can have an important effect not only on the cost of inspection but on the cost of manufacture as well. For this reason inspection procedures of any kind require careful planning. Many individuals can contribute to the successful planning of inspection.

(1) The manufacturing engineer is responsible for planning inspection and for writing a layout describing the inspection procedures.

(2) Quality control engineers generally assist in the statistical aspects of inspection planning, including the selection of suitable quality levels and the provision of suitable inspection methods. In addition to this, they help to check the reasonableness and economy of inspection plans and make sure that consistent practices are followed throughout the plant. They frequently assist in the writing of inspection layouts.

(3) Inspection supervisors contribute many helpful suggestions with respect to inspection planning. Their experience provides a valuable source of information for the manufacturing and quality control engineers.

(4) Shop supervisors should also take part in the planning of inspection, since it has a direct effect on shop procedures and on manufacturing costs. It is advisable for the Quality Control Team to discuss in advance any proposed changes in inspection procedures. This serves to promote good understanding as well as to make sure that the procedures adopted will be practical and economical.

For the purpose of planning or discussing inspection, the inspection supervisor may serve as a temporary member of the Quality Control Team.

PART B

Acceptance Sampling

———————— ✦ ————————

B-1 ELEMENTARY CONCEPTS

B-1.1 General

Suppose we have a large amount of product which is 4% defective. If we were to take a sample of 100 pieces from this product, and if the sample were exactly representative of the product, we would expect to find four defective pieces in the sample. However, we find from experience that our sample of 100 may contain more or less than four defective pieces. The following is a record of what was actually observed in a series of samples of 100 from product that was known to be 4% defective.

Product Is Actually 4% Defective	
Sample Number	Number of Defective Pieces in Sample
1	3
2	2
3	6
4	4
5	3
6	5
7	7
8	5
9	1
10	4

Fig. 226. Varying numbers of defective pieces in samples of 100.

In process control we would plot such samples on a p-chart, and the chart would plainly show a fluctuating pattern. In sampling inspection the results are not ordinarily plotted on p-charts, but use is made of the fluctuating pattern.

A sampling plan establishes a certain limit called an "acceptance number" which defines the maximum allowable number of defects or defectives in a sample. When the sampling fluctuation is such that the allowable number is exceeded, the inspector rejects the product. When the sampling fluctuation is such that the allowable number is not exceeded, the inspector accepts the product. Product of poor quality will have a different fluctuating pattern from product of good quality and because of this the sampling plan will reject a greater proportion of the poor quality product.

A simplified picture of the operation of a sampling plan is shown on page 238.

In the case described, the inspector was told to take samples of 100 and use an acceptance number of 5. At first the incoming product was 4% defective, and two out of 10 samples exceeded the acceptance number. The inspector rejected the product represented by those samples. Later on, when the product became 8% defective, eight of the inspector's samples exceeded the acceptance number. He therefore rejected the product represented by those eight samples.

If the inspector had been told to use an acceptance number of 4, he would have rejected more product which was 4% defective, and almost all of the product which was 8% defective.

Two important things about the operation of a sampling plan are illustrated in this example:

(a) When the product becomes worse, the sampling plan does not necessarily reject all the product which is submitted. It only rejects a larger *proportion* of the product as the quality becomes poorer.

(b) An individual quantity of product which is rejected by the sampling plan is not necessarily worse than a quantity of product which is accepted. A sampling plan is based on the proportion of product, *represented by a long series of samples*, which will, in the long run, be accepted or rejected.

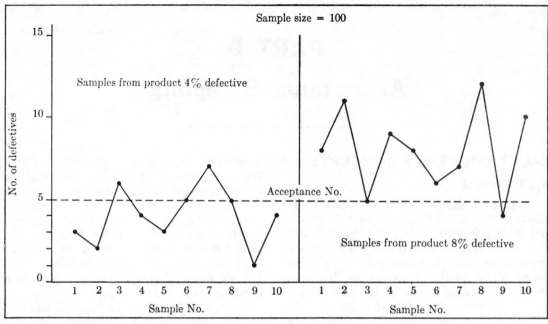

Fig. 227. Operation of a sampling plan as the quality of the product becomes poorer.

B-1.2 Sample size and acceptance number

The sample size is the number of pieces selected to be inspected. It is represented by the symbol "n." The acceptance number, as indicated above, is the largest number of defectives (or defects) in the sample that will permit the product to be accepted. It is represented by the symbol "c." Together, the sample size and acceptance number determine what proportion of product of a given quality will in the long run be accepted or rejected.

In the case of "double" or "multiple" sampling the inspector is given more than one sample size and acceptance number.

B-1.3 Probability of acceptance

The "probability of acceptance" of a sampling plan is the percentage of samples out of a long series of samples which will cause the product to be accepted. If the product is 4% defective and we tell the inspector to take samples of 100 and allow an acceptance number of 5 (as shown in Figure 227), the inspector will in the long run accept about 80% of the product. We say that the probability of ac-

ceptance for such product is about 80%. If the product is 8% defective and we tell the inspector to take samples of 100 and use an acceptance number of 5 (as shown in Figure 227), the inspector will in the long run accept about 20% of the product. We say that the probability of acceptance for such product is about 20%.

It is possible to calculate the probability of acceptance for product of any quality using any desired combination of sample size and acceptance number. The probability of acceptance is usually expressed in decimal form rather than as a percentage. It is represented by the symbol "P_a."

B-1.4 OC curves

It is characteristic of sampling plans that the probability of acceptance is large as long as the product is very good and becomes less as the product becomes worse. A complete plotting of the probability of acceptance for product at all possible levels of percent defective is known as an "Operating Characteristic Curve." This term is frequently abbreviated to "OC curve."

Some typical examples of OC curves are shown on page 243. The OC curve for the

238

sampling plan in Figure 227 is shown below.

The OC curve is interpreted as follows:

To find what proportion of product will be accepted if the product is 4% defective, find .04 along the scale at the base of the curve and draw a line vertically upward until it intersects the curve. (See dotted line in Figure 228.) The probability of acceptance can then be read along the left-hand scale opposite the point of intersection.

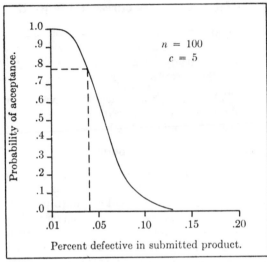

Fig. 228. OC curve for the sampling plan $n = 100$, $c = 5$.

In the above example, the probability of acceptance for product 4% defective is a little less than .8. This means that slightly less than 80% of such product will be accepted. Another way of saying this is that slightly more than 20% will be rejected.

If the product submitted by Operating were 6% defective, about 45% would be accepted and 55% rejected. If the product submitted by Operating were 12% defective, practically all of it would be rejected by an inspector using this plan.

The probabilities of acceptance shown by an OC curve are based on the assumption that samples are drawn at random from the submitted product. If samples are not drawn at random, the calculated probabilities do not apply. A random sample is defined as one selected in such a way that every unit in the product has an equal chance of being chosen in the sample.

By a suitable combination of sample size and acceptance number, it is possible to devise a sampling plan that will reject most of the product that we would like to have rejected and accept most of the product that we would like to have accepted. In most cases the actual choice of a sampling plan is dictated by economic considerations as well as by the probabilities of acceptance and rejection.

B-2 METHODS OF CALCULATING THE PROBABILITY OF ACCEPTANCE

For attributes sampling plans, where each unit of product is classified merely as defective or non-defective, there are three equations which can be used to calculate the probability of acceptance. These are:

a. The Hypergeometric.
b. The Binomial.
c. The Poisson.

Discussions of these equations and their uses can be found in the standard texts. A simplified explanation is given in Reference No. 20.

The Poisson equation is the most widely used of these three. It is used, with certain restrictions, not only where the inspector counts the *defective units*, but also where he counts the *actual number of defects*. Since the Poisson equation is used in many of the situations encountered in practical work, all examples of probabilities of acceptance in this Handbook, unless otherwise noted, will be Poisson probabilities.

The Poisson probabilities can be found in convenient published tables and curves. Two useful sources are the following:

(1) The numerical probabilities, carried out to 6 decimal places, are given in the book "Poisson's Exponential Binomial Limit" by E. C. Molina (D. Van Nostrand Company, New York, 1947). Two tables are provided—individual terms in Table I and cumulative terms in Table II.

239

(2) The probabilities can also be read more roughly from a set of curves based on the Poisson equation. A set of Poisson curves is shown in Figure 229.

To determine the probability of acceptance, using the Poisson tables or curves, begin by determining:

"n" (the size of the sample).
"p" (the proportion of defectives or defects in the product).
"c" (the acceptance number which is to be used by the inspector).

It is not necessary to know p and n individually if we know the product of these two — the "expected number of defects," pn.

In Molina's tables the product of n x p is called "a." On the curves in Figure 229 the product of n x p is called "pn."

B-2.1 How to use Molina's Tables

To calculate the probability of acceptance for a single sampling plan (that is, a plan which tells the inspector to accept or reject on the basis of a single sample), proceed as follows:

(1) Start with the combination of sample size and acceptance number which you wish to study. Call the sample size "n" and the acceptance number "c."

(2) Take any percent defective value in which you are interested. Express it as a decimal. Call this "p."

(3) Multiply n x p to obtain "a."

(4) Consult Molina's Table II (Cumulative Terms). Look up the value of "a" obtained in Step 3. Follow down in the table until you come to $c + 1$ defects. For example, if the acceptance number in your sampling plan is 4, follow down in the Table until you come to 5. The probability opposite $c + 1$ defects is the probability of rejection.

(5) Finally calculate the probability of acceptance. This is always 1 minus the probability of rejection.

Example:
For the sampling plan $n = 100$, $c = 5$,

find the probability of acceptance where $p = 8\%$.

$$n \text{ x } p = 100 \text{ x } .08 = 8$$

Look up "$a = 8$" in Molina's Table II. Follow down in the table until you come to $5 + 1$ (or 6) defects. The probability of rejection is .808764.
Subtracting this from 1, we get .191236. This is the probability of acceptance. It can also be expressed as 19.1%.

B-2.2 How to use the curves in Figure 229

(1) Start with the combination of sample size and acceptance number which you wish to study. Call the sample size "n" and the acceptance number "c."

(2) Take any percent defective value in which you are interested. Express it as a decimal. Call this "p."

(3) Multiply n x p to obtain "pn."

(4) Look up the value of "pn" on the scale at the bottom of Figure 229. Follow upward along that vertical line until it intersects the curve which corresponds to the acceptance number "c." Then move horizontally to the left and find the probability of acceptance along the left-hand vertical scale.

Example:
For the sampling plan $n = 100$, $c = 5$, find the probability of acceptance where $p = 8\%$.

$$n \text{ x } p = 100 \text{ x } .08 = 8$$

Read up on the vertical line at 8 to the heavy curve marked 5. Then read across to the left-hand scale. The probability of acceptance is approximately .19, or 19%.

B-2.3 Calculating and plotting an OC curve

To plot an OC curve for a single sampling plan proceed as follows:

(1) Set up a table of various values of percent defective as shown in Figure 230.

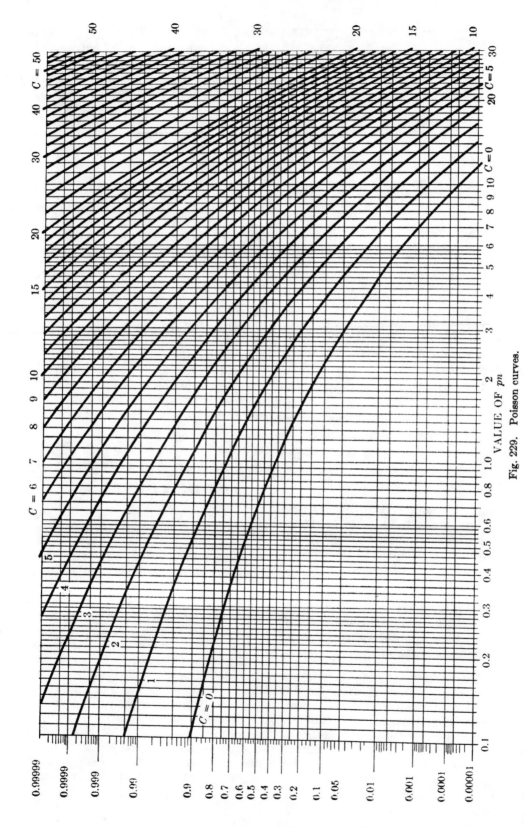

VALUE OF *pn*

Fig. 229. Poisson curves.

241

Sampling Plan $n = 100$, $c = 5$		
p	"pn" or "a"	Probability of Acceptance
.01	1	.999
.02	2	.983
.03	3	.916
.04	4	.785
.05	5	.616
.06	6	.446
.07	7	.301
.08	8	.191
.09	9	.116
.10	10	.067
.11	11	.048
.12	12	.020
.13	13	.011

Fig. 230.   Calculations required for plotting an OC curve.

Express "p" (the percent defective) as a decimal fraction. Make the values of "p" cover a suitable range of both good and bad product.

(2) Fill in the second column in the table by multiplying each of the listed values of "p" by "n." If "n" is 100, the values in the second column will be 1, 2, 3, etc.

(3) Find the probability of acceptance by using either Molina's Tables or the curves in Figure 229.

(4) Plot the probability of acceptance corresponding to each value of "p" as shown in Figure 228. If a number of OC curves are to be compared, be sure to use the same horizontal and vertical scales.

B-2.4 Probability of acceptance for other than single sampling plans and for cases where it is not appropriate to use Poisson probabilities

For double or multiple sampling plans, where the inspector may take two or more samples before reaching a decision to accept or reject, the probability of acceptance is more difficult to calculate. The calculations are explained in Reference No. 20. It is also more difficult to calculate the probability of acceptance for a "variables" type sampling plan. A discussion of this is given in Reference No. 4.

In some situations it is necessary to use the Hypergeometric or Binomial equations rather than the Poisson. Binomial probabilities have been published in tables rather similar to the Poisson tables. One useful source is "Applied Mathematics Series No. 6, Tables of the Binomial Probability Distribution," published by the Government Printing Office in Washington, D. C.

In certain cases, particularly in the case of some of the most frequently used plans, OC curves have already been plotted and published. In these cases it is not necessary to make the calculations at all. One example of this is the Mil.-Std. 105A tables (see Reference No. 30) which show approximate OC curves for single, double and multiple sampling plans. OC curves are also available for many of the sampling plans in the Dodge-Romig tables (Reference No. 11). In Bowker and Goode's "Sampling Inspection by Variables" (Reference No. 4), OC curves are given for single and double variables-type plans.

Caution should be used in comparing, or drawing conclusions from, published OC curves, since the curves may not be plotted on comparable scales.

B-3 ECONOMIC IMPORTANCE OF OC CURVES

An OC curve can be plotted for any combination of sample size (n) and acceptance number (c). Each combination results in a different curve. Some of the most important things to remember about OC curves can be seen by comparing the curves in Figure 231.

Note that, in general, a larger sample size tends to result in a steeper curve. Such plans are said to have greater "discriminating power" than plans with smaller samples and shallower curves. Plan A has greater discriminating power than Plan B. This means that it can distinguish more sharply between products having different percents defective.

Note also that a larger acceptance number tends to change the shape of the curve, creating a flat "shoulder" at the top while retaining a thin "tail" at the bottom. Plans E and F have more pronounced shoulders than Plans G and H or plans C and O.

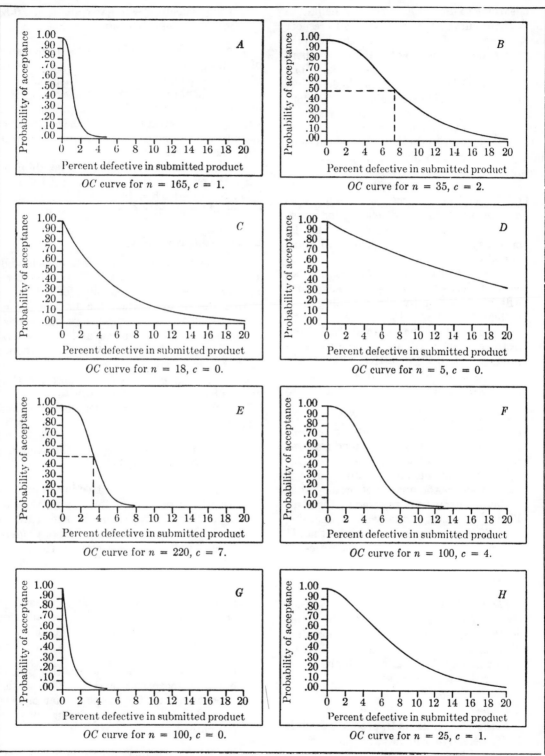

Fig. 231. OC curves for some frequently used sampling plans.

In learning to use an OC curve, it is helpful to think of the curve as "beginning" (with respect to the percent defective scale at the bottom) at zero; and as "extending" to the point where the tail approaches the bottom line. The curve in Plan G extends to about 5% defective. The curve in Plan D extends beyond the confines of this particular diagram, which is plotted only to 20% defective.

It is also helpful to think of the OC curve as having three parts in which we are primarily interested:

(1) *The shoulder (or peak) at the top.* This may be a flat portion extending for a considerable distance as in Plan F or Plan B; or it may be only a sharp peak as in Plans C and G.

This part of the curve is important because it shows the quality of product that will be accepted by the sampling plan without question. Plan F will accept practically all product up to about 2% defective. Plan A will accept practically all product up to 0.5% defective. Plan C will reject part of the product if it is anything but 0% defective.

(2) *The thin part of the tail at the bottom.* The thin part may be short and sharp as in Plans A and G, or it may extend for considerable distances as in Plans H and C.

This part of the curve is important because it shows the quality of product that is almost certain to be rejected by the plan. Plan A will reject virtually all product if it is worse than about 3% defective. Plan H will not reject comparable quantities of product unless it is more than 20% defective.

(3) *The middle portion of the curve, between the shoulder and the tail.* At the exact center of the curve, where the probability of acceptance is 50%, product of the corresponding quality has a 50-50 chance of being either rejected or accepted.

Example:
If the plan in use is B, product which is 7.5% defective will have about a 50-50 chance of being accepted.
If the plan in use is E, product which is

3.5% defective will have about a 50-50 chance of being accepted.

The above examples illustrate the importance of knowing the OC curve in selecting a sampling plan for use on a given product. In general, the engineer should make sure that the "shoulder" of the curve corresponds to the product he is willing to have accepted, and that the "tail" of the curve corresponds to the product he is willing to have rejected.

Maximum economy is likely to be obtained when the process is running at or near its capability level and when this capability matches the shoulder of the OC curve to be used.

B-3.1 Producer's risk

Sampling plans are often spoken of as having a certain "Producer's Risk." The Producer's Risk is defined as the probability or risk of rejecting the product when the lot quality or process quality, as the case may be, is relatively good. For engineers and supervisors, this means the risk that the normal product made by Operating will be rejected by Inspection. The engineer tries to see that the Producer's Risk is kept as small as possible.

To estimate the Producer's Risk of a sampling plan proceed as follows:

(1) First plot the OC curve for the sampling plan you wish to study.

(2) Find the percent defective in the process when it is running at its capability. For exploratory purposes it is sufficient to make a rough estimate. For a more accurate check, it is necessary to have a process capability study or shop control chart.

(3) Find this process capability percentage on the scale below the OC curve, and use the curve to determine the probability of acceptance.

(4) Take the difference between this probability of acceptance and 1. This is the Producer's Risk for the particular process capability which you are using in your estimate.

It would be possible to calculate the Producer's Risk directly, without first plotting the

OC curve. Merely take the process capability percentage determined in Step 2 and calculate the probability of rejection as explained on page 240. However, most engineers and supervisors are interested in the entire region around the process capability level. For this it is desirable to have the complete OC curve.

Example:

Refer to the OC curve in Figure 228. Suppose the process runs normally at 3% defective. Following up at 3% until we reach the curve, we find that this corresponds to a probability of acceptance of about 92%. The Producer's Risk, for this particular process, is the difference between 92% and 100%, or 8%.

B-3.2 Consumer's risk

Sampling plans are also said to have a certain "Consumer's Risk." The Consumer's Risk is defined as the probability or risk of accepting the product when the lot quality or process quality, as the case may be, is relatively poor. For engineers and supervisors, this means the risk that product considered unsatisfactory to the customer may be accepted by Inspection. The engineer tries to see that the Consumer's Risk also is kept as small as possible, considering the needs of the user in each particular case.

The Consumer's Risk of a sampling plan can be estimated as follows:*

(1) First plot the OC curve for the sampling plan you wish to study.

(2) Discover the percent defective which the consumer wants to reject. This is interpreted as meaning the quality which is so poor that the consumer would be willing to accept it only a small percent of the time.

(3) Find this value on the scale below the OC curve, and use the curve to determine the probability of acceptance. This gives the risk of accepting unsatisfactory qual-

---

* In "Sampling Inspection Tables," by Dodge and Romig, the term "Consumer's Risk" is defined more restrictively than it is defined here. For information on this consult the index in Reference No. 11.

ity under the conditions assumed in Step 2, *provided* that product of such poor quality is actually submitted.

As in the case of the Producer's Risk, it would be possible to calculate the Consumer's Risk directly without plotting the OC curve. However, engineers and supervisors (as well as customers) are generally interested in the entire region around the percent defective which was chosen in Step 2. For this reason, it is an advantage to have the complete OC curve.

Example:

Refer to the OC curve shown in Figure 228. Suppose the consumer wants to reject product which is 9% defective. Reading up at this point until we reach the curve and then across to the probability of acceptance, we find it is approximately 10%. This is the Consumer's Risk for product of the assumed percent defective.

In the same way, the Consumer's Risk could be calculated for any other percent defective.

It is important to note that the Consumer's Risk of 10%, which was calculated above, does not mean that the consumer has a 10% chance of receiving poor product. The meaning of the Consumer's Risk is that such product would have a 10% chance of being accepted *if it were actually submitted to Inspection.* However, if the process is running near its capability, and if that capability is near the shoulder of the curve, then product as bad as 9% defective would probably not be made. In that case no 9% defective product would be submitted to Inspection, and the real risk of receiving poor quality product would be practically zero.

B-3.3 Costs associated with Producer's and Consumer's Risks

The engineer will find that every part of the OC Curve is associated in some way with the costs of running the job. He should try to select a curve that will minimize this cost. Many of the most important costs are associated with the Producer's Risk: that is, with the risk of having product rejected when it is relatively good product.

(1) When lots are rejected unnecessarily they must not only be re-checked but must also be loaded and unloaded and trucked about from place to place.

(2) Storage space has to be provided for lots that are being held up.

(3) The unnecessary checking and rechecking may hold up testing facilities that are badly needed for more productive work.

(4) The Operating routine is interrupted unnecessarily.

(5) The repeated handling and checking may make the quality of shipped product worse instead of better.

(6) If the screening of rejected lots is done by Operating, further inspection must be done afterward before the product is finally accepted.

(7) There may be costly delays in getting hold of needed parts.

In addition to all the above, the economic gains which result from a quality control program are due primarily to the increased stability of the production process. Rejection of "normal" product to Operating does not tend, in general, to promote stability of the process.

There are also costs associated with the Consumer's Risk: that is, with the chance that unsatisfactory product will be accepted and sent out. These costs include the effect on customer good will; the cost of handling and answering complaints; the cost of investigations and conferences; a possible effect on the overall quality rates; additional expenditures of engineering effort and time.

Against these two costs the engineer must balance the cost of the inspection itself. As a rule, large sample sizes and large acceptance numbers will provide a better balance between the Producer's and Consumer's risks, but the large samples may be expensive or impractical. Among the things which can be done to avoid these large samples are the following:

(1) Set up a sampling plan with two inspection levels instead of one—the first level to be used when the process is running normally, and the second level to be used

when quality is seriously threatened. The emphasis can then be put on the Producer's Risk during normal periods and on protection of the consumer during periods of trouble. One way of doing this is shown on pages 273–274.

(2) Set up a control chart to be used during normal periods instead of a formal sampling plan. When quality is satisfactory as it comes from Operating, this plan will operate with a fairly large Consumer's Risk. However, if the incoming quality shifts to an unsatisfactory level, this will tend to show up in the pattern on the control chart. This can be used to set in motion some pre-determined action which will furnish additional protection to the consumer: for example, reversion to a standard-type sampling plan until the abnormal period is over.

B-4 CLASSIFICATION OF SAMPLING PLANS ACCORDING TO AQL, LTPD AND AOQL

B-4.1 AQL sampling plans

Suppose we have plotted the OC curves for a number of different sampling plans as on page 243. It is possible to classify these curves in various ways for convenience. For example, we might group together all the curves which have a high probability of acceptance for product 2% defective. These would include Plans B, D, E, F and H.

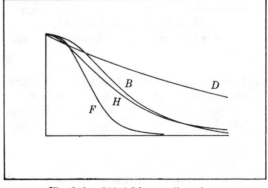

Fig. 232.   2% AQL sampling plans.

Note that these plans are fairly similar at the shoulder (the product they will accept) but are not at all similar at the tail (the product they will reject). Plans classified on this basis are called AQL (Acceptable Quality Level) sampling plans because their point of similarity is the product that will be accepted.

AQL is defined as "the maximum percent defective (or the maximum number of defects per 100 units) which can be considered satisfactory as a process average." To engineers and supervisors, this means the maximum percent defective which will be accepted regularly by Inspection, or in other words, the maximum percent defective for which the probability of acceptance is very high.

When an engineer chooses a "2% AQL sampling plan," he is choosing a plan which will regularly accept 2% defective product. The fact that the plan is classified as "2% AQL" does not tell him anything about the remainder of the OC curve—that is, about the product that will regularly be rejected.

Government purchase contracts frequently specify AQL's for various groups of inspection items. In such cases, the government inspection agency will select a sampling plan which has a high probability of acceptance at the specified AQL.

To make it easier for government inspectors to select sampling plans on this basis, the U. S. Department of Defense has published a book of sampling plans classified according to their AQL's. See Reference No. 30. This book is popularly referred to as the "Mil. Std. 105A Tables." It covers a range of AQL's from .015% defective to 10% defective. Other AQL's for use with complicated equipments and products are expressed in terms of "defects per 100 units."

These plans are widely used in industry as well as by the Army, Navy and Air Force. They provide a useful classification of sampling plans wherever we wish to make sure that the product in which we are interested will have a high probability of acceptance.

Two of the sampling plans shown on page 243 can be found in the Mil. Std. Tables: Plans H and B. These could properly be called 2% AQL sampling plans but the Mil. Std. Tables do not happen to list plans for 2% defective. Consequently, these two plans

are listed under 2.5% AQL. The instructions at the beginning of the tables tell us to use the 2.5% plans for specified AQL's ranging from 1.65% to 2.79% defective.

A typical AQL sampling table is shown in Figures 233 and 234. The captions give a general idea of how the table is used. For further information see Reference No. 30.

AQL SAMPLING TABLE

TABLE III. Sample Size Code Letters			
	Inspection Levels		
Lot Size	I	II	III
2 to 8.............	A	A	C
9 to 15............	A	B	D
16 to 25...........	B	C	E
26 to 40...........	B	D	F
41 to 65...........	C	E	G
66 to 110..........	D	F	H
111 to 180.........	E	G	I
181 to 300.........	F	H	J
301 to 500.........	G	I	K
501 to 800.........	H	J	L
801 to 1300........	I	K	L
1301 to 3200.......	J	L	M
3201 to 8000.......	L	M	N
8001 to 22,000.....	M	N	O
22,001 to 110,000...	N	O	P
110,001 to 550,000..	O	P	Q
550,001 and over....	P	Q	Q

Fig. 233. Excerpt from Mil. Std. 105A Tables: table for determining the size of the sample. To use this table proceed as follows:

(a) Determine the usual lot size in which product will be submitted.
(b) Find the corresponding letter in the column headed "Inspection Level II."
(c) Use this letter to find the appropriate sample size and acceptance number in Figure 234.

A government inspector will normally use the letters in Inspection Level II. Level I is looser than Level II, and Level III is tighter.

247

AQL SAMPLING TABLE

TABLE IV-A. Master Table for Normal and Tightened Inspection (single sampling)

Acceptable Quality Levels (normal inspection)—in percent

Sample Size Code Letter	Sample Size	0.015 Ac Re	0.035 Ac Re	0.065 Ac Re	0.10 Ac Re	0.15 Ac Re	0.25 Ac Re	0.40 Ac Re	0.65 Ac Re	1.0 Ac Re	1.5 Ac Re	2.5 Ac Re	4.0 Ac Re	6.5 Ac Re
A	2	↓	↓	↓	↓	↓	↓	↓	↓	↓	↓	↓	↓	0 1
B	3	↓	↓	↓	↓	↓	↓	↓	↓	↓	↓	↓	0 1	↑
C	5	↓	↓	↓	↓	↓	↓	↓	↓	↓	↓	0 1	↑	1 2
D	7	↓	↓	↓	↓	↓	↓	↓	↓	↓	0 1	↑	1 2	2 3
E	10	↓	↓	↓	↓	↓	↓	↓	↓	0 1	↑	1 2	2 3	3 4
F	15	↓	↓	↓	↓	↓	↓	↓	0 1	↑	1 2	2 3	3 4	5 6
G	25	↓	↓	↓	↓	↓	↓	0 1	↑	1 2	2 3	*1 2	4 5	6 7
H	35	↓	↓	↓	↓	↓	0 1	↑	1 2	2 3	3 4	†2 3	6 7	9 10
I	50	↓	↓	↓	↓	0 1	↑	1 2	2 3	3 4	4 5	3 4	8 9	12 13
J	75	↓	↓	↓	0 1	↑	1 2	2 3	3 4	4 5	5 6	4 5	11 12	17 18
K	110	↓	↓	0 1	↑	1 2	2 3	3 4	4 5	5 6	8 9	6 7	17 18	24 25
L	150	↓	0 1	↑	1 2	2 3	3 4	4 5	5 6	7 8	10 11	8 9	20 21	32 33
M	225	0 1	↑	1 2	2 3	3 4	4 5	5 6	7 8	10 11	14 15	11 12	29 30	43 44
N	300	↑	1 2	2 3	3 4	4 5	6 7	8 9	11 12	15 16	20 21	14 15	45 46	68 69
O	450	1 2	2 3	3 4	5 6	7 8	9 10	13 14	18 19	25 26	35 36	20 21	81 82	124 125
P	750	1 2	1 2	2 3	3 4	4 5	6 7	8 9	11 12	15 16	20 21	31 32	45 46	68 69
Q	1500	1 2	2 3	3 4	5 6	7 8	9 10	13 14	18 19	25 26	35 36	56 57	81 82	124 125
		0.035	0.065	0.10	0.15	0.25	0.40	0.65	1.0	1.5	2.5	4.0	6.5	10.0

Acceptable Quality Levels (tightened inspection)—in percent

* This is Plan H.
† This is Plan B.

Fig. 234. Excerpt from Mil. Std. 105A Tables: table for selecting sample size and acceptance number. To use this table, select the appropriate "sample size code letter" from Fig. 233, get the sample size from column 2 and read the acceptance number under the proper value of AQL. This table shows a "rejection number" as well as an acceptance number. The rejection number is one more than the acceptance number.

B-4.2 LTPD sampling plans

Referring again to the OC curves on page 243, we might decide to group together all the curves which have a low probability of acceptance for product 2% defective. These would include Plans A and G.

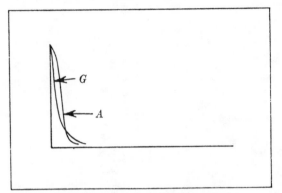

Fig. 235. 2% LTPD sampling plans.

These plans are fairly similar at the tail (the product they will reject) but are not necessarily similar at the shoulder (the product they will accept). Plans classified on this basis are called LTPD (Lot Tolerance Percent Defective) sampling plans because their point of similarity is the quality level or percent defective which can just be tolerated in a small percentage of the product.

LTPD is defined in the Dodge-Romig "Sampling Inspection Tables" as "an allowable percentage defective; a figure which may be considered as the borderline of distinction between a satisfactory lot and an unsatisfactory one." To engineers and supervisors this means the percent defective which will regularly be rejected by Inspection—that is, the percent defective for which the probability of acceptance is very low.

When an engineer chooses a "2% LTPD sampling plan," he is choosing a plan which will regularly reject 2% defective product. The fact that the plan is classified as "2% LTPD" does not tell him the characteristics of the remainder of the OC curve—that is, what quality of product will regularly be accepted.

Customers sometimes specify a certain value of LTPD for a particular product. In such cases, the manufacturer of the product will try to select a sampling plan which has a low probability of acceptance at the specified LTPD.

To make it easier to select sampling plans on this basis, Dodge and Romig have published tables of sampling plans classified according to their LTPD's. See Reference No. 11. The values of LTPD range from 0.5% to 10% defective. These tables provide a useful classification of sampling plans wherever we wish to make sure that product of a particular quality will have a low probability of acceptance.

Both of the sampling plans shown in Figure 235 can be found in the Dodge-Romig LTPD Tables. In Dodge-Romig notation, LTPD is denoted by the symbol "$p_t\%$."

A typical LTPD sampling table is shown on page 250. The caption gives a general idea of how the table is used. For further information see Reference No. 11.

B-4.3 AOQL sampling plans

It is possible to classify sampling plans on a third basis also, according to their AOQL (Average Outgoing Quality Limit). The AOQL is a value which can be calculated for any sampling plan that is used for product which can, if necessary, be 100% inspected. The AOQL is a "limiting value of percent defective" which becomes associated with the sampling plan as soon as we make provision for doing 100% inspection on all lots rejected by the plan. In any case where 100% inspection cannot or will not be done on all rejected lots, do not attempt to select a sampling plan on the basis of its AOQL.

The meaning of the term AOQL can be illustrated as follows. Consider the sampling plan labeled "C" on page 243. When product is 2% defective, this plan will accept approximately 70% of it; when product is 4% defective, it will accept approximately 50%; when product is 8% defective, it will accept approximately 25%, etc.

Suppose we make a rule that all lots rejected by this sampling plan must be 100% inspected; that all defective units found by this inspection must be replaced with good units; and that the rejected lots which have had all defects removed must then be considered together with the accepted lots in such a way as to make one total quantity of product. It is possible to

LTPD SAMPLING TABLE

TABLE SL-7. Lot Tolerance Percent Defective = 7.0%

Process Average, %	0–.07			.08–.70			.71–1.40			1.41–2.10			2.11–2.80			2.81–3.50		
Lot Size	n	c	AOQL, %	n	c	AOQL, %	n	c	AOQL, %	n	c	AOQL, %	n	c	AOQL, %	n	c	AOQL, %
1–25	All	0	0	All	0	0	All	0	0	All	0	0	All	0	0	All	0	0
26–50	24	0	.80	24	0	.80	24	0	.80	24	0	.80	24	0	.80	24	0	.80
51–100	28	0	.95	28	0	.95	28	0	.95	28	0	.95	28	0	.95	28	0	.95
101–200	30	0	1.0	30	0	1.0	49	1	1.3	49	1	1.3	49	1	1.3	65	2	1.4
201–300	31	0	1.1	31	0	1.1	50	1	1.4	70	2	1.5	85	3	1.6	85	3	1.6
301–400	32	0	1.1	55	1	1.4	70	2	1.6	90	3	1.7	105	4	1.8	125	5	1.8
401–500	32	0	1.1	55	1	1.4	75	2	1.6	90	3	1.8	110	4	1.9	140	6	2.0
501–600	32	0	1.1	55	1	1.4	75	2	1.7	95	3	1.8	125	5	2.0	145	6	2.1
601–800	32	0	1.1	55	1	1.4	75	2	1.7	110	4	2.0	130	5	2.1	160	7	2.2
801–1,000	33	0	1.1	55	1	1.4	95	3	1.9	110	4	2.1	145	6	2.2	180	8	2.4
1,001–2,000	55	1	1.5	75	2	1.8	95	3	2.0	130	5	2.3	185	8	2.5	230	11	2.8
2,001–3,000	55	1	1.5	75	2	1.8	115	4	2.1	150	6	2.4	215	10	2.8	300	15	3.0
3,001–4,000	55	1	1.5	75	2	1.8	115	4	2.2	165	7	2.6	235	11	2.9	330	17	3.2
4,001–5,000	55	1	1.5	75	2	1.8	130	5	2.4	185	8	2.7	250	12	3.0	350	18	3.3
5,001–7,000	55	1	1.5	75	2	1.8	130	5	2.4	185	8	2.7	270	13	3.1	385	20	3.4
7,001–10,000	55	1	1.5	95	3	2.0	150	6	2.5	200	9	2.9	285	14	3.2	415	22	3.6
10,001–20,000	55	1	1.5	95	3	2.0	*150	6	2.5	220	10	2.9	320	16	3.3	470	25	3.7
20,001–50,000	55	1	1.5	115	4	2.2	170	7	2.6	235	11	3.1	355	18	3.5	530	29	3.9
50,001–100,000	55	1	1.5	115	4	2.2	185	8	2.7	270	13	3.1	370	19	3.5	530	29	3.9

n = Size of Sample; entry of "All" indicates that each piece in lot is to be inspected.

c = Allowable Defect Number for Sample.

AOQL = Average Outgoing Quality Limit. This is given as supplementary information.

* This plan appears also in Figure 240.

Fig. 236. Excerpt from "Sampling Inspection Tables" by Dodge and Romig: 7% LTPD. To use this table, determine (1) the usual lot size and (2) the "process average" (percent defective at which the product normally runs). The sample size is given in column "n" under the applicable process average, and the acceptance number is given in column "c." Ignore the AOQL column unless you plan to use this as an AOQL plan also.

calculate the percentage of defectives which will be left in the mass of product if this procedure is followed. For example, when product is 4% defective, about 50% of the lots will be passed without screening while 50% will be rejected and then "100% inspected." Since half of the product will now be free from defects (theoretically) and the other half of the product will still be 4% defective, the average percent defective in the total product will be half of 4%, or 2% defective.

This is expressed as follows:

$$AOQ = p \times P_a \times \frac{N - n}{N}$$

where

AOQ = the Average Outgoing Quality.

p = the percent defective.

P_a = the probability of acceptance.

n = size of the sample.

N = size of the lot from which the sample is taken.

This equation can be used to calculate the AOQ value for various sampling plans and various values of percent defective. For example, assume that we are using the sampling plan labeled "C" on page 243, and that the lot size is 2000. We first calculate the probability of acceptance using Molina's tables and, from this, the average outgoing quality.

Incoming % Defective	Probability of Acceptance	AOQ
2%	.698	1.38%
4%	.487	1.93%
8%	.237	1.88%
12%	.115	1.37%
16%	.056	0.89%

These values of AOQ may be plotted on a chart having an appropriate vertical scale for AOQ (in percent defective) and having the same horizontal scale for the incoming product (in percent defective) that was used in Plan "C." The AOQ curve is shown in Figure 237.

This curve shows that when the incoming product is 10% defective, the outgoing product will be only 1.6% defective—provided the requirements of the sampling plan, including 100% inspection, have been faithfully carried out.

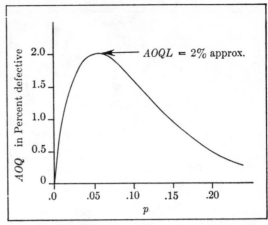

Fig. 237.   AOQ curve for the sampling plan $n = 18$, $c = 0$.

Note that the AOQ curve rises until it reaches a certain maximum point, after which it falls off again as a result of more and more product being "100% inspected." The AOQL is the maximum point which is reached by the AOQ curve.

The AOQL of a sampling plan is therefore defined as follows: The AOQL is the worst average quality that can exist, in the long run, in the outgoing product, after the rejected lots have been 100% inspected and all the defectives have been replaced by good units.

B-4.4 Calculation of AOQL

There are two ways to calculate the AOQL of a sampling plan. One is to calculate a series of AOQ values, as shown above, plot them on a graph and determine the maximum point on the curve. By this method we determine that the AOQL of the sampling plan called "C" (page 243) is approximately 2%. See Figure 237.

The same result could be obtained more rapidly by the following equation.

$$AOQL = \frac{y}{n} - \frac{y}{N}$$

where y is a factor depending on the acceptance number of the sampling plan as shown in Figure 238, n is the sample size and N is the lot size. The values in Figure 238 are taken from page 49 of the Dodge-Romig "Sampling Inspection Tables." See Reference No. 11.

251

c	0	1	2
y	0.368	0.841	1.372
c	3	4	5
y	1.946	2.544	3.172
c	6	7	8
y	3.810	4.465	5.150
c	9	10	11
y	5.836	6.535	7.234

Fig. 238. Table for values of "y," to be used in calculating AOQL.

This table can be used wherever we would normally use Poisson probabilities.

For the sampling plan called "C" (page 243),

$y = 0.368$ (because the acceptance number is zero).

$n = 18.$

Assume that the lot size is $N = 2000$.

$$AOQL = \frac{0.368}{18} - \frac{0.368}{2000} = .0204 - .0002$$

$$= .0202, \text{ or } 2.02\%$$

This agrees with the AOQ curve in Figure 237.

The following are the AOQL values for each of the sampling plans on page 243:

Plan	n	c	AOQL
A	165	1	0.47%
B	35	2	3.86%
C	18	0	2.02%
D	5	0	7.34%*
E	220	7	1.81%
F	100	4	2.41%
G	100	0	0.35%
H	25	1	3.32%

* If we used Binomial probabilities for this plan, the calculated AOQL would be 6.68% instead of 7.34%.

B-4.5 Classification of sampling plans according to their AOQL

Suppose we wish to group together plans having similar AOQL's. From the above list, we would group together Plans C and E, since both have AOQL's of approximately 2%.

These plans are not alike at the shoulder (the product they will accept). Neither are they alike at the tail (the product they will reject). Their only similarity is that, when they are used with 100% inspection of all the rejected lots, the outgoing product will not, on the average, be worse than 2%.

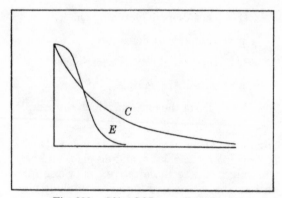

Fig. 239. 2% AOQL sampling plans.

When an engineer chooses a "2% AOQL sampling plan," he is choosing a plan which will limit the outgoing product, in the long run, to a 2% average or less. The outgoing quality may be, and frequently is, limited to some point much lower than the stated AOQL. For example, the curve in Figure 237 shows that if the submitted product were 20% defective, this particular plan would force the shop to do sufficient screening to cut it down (theoretically) to 0.5%. The plan imposes, under these circumstances, a much tighter standard of quality than the stated 2%.

The fact that a sampling plan is classified as "2% AOQL" does not tell the engineer anything about any part of the OC curve. He is not able to tell what quality of product will be regularly accepted, or what quality will be regularly rejected.

Just as it is possible to specify an AQL value or LTPD value (paragraphs B-4.1 and B-4.2)

AOQL SAMPLING TABLE

TABLE SA-2.5. Average Outgoing Quality Limit = 2.5%

Process Average, %	0–.05			06–.50			.51–1.00			1.01–1.50			1.51–2.00			2.01–2.50		
Lot Size	n	c	p_t, %	n	c	p_t, %	n	c	p_t, %	n	c	p_t, %	n	c	p_t, %	n	c	p_t, %
1–10	All	0	—	All	0	—	All	0	—	All	0	—	All	0	—	All	0	—
11–50	11	0	17.6	11	0	17.6	11	0	17.6	11	0	17.6	11	0	17.6	11	0	17.6
51–100	13	0	15.3	13	0	15.3	13	0	15.3	13	0	15.3	13	0	15.3	13	0	15.3
101–200	14	0	14.7	14	0	14.7	14	0	14.7	29	1	12.9	29	1	12.9	29	1	12.9
201–300	14	0	14.9	14	0	14.9	30	1	12.7	30	1	12.7	30	1	12.7	30	1	12.7
301–400	14	0	15.0	14	0	15.0	31	1	12.3	31	1	12.3	31	1	12.3	48	2	10.7
401–500	14	0	15.0	14	0	15.0	32	1	12.0	32	1	12.0	49	2	10.6	49	2	10.6
501–600	14	0	15.1	32	1	12.0	32	1	12.0	50	2	10.4	50	2	10.4	70	3	9.3
601–800	14	0	15.1	32	1	12.0	32	1	12.0	50	2	10.5	50	2	10.5	70	3	9.4
801–1000	15	0	14.2	33	1	11.7	33	1	11.7	50	2	10.6	70	3	9.4	90	4	8.5
1,001–2,000	15	0	14.2	33	1	11.7	55	2	9.3	75	3	8.8	95	4	8.0	120	5	7.6
2,001–3,000	15	0	14.2	33	1	11.8	55	2	9.4	75	3	8.8	120	5	7.6	145	6	7.2
3,001–4,000	15	0	14.3	33	1	11.8	55	2	9.5	100	4	7.9	125	5	7.4	195	8	6.6
4,001–5,000	15	0	14.3	33	1	11.8	75	3	8.9	100	4	7.9	*150	6	7.0	225	9	6.3
5,001–7,000	33	1	11.8	55	2	9.7	75	3	8.9	125	5	7.4	175	7	6.7	250	10	6.1
7,001–10,000	34	1	11.4	55	2	9.7	75	3	8.9	125	5	7.4	200	8	6.4	310	12	5.8
10,001–20,000	34	1	11.4	55	2	9.7	100	4	8.0	*150	6	7.0	260	10	6.0	425	16	5.3
20,001–50,000	34	1	11.4	55	2	9.7	100	4	8.0	180	7	6.7	345	13	5.5	640	23	4.8
50,001–100,000	34	1	11.4	80	3	8.4	125	5	7.4	235	9	6.1	435	16	5.2	800	28	4.5

n = Size of Sample; entry of "All" indicates that each piece in lot is to be inspected.
c = Allowable Defect Number for Sample.
p_t = Lot Tolerance Per Cent Defective corresponding to a Consumer's Risk (P_c) = 0.10.

* This plan appears also in Figure 236.

Fig. 240. Excerpt from "Sampling Inspection Tables" by Dodge and Romig: 2.5% AOQL. To use this table, determine (1) the usual lot size and (2) the "process average" (percent defective at which the product normally runs). The sample size is given in column "n" under the applicable process average, and the acceptance number is given in column "c."

In addition to having a stated AOQL (in this case, 2.5%), each of the above plans will have a particular value of "lot tolerance percent defective" or LTPD. This is given in the column marked "p_t %." While it is not a necessary part of the AOQL plan, this figure is often useful in showing how bad a lot might be and still have a 10% chance of being accepted. Note that the same sampling plan may be listed under AOQL and also LTPD (shown by asterisk and note).

so it is possible to specify an AOQL. When an AOQL is specified for a particular product, we try to select a sampling plan whose AOQL is equal to the specified value.

To make it easier to select plans on this basis, Dodge and Romig have published tables of sampling plans classified according to their AOQL's. See Reference No. 11. The values of AOQL range from 0.1% to 10% defective.

The plans in these tables are arranged in such a way that, if the engineer selects a plan under the correct "process average," he will minimize the total number of pieces which must be looked at, including both sampling and 100% inspection. Values of "$p_t\%$" (lot tolerance percent defective) are included as supplementary information.

These tables are useful wherever we are chiefly interested in setting a fixed maximum limit on outgoing quality and are willing to achieve this by a combination of sampling and 100% inspection. Both of the sampling plans shown in Figure 238 can be found in the Dodge-Romig AOQL Tables.

A typical AOQL sampling table is shown in Figure 240. The caption gives a general idea of how the table is used. For further information see Reference No. 11.

B-4.6 Precautions to be taken in using AOQL sampling plans

Every sampling plan can be classified in all three of the ways described above. The same sampling plan might be called a "1% AQL sampling plan," an "8% LTPD sampling plan" and (if all lots which fail to meet the acceptance number of the plan are inspected 100%) a "2.5% AOQL" sampling plan. Many of the sampling plans used at Western Electric are selected on the basis of AOQL rather than on the basis of AQL or LTPD.

Since AOQL plans involve a combination of sampling and 100% inspection, these plans are often subject to misinterpretation and misuse. Engineers and inspection supervisors should guard against the following errors.

(1) We sometimes hear of "AOQL sampling plans" being used in connection with destructive tests, or in Receiving Inspec-

tion where the rejected lots are junked, returned to the supplier or accepted on an outside limit basis, but where there is no intention whatever of doing 100% inspection on the lots which fail to meet the acceptance number of the plans. It should always be remembered that unless the prescribed 100% inspection is done, we will not get the protection promised by an AOQL sampling plan.

(2) If the product contains defects to begin with, an AOQL sampling plan will depend on the presence of the rejected lots, which have been made perfect by screening, to dilute the percentage of defectives which may still be present in the lots accepted. People using AOQL sampling plans sometimes make the mistake of sending the accepted lots to one customer (or user) and the rejected lots to another. The first customer may get highly defective product. Also, if the accepted lots are sent to the storeroom during the time when the rejected lots are being sorted and repaired, the product in the storeroom during that time may be much worse than the AOQL. The same thing may be true of accepted lots which are sent to the next Operating department to be assembled while the rejected lots are being gone over. Until the rejected lots catch up with the accepted lots and can be considered in combination with them, there is no guarantee that the product will be meeting the AOQL.

B-4.7 What the Operating organization should know about AOQL sampling plans

Operating people often assume that a "2% AOQL sampling plan" will accept product which is 2% defective. That is, if Inspection is using a 2% AOQL plan, and if Operating submits product which is actually 2% defective, they feel that all or most of the submitted product should pass the inspection plan. Engineers also frequently make this assumption in discussing suitable quality levels for sampling or in agreeing to the use of some specific proposed plan. However, unless the AOQL sampling plan is deliberately chosen with this in mind, a 2% plan may reject large portions of 2% defective product. The following example will show why it is necessary to restrict the choice of plans.

Suppose a sampling plan were to be chosen solely for its AOQL. The following plans will have an AOQL of 2% when used for lots of approximately 1000.

$$\text{(a) } n = 18, c = 0$$

$$\text{(b) } n = 40, c = 1$$

$$\text{(c) } n = 65, c = 2$$

$$\text{(d) } n = 90, c = 3$$

While all of these plans have a 2% AOQL, they will reject very different amounts of 2% defective product.

2% AOQL Sampling Plans	Approximate Percentage of Product Rejected (if product is running at 2% defective)
(a) $n = 18, c = 0$	30%
(b) $n = 40, c = 1$	19%
(c) $n = 65, c = 2$	14%
(d) $n = 90, c = 3$	11%

In all four cases the amount of product rejected is quite large. If the Operating department wishes to avoid these rejections, it will have to maintain a quality level considerably better than 2%.

To find how good the product must be in order to avoid rejection, proceed as follows:

(1) Plot the OC curve of the sampling plan in question.

(2) Find the point where the curve drops away from the 1.00 probability of acceptance.

(3) The corresponding percent defective is the point at which Operating must aim if it wishes to have its product accepted regularly by Inspection.

The following are the points at which Operat-

ing should aim in the case of the plans shown above.

2% AOQL Sampling Plans	Necessary Level of Quality to assure regular acceptance (where "regular acceptance" means acceptance about 98% of the time)
(a) $n = 18, c = 0$	0.1% defective
(b) $n = 40, c = 1$	0.5% defective
(c) $n = 65, c = 2$	0.9% defective
(d) $n = 90, c = 3$	1.1% defective

Both Operating and Engineering need to know this "target value" whenever Inspection is using AOQL sampling plans.

All four of the above plans are taken from the Dodge-Romig 2% AOQL Single Sampling Table. Plan (d) is the one recommended in the Table for product which is running 2% defective.

To guard against excessive rejections like those shown above, avoid choosing AOQL sampling plans from the incorrect column for "process average." Plot the OC curve for each sampling plan chosen, and determine a suitable target value for Operating as indicated above. If the target value is not one which can be met economically, it may be necessary to revise the choice of AOQL.

B-5 SAMPLING PLANS FOR CONTINUOUS PROCESSES

Sampling plans may be divided into three principal types.

(1) Plans for continuous processes.

(2) Plans for lot-by-lot inspection.

(3) Special plans which involve, in a sense, lot-by-lot inspection but which are applied to a series of lots considered as a group.

The plans to be considered in this Sub-section are of the continuous type.

Continuous process sampling plans are used for production processes where no separate "lots" exist. They are generally used on conveyors but are applicable to any continuously-running operation where we do not wish to accumulate the product into lots for purposes of inspection. All of the continuous sampling plans which are available at present are of the AOQL type.

B-5.1 General idea of continuous sampling

Suppose we have a continuous flow of product which is 4% defective. We begin to inspect this product, classifying each unit in order as defective or non-defective. If O represents a non-defective unit and X a defective one, the record of inspection results would be similar to the following:

OOOOX OOOOOOOOX OX OOOOOOOOOO

OOOOOOOOOOOX OOOOOOOOOOOOOOOO

OOOOOOOOOX OOOOOOOOOOOOOOOO

In lot-by-lot inspection we would count the total number of defectives in a sample from a given lot. In continuous inspection we have no clearly defined lot. Therefore, instead of counting the total number of defectives, we count the number of good units between two successive bad ones. It is possible to set up an acceptance standard for a sampling plan in terms of some required number of successive units which must be found "clear of defects" in order to permit the product to be accepted.

The number which must be found clear of defects is called the "clearing sample," i.

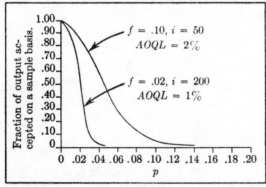

Fig. 241. OC curves for continuous sampling plans CSP-1.

B-5.2 Operation of the continuous sampling plan CSP-1

The operation of a continuous sampling plan is shown on page 257.

This sampling plan is known as "CSP-1." It calls for clearing when a single defect is found. Other continuous sampling plans (CSP-2 and CSP-3) do not call for clearing on the occurrence of a single defect during sampling, provided no further defect is found in a specified number of units thereafter. Details of these plans can be found in Reference No. 8.

In continuous sampling there is no fixed sample size, "n." Instead, the inspector selects a specified fraction of the product, "f." He uses a clearing sample, "i," to determine whether it is satisfactory to ship the product without clearing. The two values "f" and "i" determine the characteristics of the plan and are used in calculating its OC curve. The OC curve shows the percentage of total production that will be accepted on a sampling basis.

Figure 241 shows OC curves for two continuous sampling plans which have AOQL's of 1% and 2% respectively. The 2% plan may be compared with other 2% AOQL plans—for example, C and E on page 243.

The curves on page 258 are used (in place of sampling tables) to select continuous sampling plans CSP-1. Select the curve representing the desired AOQL (in percent). Then read "f" in percent on the scale at the left, and "i" in units of product on the scale at the bottom.

B-5.3 Field of application for continuous sampling

Continuous sampling plans are suitable for much wider application than the obviously continuous or conveyorized processes. In modern manufacture most of the operations are essentially continuous in nature, and when product is accumulated into "lots" it is mainly for convenience in inspection, handling and shipment. Wherever the product lots are formed artificially and for convenience, continuous sampling could be employed in place of lot-by-lot sampling.

As in the case of any AOQL sampling plan, protection depends primarily on the sorting or "clearing." Further information on continuous sampling can be found in Reference No. 8.

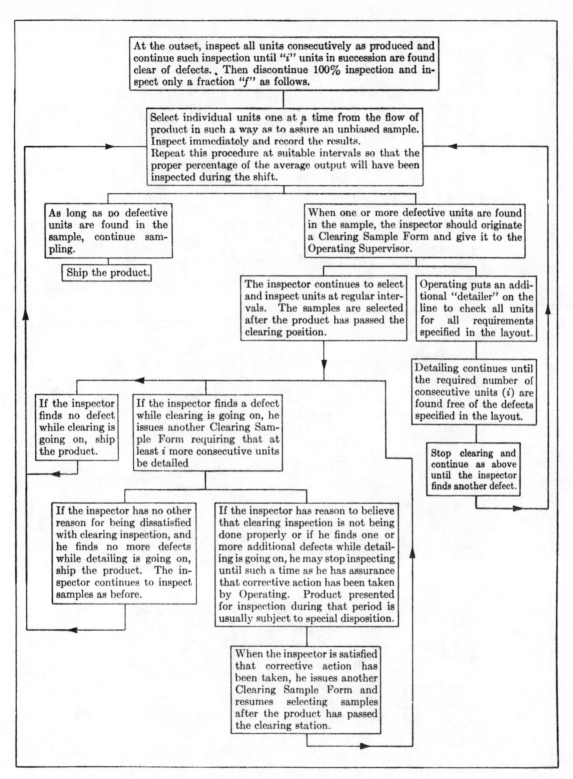

At the outset, inspect all units consecutively as produced and continue such inspection until "i" units in succession are found clear of defects. Then discontinue 100% inspection and inspect only a fraction "f" as follows.

Select individual units one at a time from the flow of product in such a way as to assure an unbiased sample. Inspect immediately and record the results.
Repeat this procedure at suitable intervals so that the proper percentage of the average output will have been inspected during the shift.

As long as no defective units are found in the sample, continue sampling.

Ship the product.

When one or more defective units are found in the sample, the inspector should originate a Clearing Sample Form and give it to the Operating Supervisor.

The inspector continues to select and inspect units at regular intervals. The samples are selected after the product has passed the clearing position.

Operating puts an additional "detailer" on the line to check all units for all requirements specified in the layout.

Detailing continues until the required number of consecutive units (i) are found free of the defects specified in the layout.

If the inspector finds no defect while clearing is going on, ship the product.

If the inspector finds a defect while clearing is going on, he issues another Clearing Sample Form requiring that at least i more consecutive units be detailed

Stop clearing and continue as above until the inspector finds another defect.

If the inspector has no other reason for being dissatisfied with clearing inspection, and he finds no more defects while detailing is going on, ship the product. The inspector continues to inspect samples as before.

If the inspector has reason to believe that clearing inspection is not being done properly or if he finds one or more additional defects while detailing is going on, he may stop inspecting until such a time as he has assurance that corrective action has been taken by Operating. Product presented for inspection during that period is usually subject to special disposition.

When the inspector is satisfied that corrective action has been taken, he issues another Clearing Sample Form and resumes selecting samples after the product has passed the clearing station.

Fig. 242. Operation of a continuous sampling plan: CSP-1.

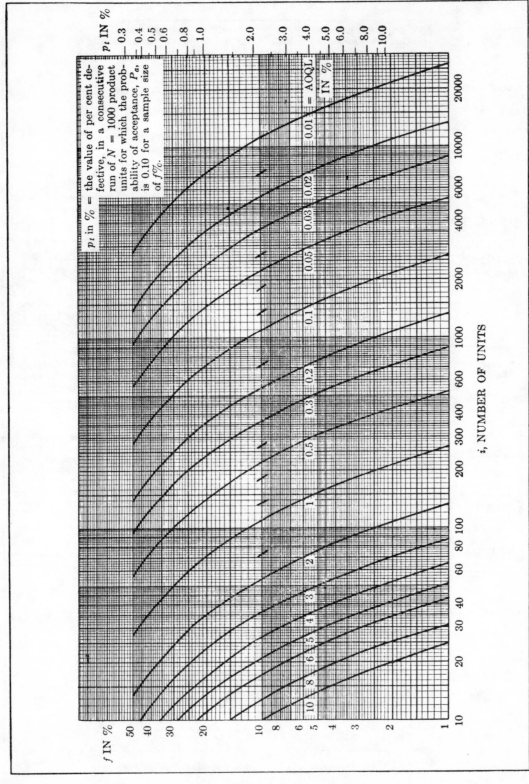

Fig. 243. Curves for selecting continuous sampling plans CSP-1.

258

B-6 SAMPLING PLANS FOR LOT-BY-LOT INSPECTION

Lot-by-lot sampling plans may be used wherever the product to be inspected can be conveniently accumulated into lots. A "lot" is defined as a collection of similar pieces submitted at one time for inspection. The number of pieces in the lot is called the "lot size." The lot size may be the number specified on the delivery ticket, or it may be simply the number produced in one hour or one shift or some other natural division of time. The "lot" to be used for any specific sampling plan should be clearly stated in the Inspection Layout.

Lot-by-lot plans are called "single sampling" if acceptance or rejection is based on a single sample, and "double" or "multiple sampling" if there is provision under certain circumstances for taking a second or subsequent samples.

The "sample size" in a lot-by-lot inspection plan is the number of parts selected at random from the lot. In lot-by-lot sampling this is always a definite number, never a percentage. The sample size is designated as SS or "n."

The "acceptance number" in a lot-by-lot sampling plan is the maximum number of defective units (or defects) in the sample or samples under consideration that will permit the acceptance of the inspection lot. The acceptance number is designated as AN or "c."

B-6.1 Description of single, double and multiple sampling

Single sampling means that the decision to accept or reject is based on the inspection of a single sample.

Double sampling means that inspection of the first sample leads to a decision to accept, reject or take a second sample. Inspection of a second sample, when required, leads to a decision to accept or reject.

Sequential sampling means that after each unit is inspected, a decision is made to accept, reject or inspect another unit. Inspection is continued as long as may be necessary to reach a decision to accept or reject. In some cases, a sequential plan provides for taking a series of *groups of units*, rather than a series of individual units. This is called "group sequential sampling."

Multiple sampling is a form of group sequential sampling in which the plan is "truncated"; that is, a maximum limit is set on the number of groups which need to be inspected in order to reach a decision to accept or reject.

In all of these plans the inspector is given specific instructions on how to dispose of the product on the basis of the findings in his sample. Diagrams showing the operation of single, double and unit sequential sampling plans are given in Figures 244–246.

A *single sampling plan* gives the inspector one sample size and one acceptance number. If a "rejection number" is stated, it is simply one more than the acceptance number.

Sample	Acceptance Number	Rejection Number
110	4	5

A *double sampling plan* gives the inspector two sample sizes (n_1 and n_2) and two acceptance numbers (c_1 and c_2). The second acceptance number applies to both samples combined. If a rejection number is stated, it is one more than the acceptance number for the first and second samples combined.

Sample		Acceptance Number	Rejection Number
n_1	75	2	8
n_2	150	—	—
Combined	225	7	8

A *multiple sampling plan* gives the inspector a series of sample sizes, and for each of these an acceptance number and a rejection number. The inspector takes the first sample and compares his findings with both the acceptance and rejection numbers. If the number of defectives (or defects) is equal to or less than the acceptance number, he accepts. If it is equal to or greater than the rejection number, he rejects. If it falls between the acceptance and rejection numbers, he must inspect another sample. As in the case of double sampling, the acceptance and rejection numbers apply to the combined samples.

Sample		Acceptance Number	Rejection Number
First	30	—	3
Second	30	1	4
Third	30	2	5
Fourth	30	4	6
Fifth	30	5	7
Sixth	30	6	8
Seventh	30	7	8

The "unit sequential" sampling plan shown in Figure 246 is similar to multiple sampling except that each sample consists of one unit.

The advantages of single sampling are:

(1) A constant inspection load (provided rejected lots are sent back to Operating).

(2) Simplicity of administration.

(3) Better control of inspection piece rates.

(4) Low cost of selecting samples.

(5) Smallest amount of record keeping.

The advantages of double sampling are:

(1) Smaller average amount of inspection, particularly when the incoming product is very good or very bad.

(2) A possible psychological advantage associated with the idea of giving the lot a "second chance."

The advantages of sequential sampling are similar to those of double sampling.

Sequential sampling usually requires the smallest average amount of inspection in the long run.

In any comparison of single, double and multiple sampling plans, care should be taken to assure that the plans being compared have similar OC curves. Some of the apparent advantages of a particular plan may be at the cost of less protection for the producer or consumer or both.

B-6.2 Factors to be considered in determining the size of a lot

The choice of lot size is important in determining the economy of a lot-by-lot sampling plan. For a given quality protection the sample will generally be a smaller proportion of the lot as the lot size increases. There is, therefore, a definite advantage in making the lots large. However, the following limitations should be considered in determining the most economical size of lots.

(1) *Physical considerations involved in accumulating, storing, handling and selecting samples from very large lots.* The size of inspection areas, the size and number of storage areas, and the available facilities for handling product between these areas must be considered.

(2) *Disruption of the orderly flow of product caused by accumulation of a large lot.* The product being inspected is usually scheduled for immediate stocking or shipment. Supplies of parts and assemblies may be unduly delayed if we wait for the accumulation of very large lots.

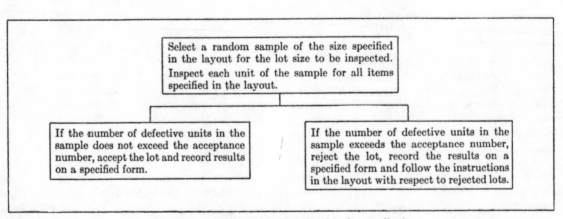

Fig. 244. Lot-by-lot sampling plan (single sampling).

(3) *The effect of mixing product from different cause systems.* Large lots increase the difficulty of selecting a random sample. They also make it difficult or impossible to identify the source of work and tend to prevent the efficient tracing of causes.

(4) *Difficulties encountered when large lots are rejected.* Losses and other difficulties increase when large lots are shipped back to suppliers or have to be held for detailing or rerouted to other departments for repairing or scrapping.

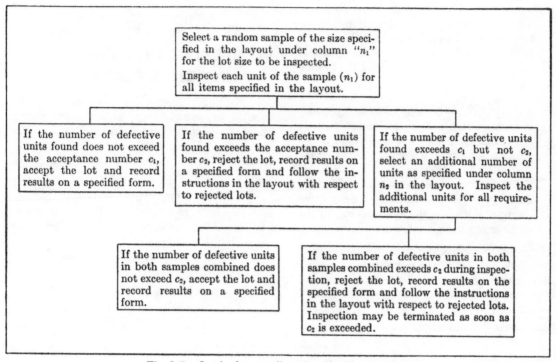

Fig. 245. Lot-by-lot sampling plan (double sampling).

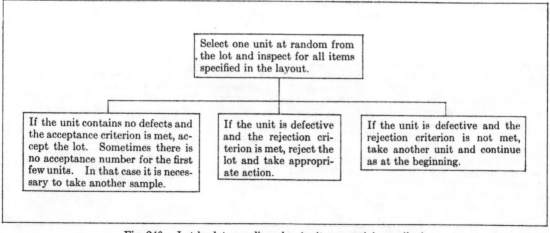

Fig. 246. Lot-by-lot sampling plan (unit sequential sampling).

261

(5) *Delay in picking up a prompt warning of trouble because of having fewer samples.* The engineer and the shop often rely on the acceptance procedure to give them a warning when something has gone wrong. This can sometimes be as important as the mathematical limitation of defectives which is provided by the plan. The delay we can expect to experience before a warning of trouble is given is directly related to the number of samples taken. The use of large lots and therefore fewer samples tends to increase the delay, with the following bad effects:

During the time of delay more bad product may be made. This can result in new costs, including the cost of disposal or repair, possible shortage of critical materials, and waste of valuable time. One such unnecessary delay could result in such added cost to the job that it would render quite unimportant the calculated saving in the number of pieces inspected.

In order to control the amount of inspection performed in connection with lot-by-lot sampling, the engineer should specify the desired or normal lot size in the manufacturing layout.

The inspection layout need then provide only for the usual range of lot sizes that will be submitted for inspection. Where process control is used in the shop, inspection lot sizes should be related to the process control activities. One of the by-products of Operating control charts is that they make it possible for Inspection to obtain more homogeneous and more suitably-sized lots.

B-7 SPECIAL TYPES OF SAMPLING PLANS

While most inspection problems can be handled by using either continuous sampling plans or lot-by-lot sampling plans, as shown in Sub-sections B-5 and B-6, occasionally the need arises for a special type of plan. Among such plans are the following:

Chain sampling plans—Reference No. 10
Skip-lot sampling plans—Reference No. 9
Variables acceptance plans—Reference No. 4
Narrowed limit plans—References No. 34 and 43

Frequently it is found that Inspection can

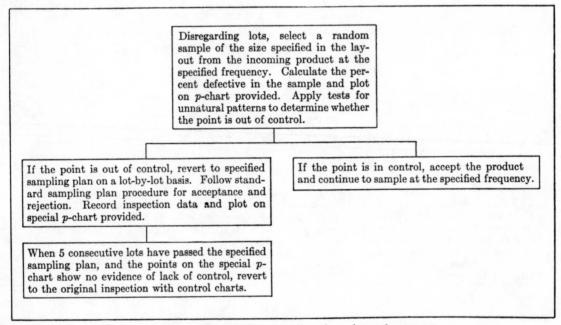

Fig. 247. Control chart sampling plan using *p*-charts.

benefit by using a control chart instead of the more usual type of plan. When control charts are used for acceptance or rejection, rather than for process control, they are known as "control chart sampling plans" rather than as "process control charts." A plan of this type is shown in Figure 247. See also the plans for "Minimum" or "Audit" inspection on page 274.

Any type of chart may be used: $\bar{X}$ and R chart, p-chart, c-chart, chart for individual measurements, etc.

When control charts are used for acceptance purposes, it is necessary to specify

(1) What shall be taken to be evidence of unsatisfactory quality.

(2) What action shall be taken with respect to (a) the product from which the sample was taken, (b) the previous product and (c) the subsequent product.

(3) What shall be used as a criterion for deciding that the chart is back in control.

One commonly used procedure is indicated in Figure 247. In critical cases the engineer may instruct the shop (or the inspector) to do 100% inspection of all product associated with an out-of-control point on the chart.

Note that this is quite different from the use of control charts for process control. In process control it may only be necessary to correct the process with reasonable promptness. It is not usually necessary to sort the product associated with out-of-control samples.

B-8 PROPER GROUPING OF INSPECTION ITEMS

Theoretically, sampling plans should be applied to one characteristic at a time. However, it is permissible to group inspection items for convenience provided certain conditions are met. The principal condition is that it must be possible to treat the group of characteristics as if they were one. Failure to keep this point in mind is responsible for many of the errors made in acceptance sampling.

Grouping a number of items on one sampling plan may simplify the inspector's job and make it faster. Inspection records are also reduced in number, since the inspector is required to keep separate records for each sampling plan used. In Final Inspection it is sometimes possible to use more generous AOQL's for a group of items than if the items were divided into several plans.

Grouping of inspection items, however, requires careful study. The result of each suggested grouping should be carefully examined in the light of its effect on both Inspection and Operating. Inappropriate groupings may result in unnecessary interference with production and may tend to increase Operating and Inspection costs.

In general, avoid grouping together defects with different degrees of seriousness; characteristics that require widely different inspection times; defects that occur frequently with defects that occur very seldom. Remember that sampling plans have to be designed to give protection under the most unfavorable conditions, and this means that they may be forced to reject a certain number of normally acceptable lots. To minimize the cost of screening such lots it is advisable not to include too many items in one group. *Do not include more items in one group than the shop will be able to screen for conveniently when a lot is rejected.*

In handling defects having different degrees of seriousness, first group the defects into two or more classes as follows:

Critical • Major • Minor.

The "demerit" lists issued by Quality Assurance (see page 270 and Reference No. 36) can be used as a guide in judging the seriousness of each defect. Arrange to keep the minor defects separated from the major and critical defects as much as possible.

Avoid grouping troublesome items (most likely to cause rejection) with other items which rarely cause trouble. Lump together items that (a) occur very infrequently or (b) can be readily checked at one time. Inspection piece rates should also be consulted in arranging suitable groups.

B-9 HOW TO SELECT A QUALITY LEVEL FOR SAMPLING

The most difficult decision which an engineer has to make in connection with sampling is the choice of an appropriate quality level. The choice of a suitable level depends on finding the proper balance between quality and cost. Any information which the engineer has on (1) quality requirements, or (2) normal manufacturing operations and costs, will help him to work out this balance satisfactorily.

B-9.1 Quality requirements

Quality requirements are defined, in one way or another, by the organizations or people who are to use the product. Sometimes these requirements are stated very explicitly. Sometimes they are only implied. Those responsible for setting up inspection plans are often forced to estimate the probable needs of the user on the basis of judgment and past experience. The more specifically the needs of the user are defined, the easier it is, in general, to make a decision on the quality level to be used in sampling.

At Western Electric we usually distinguish two different situations:

(a) Final inspection of finished product which is ready to be shipped to an outside customer.

(b) Inspection of sub-assemblies, piece parts and raw materials which are to be used by other departments within Western.

Final Inspection (product to be shipped to customer)

In this case, overall quality requirements have probably been established in the past by Quality Assurance. These standards are expressed numerically, usually in the form of "demerits-per-unit." It is possible for the engineer to obtain the numerical standards from Quality Assurance and convert these directly into appropriate levels to be used in Final Inspection. The details of this are beyond the scope of the present Handbook but full instructions are given in Reference No. 46 (Since this reference contains proprietary information it is available for use only in connection with Company work). These instructions tell how to set up plans for Final Inspection which will meet the "demerit" standards and still provide for maximum economy in inspection. The plans provide for the use of Tight, Normal, Reduced and Minimum inspection levels.

Where demerit standards have not been established for a product, proceed as in the case of piece parts or sub-assemblies.

Sub-assemblies, piece parts and raw materials

For sub-assemblies, piece parts and raw materials the quality requirements are not so clearly defined. The engineer's principal information comes from:

- Complaints from the user (the Assembly Department or other department which must process the material).
- Records of dropouts at subsequent operations.
- The process average (that is, the actual percent defective in the product) during a time when subsequent operations were reasonably free from trouble.

The last point is particularly important. If the process has been delivering product 4% defective for many months without causing trouble, it is not advisable to institute a 1% LTPD sampling plan.

Unless there is a reason for doing otherwise, choose (a) a sampling plan with an OC curve related to the quality regularly produced by the shop in the past (that is, a plan that will accept the normal product practically all of the time); or (b) a plan of the AOQL or LTPD type which is related to the quality which has been accepted in the past by the using organization. For example, if the customer is willing to accept product 3% defective on the average, use a 3% AOQL plan. If the customer is willing to accept product 3% defective only occasionally, use a 3% LTPD plan.

If the engineer knows that there have been quality complaints associated with the product, he may need to tighten the quality standard in order to reduce the complaints. If it is difficult to establish whether there is a real connection between the complaints and the specific requirements to be included in the sampling plan, the engineer should get information on this by making a process capability study.

In general, use tight plans for critical characteristics or characteristics easy to control, and looser plans for others. The demerit lists prepared by Quality Assurance can be used as a guide to the recognized importance of many characteristics.

B-9.2 Cost considerations

The cost considerations which the engineer should keep in mind are the following:

- What is the process average or current level of percent defective?
- Does this process average represent the real capability of the process? That is, is the shop using control charts and are the shop people working with the charts effectively to bring the process into control?
- If the shop has not yet started to use control charts, it may actually be possible to save money by running the process with fewer defectives. In that case the engineer should adopt tentative quality standards for his sampling plans, using his best engineering judgment, and at the same time see that control charts are installed immediately to improve the process average.
- If the shop is using control charts and the process is running near its capability, the engineer should try to set up sampling plans which will accept the normal product. See Paragraph B-4.7. If the OC curve is not carefully chosen, the shop may be harassed with continual rejections even when the process is being run properly.

B-9.3 Conflict between quality requirements and cost considerations

If the engineer finds that the quality requirements are tighter than the normal process capability, he should attempt to resolve this conflict by some economical means. This may include instructing the Operating people to sort all or part of the product prior to sending it to Inspection. However, operational sorting is expensive, and the engineer should make certain that it is really necessary before specifying it in a layout. In most cases the process capability can be improved beyond any previous expectations through the joint efforts of a Quality Control Team.

B-10 FACTORS DETERMINING THE CHOICE OF A PARTICULAR PLAN

The following is a summary of the factors to be considered in choosing an inspection plan.

(1) First consider the number of characteristics to be checked during inspection.

(2) Decide on the way in which these characteristics should be grouped.

(3) For each group, decide on a suitable quality level in terms of percent defective, number of defects per unit or (in the case of variables inspection) the required center or spread of the distribution.

(4) Indicate whether this quality standard is to represent an AQL value (acceptable most of the time), an LTPD value (rejectable most of the time) or an AOQL.

(5) Determine the process capability (or normal process average) for each group.

(6) In lot-by-lot sampling, decide on the most suitable size for the lots.

(7) Consult an appropriate set of sampling tables (or sampling curves) and select a combination of sample size and acceptance number. Immediately obtain or plot the OC curve for the chosen plan.

(8) As far as possible make any necessary adjustments between the process capability and the OC curve of the plan.

(9) In any case where control charts are being used in the shop, consider the possibility of substituting a control chart acceptance procedure as outlined on page 274.

PART C
General Instruction for Inspection

The following is a general instruction for inspectors which will apply to most inspections performed in Western Electric plants. All members of the Inspection Organization, including inspectors and their supervisors, should be familiar with this instruction.

Departures from these procedures are sometimes made necessary by special circumstances. Such departures are usually covered in the individual Inspection Layout.

Instructions for Inspection

1.0 GENERAL

1.1 Purpose

1.11 The purpose of this instruction is to provide general information on inspection procedures and to supplement the inspection information given in the Manufacturing and Inspection Layouts.

1.12 All inspection should be carried out in accordance with this instruction unless otherwise stated in the Inspection Layout.

1.2 Definitions

1.21 Defect
A "defect" is a deviation from a single requirement.

1.22 Defective
A "defective" is a unit of product having one or more defects.

1.23 Lot Size
The lot size is the number of similar parts submitted to Inspection in one group.

1.24 Sample Size
The sample size is the number of parts to be selected at random from the product. In continuous sampling the sample size is expressed as a percentage.

1.25 Acceptance Number
The acceptance number is the maximum number of defective units (or defects) that may be found in a sample without (a) rejecting the product or (b) initiating 100% inspection.

1.26 Clearing Sample
In continuous sampling the clearing sample is the number of successive parts that must be found free of defects before 100% inspection can be discontinued and sampling can be resumed.

1.27 Obvious Defect
An obvious defect is a defect that is immediately apparent and does not require close scrutiny on the part of the inspector.

2.0 WHEN TO INSPECT
The points in the sequence of manufacturing operations where inspection should be performed are indicated in the Manufacturing Layout.

3.0 SELECTION OF SAMPLES

3.1 Random Samples

3.11 Samples should be selected at random from the submitted product.

267

3.12 In lot-by-lot inspection this means that each unit in the lot should have an equal chance of being selected as the first item in the sample, and after the selection of the first item each remaining unit should have an equal chance of being selected, and so on.

3.13 In continuous sampling, where the units come to the inspector in the order of production, it is assumed that they are already arranged in a random order. The inspector should therefore select individual units (or small groups of units) from the continuous flow of product in such a manner as to assure an unbiased sample.

3.2 *Lot-by-lot Inspection*
Where the product to be inspected consists of a specific number of separate articles or pieces, each sample should be a group of articles taken at random from different locations throughout the lot. The units should be selected without regard to any distinguishable physical differences between the units.

3.3 *Continuous Sampling*
Where the product to be inspected consists of a portion of a continuous flow of product, as on a conveyor, the inspector should select enough units to make up the specified sample by choosing the units one at a time or in small groups from the continuous flow of product. The units should be selected without regard to any distinguishable physical differences between the units, and the intervals between the selection of units should be determined in such a manner as to assure that the sample is unbiased.

3.4 *Control Chart Acceptance Sampling*
Where the product to be inspected consists of the pieces made during the last half hour, the last shift, or some other specified time interval, each sample should be a group of articles taken at random from different locations throughout the quantity of product. The units should be selected without regard to any distinguishable physical differences between the units.

3.5 *Verification Sampling*
Where the product to be inspected is the immediate portion of the output which is being produced at the time when the inspector takes his sample (as in verifying an operator's control chart), each sample should consist of a group of units produced consecutively. The time of selecting the sample should be determined in a random manner in such a way as to assure an unbiased sample.

4.0 *INSPECTION OF SAMPLES*

4.1 *General Procedure*
Each unit of the sample should be inspected for all items listed in the Inspection Layout, using the drawings and the methods or facilities specified. Each unit should also be inspected for obvious defects not specified. See definition of "obvious defect" in Paragraph 1.27.

4.2 *Workmanship Standards*
The degree to which workmanship defects may be present without violating standards of acceptable workmanship should be defined by the product engineer. If necessary, the product engineer should authorize the use of "marginal quality units" to be maintained and stored by the Inspection organization. To obtain such standards the Inspection organization may select units of product considered marginal, acceptable or rejectable, and submit them to the product engineer. The engineer, if he agrees with the quality evaluation, should identify, date and initial the submitted samples. These units may be voided or replaced at any time by the product engineer.

4.3 *Formal Observational Standards*
Formal observational standards are generally furnished where necessary by BTL. The use of such standards should be specified by number on the Inspection Layout. All units of the sample should be compared with these standards.

4.4 *Inspection Records*
The results of inspection should be recorded

on suitable forms as specified in the layout. The following information should be recorded:

1. Lot size (in lot-by-lot inspection.)
2. Sample size.
3. Number and kind of defects.
4. Disposition of lot or product.
5. Identification of part or apparatus.
6. Identification of inspector.

A separate inspection record should be maintained for each sampling plan used, and for each group of items inspected under a common sampling plan. The separate records may appear on the same sheet, provided it is possible to identify them separately.

Records of re-inspection (that is, the inspection of lots re-submitted after they have once been rejected) should be kept separate from the records of initial inspection.

5.0 ACTION TO BE TAKEN WHEN DEFECTS ARE FOUND

5.1 General

When the acceptance criterion of the sampling plan is exceeded, the inspector should take action as specified in the layout.

5.2 Obvious Defects

Obvious defects not listed in the layout should be set aside for repair. They should not, however, be counted against the acceptance number of the sampling plan. For acceptance purposes, only the listed defects should be counted.

If obvious defects not listed in the layout are numerous or appear consistently in the samples, this condition should be called to the attention of the Operating organization and the product engineer.

5.3 Defective Parts in the Sample

All defective parts found in the inspector's sample should be plainly marked and should be returned to the Operating organization. The Operating organization should either repair or junk the parts.

5.4 "Outside Limit" or Non-Conforming Material

When investigation reveals that rejected material can be used advantageously, the lots should be treated in accordance with standard Manufacturing Instructions. Notification of any special treatment of rejected lots should be forwarded promptly to the Operating organization.

5.5 Rejected Lots (in lot-by-lot inspection)

5.51 Rejected lots should be assigned a serial number and recorded on a specified form. The serial number should also appear on the ticket which accompanies the lot when it is returned to the Operating Department.

5.52 The Operating organization receiving the rejected material should sort out all defective units and repair or junk all those parts which fail to meet requirements.

5.6 Clearing (in continuous sampling)

When clearing becomes necessary under a continuous sampling plan, the Operating organization is required to sort the product 100% until the specified number of units has been found free of defects. Whenever a defect is found, the sorter should start over in counting the satisfactory units.

5.7 Reinspection

Sorted product, when resubmitted for inspection, should be sampled in accordance with the Inspection Layout involved. The sample should be inspected for all requirements specified in the layout. The acceptance number for previously rejected product is usually specified to be zero.

Layouts

In addition to the general instructions given above, all inspection activities should be covered in formal Inspection Layouts. The layout should include:

(1) Identification data describing the product, operation, etc.

(2) Points in the sequence of operations where inspection is to be performed.

(3) Sample size, lot size and acceptance number (or clearing interval).

(4) Method of selecting the sample.

(5) Characteristics to be checked (properly grouped).

(6) Method of measurement or classification.

(7) Information to be recorded or plotted.

(8) Action to be taken.

If certain of these items are covered adequately in the General Instruction, the layout may refer to the General Instruction instead of covering the points in detail.

Quality Assurance

The instructions above do not cover the Quality Assurance continuing independent audit sampling of products and services sold by the Company at the point where they are ready for release to the customer. Quality Assurance appraisals are in terms of demerits. These are compared with certain established standards, also in terms of demerits, in accordance with the demerit system of "quality rating."

Since Quality Assurance is not part of the quality control program, no attempt is made in this Handbook to describe the system of quality audit rating. For information on these procedures see References No. 36 and 46 (Since these two references contain proprietary information their distribution is limited to AT&T personnel, however, a copy of the copyrighted booklet "Quality Assurance in Western Electric" is available from the Company upon request). The former is a complete description from the point of view of Quality Assurance. The latter is a simple explanation from the point of view of Quality Control.

The standards and definitions established by Quality Assurance are often used in planning quality control programs.

Inspection Dept.	1782 (3)	Inspection Layout No. P-457954-A
Results Dept.	1721	Issue Date 9/1
Operating Dept.	1732	Replacing Issue 6/27
Insp. Control Dept.	5326 (2)	Inspect in accordance with General Instruction No. ----.

Defect Code	Requirement	Equipment
	SAMPLING SCHEME SA2	
	Applies to Groups I and II individually	

Lot Size	SS	AN
1,000– 7,000	42	1
7,001–50,000	70	2

Group I

Defect Code	Requirement	Equipment
1	Secure clinching	Visual & by feel
3	Springs to be flat on front insulator (at leading edge)	Visual & .006" feeler

Group II

Defect Code	Requirement	Equipment
101	Incomplete	Visual
102	Burrs	Visual
103	Cracked insulators and lugs	Visual
105	Slivers	Visual
112	Oil excessive	Visual
113	Foreign material	Visual
114	Bent springs	Visual

Fig. 248. Example of inspection layout: AOQL sampling. The designation "SA2" stands for single sampling AOQL, 2%. SS is the sample size; AN is the acceptance number. The numbers beside the defects refer to a list describing possible defects which is furnished to the inspector.

LOT BY LOT RECORD OF STATISTICAL SAMPLING INSPECTION

INSPECTION SECTION _____

MATERIAL INSPECTED _____

INSPECTION OPERATIONS _____

OPERATING DEPT. OPERATIONS _____   OPER. DEPT. NO. _____

LIST OF DEFECTS 1st SAMPLE

AOQL ____ %

DEFECT — NO. / CHGE. / CLASS

OPERATOR OR GROUP NUMBER
INSPECTOR'S CLOCK NO.
DISPOSITION OF LOT PASS. REJECT. ETC.
REMARK NUMBER

	YEAR / DATE	CODE OR P. NO.	TOTAL AMOUNT IN LOTS	SAMPLE INSPECTION — 1st SAMPLE TOTAL	DEFEC-TIVES	TOTAL SAMPLE TOTAL	DEFEC-TIVES	DETAILED INSPECTION TOTAL	DEFECTIVES
1									
2									
3									
4									
5									
6									
7									
8									
9									
10									
11									
12									
13									

Fig. 249. Form for recording inspection data: Lot-by-lot sampling. In continuous sampling, a form is provided which shows the results on each unit (or group of units) inspected. Colored squares may be used to show the occurrence of defects, the period of "clearing" by Operating, etc.

PART D
Inspection Levels

<hr>

For most Western Electric products the final quality requirements are necessarily very strict. This results in setting standards for Final Inspection which are often extremely tight. While these tight standards may be necessary in periods of trouble, it should not be necessary to inspect to such severe standards during periods when the process is in a normal state of control. For this reason engineers frequently specify more than one set of sampling plans to be applied to the same product.

The tight plans which may be necessary in emergency are known as Tight Inspection plans. Looser plans to be used in normal periods are called Normal, Reduced and Minimum (or Audit) Inspection plans. In general, the better the process control, the more it is possible to relax the plans for inspection.

The following is one frequently used method of providing for different inspection levels. It applies to a case where the quality standard is expressed in terms of AOQL. It is assumed that AOQL standards have been selected previously as described on page 264.

In the case of finished product, AOQL's may be calculated from the official Quality Assurance quality rates as explained in Reference No. 46.

The engineer begins by selecting a plan for Tight Inspection. From this he derives the other levels in succession, as shown in the following steps:

(1) Tight Inspection

Select a sampling plan whose AOQL is the same as the required quality standard. Call this Tight Inspection (sometimes referred to as Level 1). Here the inspection itself is intended to give complete protection against unsatisfactory quality. There is no reliance on the shop's process control.

A plan of this type usually requires very large samples. Since it has to be designed to give adequate protection in emergency, it may also reject, during normal periods, a considerable quantity of the shop's normal product. To avoid this, set up a second plan as shown in step (2).

(2) Normal Inspection

Select a sampling plan whose AOQL is twice as large as the required quality level. Call this Normal Inspection (sometimes known as Level 2). This inspection is intended to do the following:

(a) Detect a sudden or gradual breakdown in the shop's process control, at which point Inspection should be shifted onto the Tight Inspection basis.
(b) Protect against an unusual deterioration of quality by direct rejection of lots.

Normal Inspection implies a certain amount of knowledge of, or confidence in, the shop's process control. The primary protection, however, remains in the hands of the Inspection department.

While this inspection plan will call for smaller samples than were required in step (1), and will not usually reject a large amount of normal satisfactory product, it may still be possible to reduce inspection further as shown in step (3).

(3) Reduced Inspection

Select a sampling plan whose AOQL is three times as large as the required quality standard. Call this Reduced Inspection (sometimes known as Level 3). This inspection is intended to detect a sudden or gradual breakdown in the shop's process control, at which point inspection should be shifted onto the Tight Inspection basis. It implies a definite degree of confidence in the shop's process control.

Reduced Inspection plans call for very small samples and consequently offer little protection by means of direct rejection of lots. Protection comes primarily from knowledge of shop control. If necessary, inspection can be reduced still further as shown in step (4).

(4) Minimum (or Audit) Inspection

This type of plan may be used wherever process control charts are being used in the shop and where these charts can be expected, under normal circumstances, to show reasonably good control. The inspection is merely an audit, by the inspector, of the shop's own process controls. Under this system, the AOQL is considered unimportant as long as proper control is maintained. Inspection takes only a "verification sample" at specified intervals and plots the result on the chart used by the shop.

This is called Minimum (or Audit) Inspection and is sometimes referred to as Level 4.

As long as the Inspection samples could reasonably be expected to be part of the same statistical pattern shown by the shop, and as long as the shop chart remains in reasonably good control, this indicates that the process is running as it should and that there is no essential conflict between Operating and Inspection findings. The shop chart is therefore used as the basis for accepting product. In event of conflict between Operating and Inspection results, or if the pattern changes and is found to be out of control, Inspection reverts to the Normal or Tight Inspection plans described in step (2) or step (1). Normal or Tight Inspection is continued until the conflict is resolved.

This inspection can be used for single characteristics, groups of characteristics or entire products where it is possible to place reliance on process control. It tends to call for extremely small Inspection samples and at the same time furnishes a high degree of assurance because of the pattern on the control chart. The details of acceptance or rejection for this type of plan are provided specifically in the Inspection Layout.

By selecting an appropriate inspection level to begin with, and providing suitable means for changing the inspection level in accordance with the state of process control, the engineer will be able to reduce or minimize his inspection costs.

The following is a summary of the steps to be taken in keeping inspection costs low.

(1) Set up process controls in the Operating organization (including sorting by Operating if necessary) such that the product that leaves Operating will, under normal conditions, meet the shipped quality standards.

(2) For normal use give Inspection a sampling plan which calls for relatively small samples. The samples may be too small to protect the quality standards by themselves, but they must be large enough to detect a breakdown in the Operating controls.

(3) For use when the Operating controls break down, give Inspection a tighter plan which will, under emergency conditions, place the necessary protective power in the hands of Inspection.

(4) Concentrate on restoring the Operating controls as soon as possible, in order to get rid of the uneconomical inspection.

ACKNOWLEDGMENTS

The following material has been used in this book with the kind permission of the copyright owners.

On pages 12, 17, 20, and 21, the control chart factors and formulas.	Taken by permission from the *ASTM Manual on Quality Control of Materials*, STP 15-C, copyright 1951, American Society for Testing Materials, Philadelphia, Pa. Some of this material was originally published in *British Standards* 600: 1935, (E. S. Pearson, "The Application of Statistical Methods to Industrial Standardization and Quality Control") and in *British Standards* 600R: 1942 (B. P. Dudding and W. J. Jennett, "Quality Control Charts"), British Standards Institute, London, England.
On page 115, the table of random numbers.	Taken by permission from Table XIX "Random Sampling Numbers" from the book, *Statistical Tables and Formulas*, by A. Hald. John Wiley & Sons, Inc., New York, 1952.
On pages 133, 135 and 136 probabilities for the normal law and the second approximation to the normal law.	Taken by permission from *Biometrika Tables for Statisticians*, by E. S. Pearson and H. O. Hartley, Cambridge University Press, 1954.
On page 145, diagram for calculating a line of regression.	From *Facts from Figures* by M. J. Moroney, 95¢, a Pelican Book published by Penguin Books Inc., 3300 Clipper Mill Road, Baltimore 11, Md.
On page 147, form for calculating the coefficient of correlation.	Reprinted by permission from Hawthorne Club Evening School Manual AM-8, *Statistical Methods Applied to Manufacturing Problems*, Western Electric Co., Inc., 1945.
On page 241, curves for calculating the probability of acceptance.	Reprinted by permission from *Sampling Inspection Tables*. by H. F. Dodge and H. G. Romig. John Wiley & Sons, Inc., New York, 1944.
On pages 247–248, excerpts from the Mil. Std. Tables 105A.	Reprinted by permission from Military Standard *Sampling Procedures and Tables for Inspection by Attributes*, United States Government Printing Office, September 1950.
On pages 250 and 253, examples of AOQL and LTPD sampling tables.	Reprinted by permission from *Sampling Inspection Tables*, by H. F. Dodge and H. G. Romig. John Wiley & Sons, Inc., New York, 1944.
On page 252, table of values of x and y for given values of c. Used in calculating AOQL.	Reprinted by permission from *Sampling Inspection Tables*, by H. F. Dodge and H. G. Romig. John Wiley & Sons, Inc., New York, 1944.
On page 258, sampling plans for continuous production.	Reprinted by permission from "A Sampling Inspection Plan for Continuous Production," by H. F. Dodge, Bell Telephone Laboratories, Inc. Published in *Transactions of the American Society of Mechanical Engineers*, Volume 66, No. 2, pages 127 to 133, February 1944.

REFERENCES

(1) Abruzzi, Adam, "Work Measurement," Columbia University Press, 1952.

(2) American Society for Testing Materials, "Quality Control of Materials," ASTM STP 15-C 1951.

(3) American National Standards Institute, "Control Chart Method of Controlling Quality During Production," ANSI Z1.3 – 1942.

(4) Bowker, A. H., and Goode, H. P., "Sampling Inspection by Variables," McGraw-Hill Book Co., Inc., 1952.

(5) Brownlee, K. A., "Industrial Experimentation," Chemical Publishing Co., Inc., 1947.

(6) Burr, I. W., "Engineering Statistics and Quality Control," McGraw-Hill Book Co., Inc., 1953.

(7) Burr, I. W., and Weaver, W. R., "Stratification Control Charts," *Industrial Quality Control Magazine*, March 1949.

(8) Dodge, H. F., "Sampling Plans for Continuous Production," *Industrial Quality Control Magazine*, November 1947.

(9) Dodge, H. F., "Skip-Lot Sampling Plans," *Industrial Quality Control Magazine*, February 1955.

(10) Dodge, H. F., "Chain Sampling," *Industrial Quality Control Magazine*, January 1955.

(11) Dodge, H. F., and Romig, H. G., "Sampling Inspection Tables—Single and Double Sampling," John Wiley & Sons, Inc., 1944.

(12) Dodge, H. F., and Torrey, M. N., "Continuous Sampling Inspection Plans," Annals of Mathematical Statistics, 1943.

(13) Duncan, A. J., "Quality Control and Industrial Statistics," R. D. Irwin, Inc., 1953.

(14) Ferrell, E. B., "Control Charts Using Midranges and Medians," *Industrial Quality Control Magazine*, March 1953.

(15) Fisher, R. A., "The Design of Experiments," Oliver and Boyd, Edinburgh, 1935.

(16) Fisher, R. A., "Statistical Methods for Research Workers," Oliver and Boyd, Edinburgh, 1938.

(17) Fisher and Yates, "Statistical Tables," Hafner Publishing Co., 1953.

(18) Freeman, H. A., "Industrial Statistics," John Wiley & Sons, 1946.

(19) Fry, T. C., "Probability and Its Engineering Uses," D. Van Nostrand Co., New York, 1928.

(20) Grant, E. L., "Statistical Quality Control," McGraw-Hill Book Co., Inc., 1952.

(21) Hald, A., "Statistical Theory with Engineering Applications," John Wiley & Sons, 1952.

(22) Heiland, R. E., and Richardson, W. J., "Work Sampling," McGraw-Hill, 1957.

(23) Hoel, P. G., "Introduction to Mathematical Statistics," John Wiley & Sons, Inc., 1947.

(24) Ireson, W. Grant, and Grant, Eugene L., "Handbook of Industrial Engineering and Management," Prentice-Hall, Inc., 1955.

(25) Juran, J. M., "Quality Control Handbook," McGraw-Hill Book Co., Inc., 1951.

(26) Kenney, J. F., and Keeping, E. S., "Mathematics of Statistics," D. Van Nostrand Co., Inc., New York, 1951.

(27) Miscellaneous Articles in Industrial Quality Control Magazine.

(28) Molina, E. C., "Poisson's Exponential Binomial Limit," D. Van Nostrand Co., New York, 1947.

(29) Moroney, J. M., "Facts from Figures," Penguin Books, Inc., 1954.

(30) Munitions Board Standards Agency, Department of Defense. Military Standard: "Sampling Procedures and Tables for Inspection by Attributes (Mil. Std. 105A)," United States Government Printing Office, 1950.

(31) Olmstead, P. S., "How to Detect the Type of an Assignable Cause," *Industrial Quality Control Magazine*, November 1952 and January 1953.

(32) Ott, E. R., "Analysis of Machine vs. Shift Performance Data," *Industrial Quality Control Magazine*, January 1952.

(33) Ott, E. R., "Variables Control Chart in Production Research," *Industrial Quality Control Magazine*, November 1949.

(34) Ott, E. R., and Mundel, A. B., "Narrow Limit Gauging," *Industrial Quality Control Magazine* Volume X, No. 5, March 1954.

(35) Pearson, E. S., "The Probability Integral of the Range in Samples of n Observations from a Normal Population," *Biometrika*, Volume 32, 1942.

*(36) Quality Assurance General Procedures Handbooks, Western Electric Co., Inc.

(37) Quality Assurance "An Introduction to the Quality Measurement Plan," Western Electric Co., Inc., 1980.

(38) Shewhart, W. A., "Economic Control of Quality of Manufactured Product," D. Van Nostrand Co., New York, 1931.

(39) Shewhart, W. A., "Statistical Method from the Viewpoint of Quality Control," United States Department of Agriculture, 1939.

(40) Simon, L. E., "An Engineer's Manual of Statistical Methods," John Wiley & Sons, 1945.

(41) Small, Bonnie B., "Control Chart Analysis of Engineering Experiments," Transactions of the Ninth Annual Convention, American Society for Quality Control, 1955.

(42) Snedecor, G. W., "Statistical Methods," Iowa State College Press, 1946.

(43) Statistical Research Group, Columbia University, "Sequential Analysis of Statistical Data: Applications," Columbia University Press, 1945.

(44) Stevens, W. L., "Control by Gauging," *Royal Statistical Society Journal*, Series B, Volume 10, 1948.

(45) "Tables of the Binomial Probability Distribution," Applied Mathematics Series No. 6 Government Printing Office, Washington, D. C., 1952.

(46) United States Department of Navy, "An Introduction to Statistical Quality Control," Government Printing Office, Washington, D. C., 1949.

*(47) Western Electric Company Training Manual No. 62 (Allentown Works) on "Sampling Plans for Final Inspection Adjusted to be Compatible with Demerit Quality Stds." OUT OF PRINT.

(48) Westman, A. E., and Lloyd, B. H., "Quality Control Charts Adjusted for Within Sub-Group Pattern," *Industrial Quality Control Magazine*, March 1949.

(49) Wilks, S. S., "Elementary Statistical Analysis," Princeton University Press, 1951.

(50) Yule, G. U., "An Introduction to the Theory of Statistics," Charles Griffin and Co., Ltd., London, 1919.

(51) Yule and Kendall, "An Introduction to the Theory of Statistics," Hafner Publishing Co., 1950.

* These references contain proprietary information and are therefore available for use only in connection with Company work.

Special References

Among the topics not covered in this book are the following:

Chi-Square Test.   See References Nos. 5 and 13.
Confidence Intervals (or Confidence Limits).   See References Nos. 3, 13 and 26.
Contingency Tables.   See References Nos. 13 and 26.
Estimating from a Sample.   See References Nos. 3 and 26.
Various Tests of Significance.   See Reference No. 26.

INDEX

A

A_2 factor, 12, 13, 14, 195, 196
Abbreviations used by clerks, 229
Abnormal
  causes, 6, 9, 150
  data, 52–53, 116–117
  measurements, 141, 160
  sources of variation, 6, 10, 35, 37, 52, 149–151
Abnormalities, 154, 156, 163
Abrupt changes
  in a curve, 164
  in a process, 11, 164, 178
Abruzzi, A., 50, 277
Absences, 11, 21
Absolute value of residual, 98, 107
Acceptance
  and rejection, 4, 38–39, 188, 233, 237–239, 254, 260–261, 268–269
  by control charts, 188, 246, 262–263, 265, 274
  on outside limit basis, 254, 269
  probability of (See Probability of acceptance)
  sampling (See Statistical sampling inspection)
  sampling by variables (See Variables sampling plans)
Acceptance number, 39, 237, 238, 240, 259, 265, 267
  in Dodge-Romig tables, 249–253, 255, 270
  in double or multiple sampling, 238, 259–260, 261
  in Mil. Std. tables, 247–248
  in single sampling, 259–260
Accidental
  damage, 163, 180
  loss of unit, 116
  shipment, 165
Accidents, 21
  (See Damage)
Accounting
  problems, 3
  records, 6, 21, 50, 189, 191, 197, 226
  standards, 35, 46, 54
Accumulation of product, 167, 246, 260–262
Accuracy
  of control limits, 52, 153
  of measurements, 49, 89, 90–91
Action
  criteria for, 208–209, 237
  in inspection, 263, 269, 270

in process capability studies, 61–63, 63–65, 67–70
  not taken as required, 217, 219, 227
  on an $\bar{X}$ and R chart, 66–72
  on an $\bar{X}$ chart, 66–67, 69–70, 228
  on control chart audits, 227
  on designed experiments, 77, 83, 87, 101, 112
  on shop charts, 25 (footnote), 63, 65, 194–195, 208–209, 217–221, 227
Activation, 91, 92, 93, 100, 101
Active causes, 217
Addition
  of distributions, 122–123
  of requirements, 61–63, 165, 175, 178
  of variables in an experiment, 101–103
Adjusting operation, 46, 49, 61, 188
Adjustment
  between process and OC curve, 244, 246, 255, 264–265
  of a machine, 16, 30, 37, 67, 153, 166, 188, 202, 203–204, 212
  of a meter, 67
  of a process, 16, 30, 37, 67, 153, 188, 202, 203–204, 265
  (See Overadjustment)
Administration
  of inspection, 234, 236, 260, 267–271
  of process control, 201–216, 217–222, 227
  of the quality control program, vii, 4, 33–41, 187–199, 201–216, 221–222, 223–229, 234
  (See Process control; Quality control program; Quality control engineering)
Administrative uses of control charts, 3, 4, 10, 21, 22, 23, 46, 225–226
Advantages
  of control chart analysis, 83–84, 91, 97
  of control charts in general, 9, 10
  of designed experiments, 75–76, 77, 91–93, 101, 187
  of joint cost reduction cases, 226
  of process capability studies, 10, 34–36, 45–47, 61–63, 71, 112, 187
  of quality control, 10, 33–38, 225–226, 233, 236, 246, 273–274

of sampling inspection, 4, 38–39. 187, 233–236
  of shop charts, 4, 10, 15–16, 19–20, 36, 37–38, 62, 187, 201–204, 216, 219–220, 221, 224, 225–226, 235, 246, 265, 274
  of unnatural variation, 35, 54, 151, 221
Adverse effect on quality, 72, 121, 246
Advice given by quality control engineer, 40, 113, 192, 228, 236
Age
  as a variable, 153, 178
  of a fixture or machine, 168
  of a person, 7
Aging of product, 153, 178
Aims
  of a cost reduction case, 226
  of a quality control program (See Objectives)
Aircraft, 21
Algebraic
  differences, 21, 22, 102–106
  value of residual, 98
Alignment, 5, 8, 19, 69, 155, 167, 175, 180
Allowances
  engineering, 35, 46, 54, 122, 125
  establishment of, 46, 54, 235, 265
  to be based on a natural pattern, 54, 59–60
  work sampling data for, 50
Alloying, 102, 104
Alternate pairs of samples, 108, 109
American Society for Testing & Materials (See ASTM)
American National Standards Institute (ANSI), 277
Amount
  of inspection, 39, 46, 225, 226, 233, 236, 262, 273–274
  of production, 71, 226 (See Efficiency; Schedules)
  of product rejected by Inspection, 226, 246, 255
  of product requiring detailing, 226, 235, 263, 265
  of record keeping, by inspection, 260, 268–269
  of sorting, 46, 226, 235, 265
Amount of data
  for statistical conclusions, 28, 62, 112, 146
  required for a control chart, 9
  required for chart of individual measurements, 50–51, 160

Amount of data, *continued*

    required for designed experiments, 28, 77, 78–79, 90, 92–93, 110, 111, 112, 113

    required for engineering studies, 50–51, 62

    required for experiments not formally designed, 77, 92

    required for process capability studies, 28, 47, 50–51, 61, 62, 63–64, 66–72

    required for studying correlation, 146

    required for studying skewness, 56

    (*See* Data)

Ampere turns, 66–71

Analysis

    of a c-chart, 72–73

    of a designed experiment, 77–84, 84–91, 91–101, 107–111, 111–112

    of an $\bar{X}$ and R chart, 15–16, 66–72

    of a p-chart, 19–20, 31, 59, 73, 157–159

    of a process capability study, 47, 51–63, 66–73

    of complex unnatural patterns, 54–56, 60, 66–71, 72–73

    of control charts, 152–180

    of control charts in an experiment, 100–101, 111–112

    of data in general, 3, 9

    of engineering data, 46

    of patterns, 53–56, 66–71, 72–73, 161–180

    of shop charts, 190, 199, 203–204, 217–219

    (*See* Formal analysis; Informal analysis)

Analysis of factorial design

    control chart method, 93, 97–101, 101–106, 107–111, 111–112

    sum of squares method, 93–97, 101

Analysis of variance

    by control charts, 93, 97–101, 101–107, 107–111

    by sums of squares, 78, 80, 81, 82, 91, 93–97, 101

    explanation of, 78, 80, 93

    for comparing averages, 80–81

    for determining components of variance, 91, 95, 96, 98

Anchoring of fixture, 55

Annual

    reports, 225–226

    savings, 226

Answers

    to questions asked by engineers, 4, 34, 36, 46–47, 75

    to questions asked by operators, 201–202

    to questions asked of machine setters, 202, 217

AOQ, 251

AOQL

    calculation of, 251–252

    choice of, 254–255, 264, 265, 273

    compared with target value for shop, 254–255

    derived from quality rates, 264, 273

    equation for, 251

    ignored in case of Minimum Inspection, 273, 274

    may hold product to tighter level than planned, 251, 252

    meaning of, 249

    misuse of, 254

    selection of values of, 263–265, 273

    used in conjunction with LTPD sampling plans, 250, 253

AOQL sampling plans, 249–251, 252–255, 256, 263–265, 273

Apparatus, 3, 189

Apparent

    complexity, 37–38, 70, 166–167

    correlation, 56, 146, 156, 176–177

    effects in data, 9, 10, 46, 75–76, 99, 103, 161

    freaks, 52–53, 58, 117, 162, 164

    savings, 246, 262

    skewness, 58, 163

    spread, 61, 123, 141

    stratification, 173–174

    trends, 160, 178, 179

    trouble with specification, 122, 204, 206

    worsening of pattern, 67, 68

Appearance

    as a variable, 12

    of chart mountings used in shop, 192

    of control charts, 192, 216, 221

Applications

    in the shop, vii, 4, 5–6, 10, 15–16, 19–20, 22–23, 33–41, 45–47, 50, 62–65, 72, 74, 75, 125, 183, 187–229

    leading to cost reduction, 226

    of control charts, in general, 33

    of designed experiments, 34, 75–117

    of process capability studies, 34, 45–47

    of quality control, 3–4, 33, 34

Approach to capability, 36, 47, 63, 64, 71, 73, 74, 83

Approval of shop charts, 189, 192, 199, 228

AQL, 119, 247, 265

AQL sampling plans, 246–248, 265

Areas

    for applying statistical quality control, 3–4, 33, 34, 46–47, 66, 187–189

    for inspection, 260

    of squares, 57

    storage, 246, 260

Arithmetic mean, 129 (*See* Averages)

Armature, 213

Arrangement

    of points on a control chart, 149, 160

    of points in a natural pattern, 24, 162, 170, 175, 176

Arrangement of data

    for calculating standard deviation, 130

    for control charts, 14, 18, 22, 72–73, 82, 86, 98, 109, 149, 151

    for correlation, 143–144, 145, 147

    for designed experiments, 76, 78, 82, 84, 86, 92, 94, 99, 102, 109, 117

    for frequency distribution, 139

    for obtaining median, 129

    for process capability studies, 51–52, 55–56, 72–73, 75

Arrows, in margin, 13–14, 16, 30–31, 65, 190, 205, 206, 212

"a's," writing of, 7

Assemblies

    complex, 3, 55, 122, 189

    methods for, 3, 46, 71, 175, 226

    parts needed for, 246, 254

    positioning of, 69, 167, 176

    problems in, 48, 61, 188, 189

    selective, 123, 127, 188

Assembly tolerances, 124–127

Assignable causes

    effect of, in setting standards, 59–60, 122, 145

    good or bad? 35–36, 54, 62, 149–151

    in a complex pattern, 66

    in a designed experiment, 79, 82–83, 87, 88, 99–101, 101–106, 106–107, 109, 111, 112, 113–114, 116–117

    in an error of measurement study, 87, 88, 89, 90, 91

    in data for an experiment, 111

    information from, 35–36, 54–56, 151, 221

    in general, 6, 145, 149–151, 217

    in process capability studies, 25 (footnote), 34, 35–36, 45, 46, 47, 51, 53, 55–56, 59–61, 66–73, 122, 150–151, 161–180

    meaning of, 9, 10, 37–38, 47, 149–151

    on a p-chart, 19–20, 48, 59, 157–159, 189

    on shop charts, 25 (footnote), 189, 212–213, 217, 218–219

patterns associated with, 11, 54–56, 60, 66–71, 72–73, 99–100, 161–180

tests for, 25 (footnote), 25–30, 180–183

tests for, within boxes in a designed experiment, 111

treatment of, 35–36, 54, 62, 122, 150–151

Assistance

in writing layouts, 192, 236

to Quality Control Team, 40, 228–229, 236

Assortment of product, 166

Assumptions

about average, 153, 154

of constancy, 78, 79, 80, 82, 114, 218

of equivalent variances, 78–80, 82

of normality, 78–79, 80, 82, 132, 134, 154

Assurance, in inspection, 274

(*See* Quality assurance)

Asterisk

used for marking control charts, 99, 100, 107, 109

used for marking effects in sum of squares analysis, 97

ASTM Manual on Quality Control of Materials, 139, 275, 277

Atmospheric conditions, 6

Attendance, 6

(*See* Absences)

Attitudes, 4, 158

(*See* Motivation)

Attributes control charts, 7–8, 11, 17–21, 48–49, 113, 144, 157–160, 188–189, 191, 196–197, 198, 204, 218, 227

examples of, 19, 72–73, 194

other than *p*-charts, 11, 20–21, 72–73, 160, 189, 191, 198

where to use, 48–49, 54, 59, 72–73, 113, 188–189, 191, 196–197, 218

(*See* *p*-Charts; *np*-Charts; *c*-Charts; *u*-Charts)

Attributes data

for control charts in general, 11, 17, 18, 31, 38, 47, 48–49, 50, 157–160

used in designed experiments, 113

used in process capability studies, 48–49, 50, 53, 54, 56, 59, 66, 72–73, 74, 144

used on shop charts, 188–189, 191, 194, 196–197, 198, 206, 210, 225, 227–228

Attributes inspection, 237–265, 267–271

Attributes measurements, 5, 6, 17, 18, 20–21, 47, 144

(*See* Attributes data)

Audit inspection

(*See* Minimum inspection; Quality rating)

Audits

of finished product, 270

of inspection, 227

of process controls, 38, 41, 198–199, 219, 223, 227, 233, 274

of various areas of management interest, 34

performed by Inspection, 233–234, 268, 274

Authorization

of questionable practices, 45, 61

of data collection, by the Quality Control Team, 41, 192, 223, 228

Automatic controls, 10, 70, 156, 171, 180, 235

Automatic timer, 70, 235

Automatic welder, 5, 19

Automation, 47

Average amount of inspection, 46, 260

Average range, 12, 56, 58, 131

Averages, 11, 137, 138

addition of, 123–124

affected by change in proportion, 153, 154

calculation of, 12, 129, 210, 213

change in, 153, 179

conclusions based on, 111

distribution of, 137–138

limits for, 16, 138

meaning of, 154

of a distribution, 63, 129, 171

of a series of samples, 137

of two related points, 109

process (*See* Process average)

should not be used for estimates, 60, 61

substitutes for, 129, 197

unreliable, 60, 61, 83

use of, in a designed experiment, 78, 80–81, 111

use of, in analysis, 78

various forms of, 129

(*See* $\bar{X}$ and R Charts)

Average value of electrical characteristic, 71, 83, 91, 101

Axiom, 217

B

Backing for shop charts, 192, 228

Back schedules, reduction of, 37, 46, 226

Bake-out, 102, 104

Balance

around a centerline, 24, 187, 208

between costs and savings, 10, 34, 36, 38, 45, 47, 61–63, 64, 71, 75, 121, 171, 217, 223–226, 246, 262, 263, 265

between cost and quality, 33, 38, 41, 45, 62, 64, 120–122, 193, 264–265

between two types of error, 25 (footnote)

in a factorial experiment, 92–93, 101

statistical, 59, 76, 93, 150, 157, 159, 170–171 (*See* Stability; Statistical control)

Ballast lamps, 224, 225

"Band" of acceptable levels, on a control chart, 63, 64, 65, 120, 193–194, 195–196

Barrel plating, 156

Bartlett's test, 78, 79–80, 83

Batches of material, 61, 62, 151, 196, 218

Batch-type operations

(*See* Intermittent operations)

Beaker, 218

Bearing, 15, 126, 219

Benches, 192, 218

Benefits

of control charts (*See* Advantages)

to shop, 36, 63, 64, 71, 219

Bent springs, 270

"Between sample" causes, 150

Bias

in a sample, 113, 116, 207, 214, 267–268

in a technique, 30, 114, 116, 204

Bias between measurements in a designed experiment, 111

Bifurcated springs, 53

Bimodal distributions

causes of, 136

examples of, 153, 154, 162, 163, 165, 169, 172, 174, 176, 179

(*See* Non-normal distributions)

Binding, 70, 71

Binomial distribution, 239, 242, 252 (footnote), 278

Bins, 167, 171

Blank charts and data sheets, 207, 210–211, 228, 271

Blindfolded driver, 216

Block design, 92

Blueprint limits, 16, 30–31, 119, 189, 205

(*See* Specifications)

Board for control charts, 209, 217, 218

"Boats" in an oven, 114

Bolts, 156

Bonding (of contact to wire), 209

Bottlenecks, 33, 77, 187, 202, 246

(*See* Delays)

Bowker, A. H., 242, 262, 277

Boxes

assignment of variables to, in an experiment, 92, 98, 102–103

identification of, in an experiment, 98

Boxes, *continued*
    number of measurements in, 93,
      111, 113
    of product, 157, 173
    shaded, 97, 106, 107, 110, 111
Breakdown
    by operations, 166
    dielectric, 20, 162
    of data, 36, 54–55, 166, 199, 218
      (*See* Production paths)
    of facilities, 163, 180
    of pattern, 55, 66–68, 72, 166
    of p-chart, 48, 59, 159
    of process controls, 233, 273–274
    of quality safeguards, 273, 274
    voltage, 20
"Bright dip" finish, 102
Broken bolts, 146
Brownlee, K. A., 79, 80, 81, 96, 97,
    101, 116, 148, 278
Budge, 54
Bulk of shop records, 228–229
"Bunching" of measurements, 11,
    31, 54, 68, 160, 161, 165–166,
    179
Burr, I. W., 101, 132, 135, 277
Burrs
    as a variable, 156, 162, 270
    example of data on, 49–50, 113
Business
    at quality control meetings, 40,
      41, 223–224, 226, 236
    unfinished, 47, 63, 122, 235–236
By-products
    of process capability studies, 34,
      36
    of shop charts, 36, 38, 233, 262

C

$\bar{c}$, 21
Cable, 3
Calculation of control limits
    as a variable, 153–154, 156, 173,
      219
    for a moving range chart, 8, 22,
      173–174, 191, 196, 197, 222
    for an $\bar{X}$ and R chart, 12–14, 82–
      83, 153–154, 191, 194–195
    for an $\bar{X}$ chart, 138
    for attributes charts, 7–8, 17–18
      20, 21, 191, 196–197
    for designed experiments, 97, 98,
      107–108, 111
    for miscellaneous control charts,
      74, 197–198, 221–222
    for process capability studies, 51–
      52, 53
Calculations
    authorized by Quality Control
      Team, 228
    correctness of, 4, 145, 162, 173, 215,
      227

in an experiment, 82, 86, 94–97,
    98, 107–109, 110
made by process checker, 192,
    208, 213, 214–215, 227
made by statistical clerk, 228–229
mistakes in, 4, 162, 163, 173, 180,
    215, 227
of average, 12, 71, 129, 137, 197,
    213
of effects in data, 94–95, 98, 103
of measurement error, 88, 89
of percentage, 18, 19, 20, 213, 215
of percentage outside of limits,
    30–31, 54, 58–59, 71, 127,
    132–136
of probabilities, 180–183, 239–242
of process capability, 53–54, 56,
    58–59, 71
of p values, 17, 18, 20, 162, 215
of range, 12, 131, 213, 214–215
of $\bar{R}$, in a designed experiment, 98,
    107–108
of residual, 96–97, 97–98, 106,
    107, 110, 111
of R points, 12, 14, 82, 86, 109,
    162
of sigma, 56, 58, 71, 88, 89, 123,
    124, 127, 130, 131, 147–148
of sigma for a line of regression,
    145
of skewness, 56, 59, 122, 131, 134–
    136, 196
of spread, 30–31, 56, 58–59, 71,
    122, 123–124, 127, 130–131,
    195
of tests for unnatural patterns, 25,
    109, 180–183
of $\bar{X}$ points, 12, 14, 82, 86, 109,
    162
optional, in an experiment, 98
shortcut methods for, 97–98, 110,
    130–131
Calibration, 53, 113, 153, 159, 165,
    175
Capability
    approach to, 36, 47, 63, 71, 73, 74
    as a percentage, 45, 56, 59
    as a percentage of defects, 235,
      244, 245, 250, 253, 265, 273,
      274
    compared with performance, 45,
      61, 74, 187–188, 265
    determination of, 53, 54, 56
    of a machine, 33, 35, 46, 170, 172,
      175, 202, 204, 207, 224, 235
    of an operator, 35, 46, 57, 73, 170,
      202, 204
    of a process (*See* Process capabil-
      ity)
    of a tool, 35, 46
    of designs, 35, 46, 47, 224
    of material, 35, 46, 224
    of methods, 35, 46, 224
    overall, 46, 48

Capacitance, 102
Capacitors, 4
Capacity, 38, 46, 224, 226
Car, 216
Care shown by operators, 33, 164,
    178, 203
Carelessness, 55, 155, 156, 167, 175,
    180, 235
Carrier tubes, 224, 225
Cases, cost reduction, 38, 47, 54, 62,
    71, 224, 225, 226
Casual checks, 190, 224
Categories
    for data, 55, 92, 101–102, 210,
      271 (*See* Production paths)
    for operations, 224–225
Cause and effect relationships as
      shown by a control chart, 10,
      11, 27, 35–38, 53, 66–73, 149–
      180, 187, 190, 218–220
    as shown by correlation, 29, 56,
      143–144, 146, 176–177
    as shown by process capability
      studies, 34–36, 46–47, 49,
      54–56
    as studied in designed experiments
      4, 75–76, 99–101, 111–112
    revealed through unnatural pat-
      terns, 6, 9, 11, 34, 35, 36,
      54–56
    verification of, 56, 177
    (*See* Correlation; Causes)
Causes
    abnormal, 6
    affecting a p-chart, 17, 48, 158–
      159, 192
    as related to correlation, 146, 176–
      177
    assignable (*See* Assignable causes)
    associated with patterns, 6, 9, 11,
      35–36, 54–56, 66–71, 99–101,
      149–161, 161–180, 212, 215,
      217–219
    associated with unstable patterns,
      55, 66–70, 166–167, 179–
      180
    "between sample," 150
    combinations of, 37–38, 67, 68,
      70, 166 (*See* Interactions)
    detectable through unnatural pat-
      terns, 6, 9, 11, 35–36, 37–
      38, 54–56, 161–180, 197, 221
    elimination of, 153
    erratic, 68, 166
    extraneous, 91, 149, 166
    found by Shop, 71, 190, 208, 212–
      213, 215, 217–219, 227
    hidden (*See* Hidden variables)
    identification of, 56, 166
    known to Operating, 48, 188, 218
    large, 6, 55, 66–67, 70
    not applicable, 69
    of a natural pattern, 170–171

of bunching, 165–166

of complex patterns, 55, 66–73, 166, 167–169, 179–180 (*See also* Mixtures; Stratification)

of cycles, 69–70, 161–162

of defects, 46, 66–71, 72–73, 233, 235, 246, 265

of disturbances on chart of individual measurements, 31, 160–161

of disturbances on various attributes charts, 157–160

of disturbances on *p*-chart, 31, 157–159

of disturbances on R chart, 30, 66–68, 154–156, 168

of disturbances on $\bar{X}$ chart, 30, 152–154

of freaks, 163–164

of gradual change in level, 164–165

of grouping, 165–166

of instability, 55, 166–167

of interaction, 167–169

of mixtures, 169–170, 171, 179–180

of natural variation, 6, 150, 171

of patterns, 149–180

of repairs, 46, 64, 188, 189

of rework, 37, 46, 188, 202

of scrap, 37, 46, 188, 202, 217

of skewness, 56–58, 70

of stratification, 53, 173–174

of sudden shift in level, 174–175

of systematic variation, 175–176

of tendency of one chart to follow another, 176–177

of trends, 10, 53, 164, 177–179

of trouble, 10, 11, 35, 36–37, 46, 187, 188, 189–190, 202, 217

of unnatural variation, 6, 35–36, 149–151 (*See* Causes detectable through unnatural patterns)

on shop charts, 71, 208, 212–213, 215, 217–219, 227

operating in combination, 37, 66–68, 70, 166, 167–168

outstanding, 70

simple, 38, 54, 72, 166, 217

single, 4, 37, 45, 68, 70, 166

susceptible to analysis, 54, 55, 67, 70

tracing of, in inspection, 261

ultimate, 166, 171

unknown, 4, 10, 34, 38, 46, 54, 66, 75–76, 188, 190, 218–219, 223

"within sample," 150

Cause system, data representative of, 50–51, 66, 76

(*See* Systems of causes)

Caution

in interpreting control charts, 66, 72, 154, 159, 160, 161, 197

in using designed experiments, 76, 112

Cavity, 152

c-Charts, 20–21, 48–49, 66, 72–73, 137, 189, 191, 196–197, 204

Cells

midpoint of, 130, 131, 140

used in calculating standard deviation, 130–131

used in making a frequency distribution, 138–140

Center

allowable shift in (of a process), 64, 65, 122, 193–194, 195–196

estimated from a process capability study, 56, 61, 62, 119

methods of adjusting, 30, 120–121, 202, 203–204

of a distribution, 30, 53, 56, 71, 121, 129, 138, 139–140, 152, 160, 188

of a distribution (as an inspection requirement), 119, 122, 265

of a process, 53, 56, 193–194, 195–196, 212

of the sampling distribution of averages, 138

shown by an $\bar{X}$ chart, 16, 30, 48, 53, 56, 62, 67, 152

(*See* Central tendency; Centerlines)

Centering

between specifications, 64, 65, 120–121, 160, 193, 220

of a distribution, 120, 121, 188, 226

of a machine, 30, 188

of a process, 30, 62, 64–65, 120–121, 167, 170, 188, 202, 220

of parts etc. (See Alignment.)

Centerlines

definition of, 152, 193–194

double, 64, 65, 193, 195–197

economic, 62, 64–65, 192, 193–194, 195–197

for shop control charts, 63, 64–65, 190, 192, 193–196, 228

on an R chart, 12, 14, 71, 87–89, 98, 100, 107–108, 131, 154–155

on an $\bar{X}$ chart, 12, 90–91, 228

on experimental control charts, 98, 100, 107–109

Central tendency

estimated from a process capability study, 56, 59–60, 61–62, 119

measures of, 30, 56, 129

on an $\bar{X}$ chart, 152, 154

Certainty

degree of, in conclusions from a control chart, 9, 10, 25 (footnote), 52, 180–183

degree of, in conclusions from an experiment, 97, 99, 100, 107, 109, 112

(*See* Risk)

Chain sampling, 262

Chamfer, 156, 235

Chance

effects due to, 24, 103, 150, 171

of accepting poor product, 245

of rejecting good product, 244–245, 255, 273

of wrong decisions, 25 (footnote), 83–84, 100, 107, 112, 237–238, 278

laws of, 6, 24, 116

second, for an inspection lot, 260

(*See* Chance causes; Certainty; Risk)

Chance causes, 24, 25 (footnote), 152

effect of, on a control chart, 9, 24, 150, 170–171

Changes

abrupt, 11, 164, 178

based on control charts, 10, 16, 37, 67, 72, 166–167, 188, 199, 202–204, 217

detected by control charts, 8–9, 25, 35–36, 37, 51–52, 83, 218, 220

effect of, on product, 46, 72, 202

engineering, 46, 62, 63–64, 69, 70, 72, 224

gradual, 11, 161, 164–165, 177–179

in a cause system, 6, 8–10, 19–20, 25, 27, 37–38, 53–54, 61 62, 66–71, 83, 141

in a fixture, 53, 69, 83, 164, 175, 213, 215, 219, 235

in a process, 6, 8–10, 19, 37, 46–47, 49, 53, 54, 61–63, 64, 66–72, 120–122, 141, 187–190, 192, 198–199, 202, 203, 206, 208, 212–213, 215, 218–220, 224, 226

in assortment of product, 166

in average, 153, 170

in calibration, 53, 113, 153, 159, 175

in design, 46, 51, 198, 224

in design of tool, 46, 212, 219

in distribution, 37, 57–58, 122, 141, 152–158, 164, 166, 174, 178, 179–180

in efficiency, 71, 158

in equipment, 47, 53, 70, 113, 174, 215

information on, in a process, 35, 37, 54, 72, 208, 215, 217, 218

Changes, *continued*
in gaging, 72
in inspection levels, 246, 273–274
in layouts, 40, 192, 198–199, 219, 223–224
in master control chart, 65, 228
in material, 30, 62, 63, 174, 176
in method of test, 165, 180, 218, 219
in methods, 30, 46–47, 62, 63, 68–70, 121, 174, 219, 226
in methods of assembly, 46, 70, 175, 226
in motion patterns, 158, 219
in operations, 187, 202
in pattern (on a chart), 55, 67, 73, 153, 155, 164–165, 166, 168, 174–175, 177–179, 203, 206, 218
in personnel, 227 (*See* New operators)
in product characteristics, 164
in proportions, 153, 157, 178, 179
in requirements, 198
in schedules, 155, 166, 178, 198, 224
in setup, 16, 30, 71, 174, 188, 202, 203–204
in shape of distribution, 57–58, 160
in shop charts, 38, 41, 65, 189–190, 198–199, 219, 223, 227–229
in specifications, 10, 34, 35, 36, 38, 46, 47, 48, 57, 61–65, 120–122, 187, 188, 198, 203–206, 219, 220, 224, 226
in spread, 71, 120, 121, 154–156, 179
in standards, 31, 158, 159, 165, 175, 178
in suppliers, 207
in test sets, 47, 165, 167, 175, 180, 218
in the design of process control charts, 189–190, 198–199, 219, 223, 224
in work habits, 158, 167, 219
of water in tank, 50
visual impressions of, 160, 178 (*See* Intuitive impressions)
Characteristics
associated with trouble, 64, 66, 121, 188
combined on a *p*-chart, 17, 48, 59, 157–159, 189, 190
effect of, on other characteristics, 46, 64, 187, 202, 218, 223 (*See* Interactions)
for inspection, 263, 265, 268, 270 (*See* Inspection items)
of a distribution, 6, 129
of a product, 48, 66, 91, 101, 180, 202, 270

of the letter "*a*," 7
plotted on a control chart, 66, 188–189
quality, 3, 132, 188, 265
to be checked, 201, 202, 209, 265, 270
to be plotted, 66, 99, 106, 108, 113, 188, 189
Charge on an electron, 6
Chart holders, 192, 228
Charts
maintained by Inspection, 39, 225, 246, 262–263, 265, 274
plotted by engineers, 53, 82, 86–88, 107–109
plotted by the Shop, 213–216
(*See* Control charts; Process control charts; Shop charts)
Charts for individual measurements
amount of data required for (in engineering studies), 50–51
apparent stratification on, 173–174
calculations for, 21–22
causes affecting, 162, 163, 165, 166, 167, 171, 175, 176, 179, 180
centerlines for, in the shop, 193–194, 196
construction of, 21–22
control limits for, 8, 11–12, 21–22
control limits for, in the shop, 194, 196
examples of, 5, 8, 22, 23
general use of, 11, 12
importance of, 12
interpretation of (*See* Interpretation)
samples for, in the shop, 191
sensitivity of, 11, 12, 160, 161
substitutes for, 198
symbols for, 21
used for correlation, 144
uses in the shop, 188, 189
where to use, in general, 11–12, 21, 22, 23, 50, 144, 160–161, 189, 196, 221–222
Checking
as a variable, 4, 31, 159, 167, 171, 180, 215–216
devices, 192, 209, 270
frequency of, 41, 192, 199, 209, 219, 227
intervals, 41, 190–192, 199–207, 214, 219, 227, 233, 262, 274
of freaks, 52, 70, 117, 163, 218
of gages, 219
of machine setter's notes, 67
of machine setting, 30, 202, 203–204, 217, 219
of possible causes, 55, 69, 161, 166, 217–218

of process controls, 41, 187, 189–190, 198, 219, 227, 233–234, 273–274
of samples, 192, 207–209, 213–216, 227, 268–269
Chemical operations, 4, 11, 21, 23, 35, 48, 114, 189, 224, 225
Chi-square test, 78, 79, 80, 82, 133, 140, 278
Chronic troubles, 188
Chronological history, 192, 228–229
Chucks, 55, 69, 176, 180, 213, 219
Circled effects, in an experiment, 95, 98
Circled *x*'s, on a control chart, 28–30
Circuit, 68
Clarity
of patterns, 54–55, 67–68, 166
of specifications, 61–63
shown by *x*'s, 67
Classical methods (other than control charts), 78–81, 83–84, 91, 93–97, 144–148, 278
Classification
basis of, for *p*-chart, 158, 159
in inspection, 268, 270
of data, 55, 56, 166
of defects, 198, 263, 270
Cleaning operations, 35, 50, 91, 93, 100, 101, 114
Clearances, 126–127, 188
(*See* Assembly tolerances)
Clearing
in continuous sampling, 256, 257, 269
interval, 256, 270, 271
sample, 256, 257, 267
Clerical work, 3, 34, 50, 228–229
Clerks, statistical, 216, 228–229
Clinching operation, 270
Clogging of fixtures, 178
Closing
of a cost reduction case, 226
of items in control chart audit, 227
Cloth, 20, 191
Clues obtained from pattern, 55, 66, 67, 68, 166
Clustering of measurements, 160, 165–166
Code numbers
referring to notes on a control chart, 208, 212
referring to product, 167, 171, 196
referring to semi-variables data, 49–50 (*See* Semi-variables)
Codes of product, 160, 167, 171, 196
Cold weld, 212
Collection of data
for shop charts, 38, 41, 63–64, 65, 77, 190–192, 201, 205–210, 213–216, 219, 223, 227, 228, 229

in a process capability study, 36, 41, 47, 49–51, 55, 62, 63–64, 66, 67, 74, 223, 228
Comb (on a relay), 19
"Combination" residual, 96–97, 110
Combinations
  of causes, 68, 70, 166, 167
  of characteristics on a p-chart, 17, 48, 59, 157, 159, 189, 190
  of distributions, 68, 121, 122–124, 126–127, 160, 166 (*See* Mixtures)
  of variables in an experiment, 91, 92, 93, 97, 100–101, 105–106, 108, 116, 117 (*See* Interactions)
Comments on control charts, 53, 66–67, 188, 208–209, 212–213, 215, 221
Comparator, 209, 213
Comparisons
  basis for, on a p-chart, 51, 159
  between process and specification, 30–31, 58–59, 61–63, 64–65, 71, 119–122, 170, 204–206, 224 (*See* Process)
  between shop chart and process capability study, 63
  of assembly techniques, 46
  of control charts with other methods, 75, 79, 82–84, 91, 93, 97, 98, 106, 110, 112, 141, 167, 203–204
  of designs, 46
  of distributions, 71, 139–141
  of engineering responsibility vs. shop responsibility, 46, 204, 224
  of instruments, 84, 89
  of machines, 36, 46, 49, 54, 90, 159, 170, 171, 172–173, 175, 202, 215, 224
  of methods, 35, 46, 53, 55, 63, 72, 90, 92, 175, 202, 218, 220, 224
  of operators, 36, 49, 55, 159, 170, 171, 175, 204, 215, 218
  of suppliers, 36, 39, 55, 162, 207
  of tools, 46, 55, 224
  of two R charts, 67–68
  of variability, 78–80, 83, 87–89, 154–156
  of variables in an experiment, 4, 91–101, 101–106, 112, 114
  to be based on natural patterns, 53–54, 58, 59, 61, 122, 170, 204–206
Compatibility
  of process with specification, 119–122
  of specifications with each other, 64, 121
Compensation for process variables, 37, 64, 220

Competence
  of inspector, 155, 218, 236
  of operator, 155, 164, 167, 175, 178, 180
  of process checker, 171, 213, 215–216, 218
Complaints, 38, 62, 226, 246, 264
Complete
  inspection of samples, 227, 260, 261, 268
  job studies, 224–225
Completion of studies made by engineer, 38, 45, 47, 61, 62, 63–65, 71, 74, 75, 221
Complexity
  causes of, 35, 36, 37–38, 54–56, 66, 67, 68, 69, 75 (*See* Instability; Mixtures; Freaks)
  in experimental designs, 76, 77, 114
  of apparatus, equipment etc., 3–4, 20, 21, 38, 55, 122–124, 166, 189
  of cause systems, 3, 4, 38, 45, 75, 171
Complex patterns
  assignable causes in, 66
  examples of, 66–67, 72
  importance of, 35, 54
  importance of R chart in analyzing, 55, 66–69, 153, 155, 168 (*See* R chart)
  in a process capability study, 54–56, 66, 67–73
  interpretation of, 54–56, 66–71, 72–73, 166
  on a c-chart, 72–73
  on an $\bar{X}$ and R chart, 66–71
  on a p-chart, 17, 48, 59, 157, 159, 162, 163, 167, 171, 173, 180, 196–197
  list of, 11, 54, 161
  simple causes for, 37–38, 54, 70, 166
  (*See* Unnatural patterns; Simplification)
Complicated variables (in a process capability study), 55, 66
Complications due to interactions, 76, 77, 91, 105–106, 167–169
Component distributions, 68, 122, 124–125, 127, 153, 155, 160 (*See* Mixtures)
Components
  of assemblies, 4, 55, 122, 124–127
  of distributions, 153
  of mixture, 166, 169–170, 171
  of variance, 75, 89, 93, 95–97, 98
  on a p-chart, 48, 59, 157, 159
Composition of chemical baths, 23, 114
Concise reports, 224, 225, 226
Conclusions
  based on averages, 61, 78, 111, 153, 154

from a control chart, 8–10, 15–16, 19–20, 30–32, 48, 53–56, 203–206
from analysis of variance by control chart method, 100–101, 111–112
from analysis of variance by sum of squares method, 81, 97
from an experiment, 76, 77, 81, 82–83, 87–89, 92, 97, 100–101, 111–112, 220
from a process capability study, 35, 36, 53–56, 58–60, 61–63, 71, 73, 75, 76, 112
Condensed history, 229
Conductive material, 165
Conductivity, 21
Conferences, 219, 246
  (*See* Meetings)
Confidence
  in control charts, 10
  in process controls, 273, 274
  intervals, 278
Conflict
  between Operating and Inspection results, 274
  between process and specification, 122 (*See* Comparisons; Specifications)
  between quality and cost, 264–265
Confusion
  between control limits and specification limits, 16, 30–31, 151, 190
  in speaking of natural tolerance, 61
Connections in an assembly, 17, 191
Consistency
  associated with a natural pattern, 150
  associated with an R chart, 30, 154
  in judgment, 50
  in shop practices, 223, 227
  of results, 48, 71, 77, 88, 89, 101 (*See* Reproducibility)
Consolidation of charts, 41, 199
Constancy
  artificial, 29, 172–174
  associated with a natural pattern, 150, 170–171
  assumption of, 78, 79, 82, 114, 218
  hypothesis of, 82, 83
  of inspection load, 260
  tests for, 25–28, 78, 82
Constant
  quantity, for a c-chart, 20, 191
  sample size, 18, 20, 191
  system of causes, 6–7, 9, 10, 45, 53, 83, 150, 170–171
Consumer's risk, 245, 246
Contacts (on a relay), 19, 154, 209

Containers, for product, 157, 173
Contingency tables, 278
Continuity in shop operations, 36, 46, 187, 202, 217, 219
Continuous
  checks on control charts, 38, 41, 64, 190, 192, 201, 217–219, 221–222, 223–225, 227
  disturbance in a process, 150
  movement of a pattern, 9, 29–30, 160, 177
Continuous sampling plans, 255–258
Contraction (as a variable), 153
Control
  automatic, 10, 70, 156, 171, 180, 235
  by machine setters, 48, 188, 202, 203–204
  by operators, 48, 188
  economical, 36, 63, 220–221
  importance of, 10, 35–38, 53–54, 59–61, 62, 75, 122, 124–127, 141, 150–151, 171, 187–190, 217, 220–221, 225–226, 233, 273–274
  meaning of, 3, 5–7, 35–36, 37–38, 53–54, 150, 171, 220–221
  of a process (See Process control)
  of inspection piece rates, 260
  of lots, 163, 164, 167, 171, 180, 260–262
  of manufacture, 226
  of shop processes, 35, 37, 63, 187, 190, 202, 217, 219, 220–222, 223–226
  reasons for lack of, 190, 219, 221
  results in savings, 10, 35, 36, 38, 46–47, 62, 187, 217, 225–226, 246, 265, 274
  state of, 6–7, 9, 10, 36, 37–38, 41, 45, 53–54, 56, 59, 71, 119, 122, 126, 127, 149, 150, 170–171, 189, 204, 205, 206, 219, 220–221, 222, 244, 246, 265, 273–274
  statistical (See Statistical control)
  (See also "In control" and "Out of control")
Control chart audits, 227
Control chart forms, 192, 207, 210–211, 228–229
Control chart formulas
  (See individual names of control charts)
Control chart patterns, 4, 5–7, 11, 23–25, 66–71, 161–180, 219
  (See Patterns; Natural patterns; Unnatural patterns; Tests for unnatural patterns; Interpretation of patterns)
  (See also the names of individual patterns)
Control charts

(See individual names of control charts: p-Charts, np-Charts, c-Charts, u-Charts, $\bar{X}$-charts, R charts, Charts for individual measurements, Demerit charts, "Dot" charts, Multi-vari charts, Summary control charts, "Sum and range" charts, "Total and range" charts, "X" charts t-Charts)
(See also Control charts in general,
Control chart sampling plans, 39, 246, 262–263, 265, 268, 274
Control charts in general
  administrative uses for, 3, 4, 10, 21, 22, 23, 46, 225–226
  advantages of, 9, 10, 36, 38, 83–84, 91, 97, 187, 202–203, 265
  appearance of, 192, 216, 221, 228–229
  as basis for correct interpretation of data, 9
  as related to assignable causes, 149–151
  as related to order of production, 151
  as foundation of a quality control program, vii, 4, 33, 187
  as source of assurance, 274
  as the central concept in statistical quality control, 4
  attributes, 5, 7–8, 11
  audits, of, 227
  based on sampling distributions, 23, 137, 151
  basis for confidence in, 10
  compared with other statistical methods, 78, 79, 82–84, 91, 93, 97, 98, 100–101, 106, 110, 131, 141, 143–144, 145
  confidence in, 10, 274
  consolidation of, 41, 199
  construction of, 12–23, 107–111, 193–197
  correlated, 121, 156, 176–177, 218, 223
  correlation on, 11, 143–144, 145, 153, 156, 161, 176–177
  durability of, 192
  effect of, in the shop, 37–38, 155, 164, 177, 187, 202–203, 235, 265
  experience in reading, 67
  formation of patterns on, 4, 149
  forms and routines for, 192, 207, 210–211, 213–215, 217–219, 227–229
  formulas for (See Control chart formulas)
  for solving problems, 31, 33, 34–36, 45–47, 63, 187, 202
  holders for, 192, 228
  improvement due to, 19–20, 164, 177, 202, 235, 265

in experimental work, 75–112, 220
interpretation of, 9, 10, 30–31, 53–56, 66–73, 152–180, 218–219
maintenance of, 192, 224, 227, 228–229
meaning of, 3, 5–10
mounting of, 192, 228
need for, vii, 9, 10, 15, 33–38, 45–47, 141, 158, 187–189, 190, 198–199, 202, 219, 265
non-random arrangement of samples on, 149, 160 (See Sequence)
plans for, in the shop (See Process control charts)
plotting of, 5–6, 12–15, 17–19, 20–21, 22, 51, 53, 65, 72–73, 143–144, 192, 213–216
plotting of, in an experiment, 82–83, 85, 98–99, 107–109, 111
properties of, 4, 10–12
random samples for, 51, 113, 114–116, 192, 207, 214
rational subgroups for, 151
reacting together, 156, 176–177, 218, 223
reading of, 67, 69 (See Interpretation)
reliability of, 10 (See Certainty; Risk)
removal of, 41, 189, 199, 219, 223, 227
results from, 10, 35–36, 38, 187, 225–226
reversion to, after sampling plan, 262, 263
right and wrong use of, in shop, 202
sequence of points on, 4, 6, 23, 29, 55–56, 72–73, 99, 109, 149, 151
simple introduction to, 5–10
simplicity of, 91, 97
statistical background of, 5–7, 23–25, 35–36, 37–38, 149
theory of, 5–7, 137–138, 149–161
types of, 10–12, 188
unnecessary, 219 (See Removal)
used as a basis for accepting product, 246, 262, 263, 274
used as sampling plan (See Control chart sampling plans)
used by inspectors, 39, 246, 262–263, 274
used by operators, 158, 164, 203, 235, 265
used in reports, 226
used to evaluate cost reduction savings, 224, 226
verification of, 10, 274
Who should plot? 216, 234

(*See* Process control charts; Process capability studies; Designed experiments)

(*See also* the individual names of control charts)

Control chart tests

(*See* Tests for unnatural patterns)

Control limits

based on R chart, 13, 14, 97, 111, 153, 156

based on residual, 97–98, 107–108

calculation of, 7–8, 12–23, 51–52, 64, 65, 74, 97, 98, 99, 107–108, 111, 191, 192, 194, 195–197, 198, 228, 229

calculation of, as a variable, 173, 219

calculation of, by statistical clerks, 229

compared with drawing limits, 16, 30–31, 62, 151

compared with spread of individuals, 13, 16, 30–31, 72–73, 137–138

confused with specification limits, 16, 30–31, 151, 190

economic, 64–65, 194, 195–197

explanation of, 7–9, 51–52, 87–88, 99, 107, 194–195

for a c-chart, 20, 72

for a chart of individual measurements, 22, 161, 173–174, 191, 196

for an np-chart, 20, 191, 229

for an R chart, 12–13, 97–98, 99, 108, 154

for an $\bar{X}$ chart, 13, 87–89, 99, 108, 138, 153–154

for a p-chart, 17–19, 191, 194, 196–197, 229

for a u-chart, 21, 191

for shop charts in general, 64, 192, 194–195, 196–197, 219, 229

in a designed experiment, 82, 87–89, 97, 98, 99, 107–108, 109

incorrect, 52, 153, 173–174, 219

inner, 99, 100, 107–108, 109

modified, 121, 195–197

outer, 99, 100, 107–109 (*See* Three sigma control limits)

precision of, 9, 52, 161

sensitivity of, 8, 9, 150, 161

special types of, 197–198

theory of, on the $\bar{X}$ chart, 138

too narrow for pattern, 11, 24, 72–73, 150, 153–154, 166

unsymmetrical, 18, 28, 182–183, 191

width of, 13, 17, 22, 87, 153–154, 173

width of, in a designed experiment, 109

Conveyors, 176, 256

Cooling, 69 (*See* Temperature)

Cooperation

between Operating and Engineering, 33, 38, 39–41, 45, 65, 74, 188, 190, 202, 219, 220, 223–226

in a cost reduction case, 226

through Quality Control Teams, 39–41, 45, 64, 66, 187–199, 201–202, 219, 220, 221, 223–229, 236

Copies of shop charts, 192, 207, 228

Core (for a relay), 64

Core plate, 58

Corrected main effects, 105, 106

Correction factor

in a sum of squares analysis, 81, 94, 96

in F-test, 79

Corrective

action, based on control charts, 41, 189–190, 198–199, 217–219, 223, 227, 263 (*See* Action)

sorting (*See* Sorting)

Correctness

of calculations, 162, 163, 173, 215, 227

of conclusions in an experiment, 77, 83–84, 92, 101, 112, 117

of conclusions in a process capability study, 54, 56, 61–63, 67, 72

of control charts, 10, 189–190, 199

of measurements (*See* Error)

of plotting, 163, 214–215, 227

of shop data, 49, 117, 214–216

Correlation, vii, 143–148

absence of 56, 143, 146

as related to cause and effect, 146, 176–177

as represented by a line of best fit, 144–145

as represented by a line of regression, 144–146

between characteristics, 35, 46, 113, 121, 176–177, 187, 218, 223

between control charts, 53, 69, 176–177, 218, 223

between specifications, 64, 120–121

between $\bar{X}$ and R points, 69, 156, 176–177

coefficient of, 145, 146–147

curvilinear, 148

degree of, 146, 147, 148, 177

discovery of, 46, 218, 223

level to level, 176–177

multiple, 148

negative, 143, 146, 156

on control charts, 143–144, 145, 156, 176, 177, 202, 218, 223

partial, 148

point to point, 69, 156, 176–177

positive, 143, 146, 156

possible effect of, on specifications, 64, 121

regression lines for, 144–145, 148

scatter diagrams for, 143

significance of, 56, 146, 147, 177

slope of, 144–145

trend arrangements for, 143–144

used as a method of simplifying patterns, 56

Cost reduction

as one of the aims in a process capability study, 34, 35, 36, 46, 47, 54, 62, 63, 71, 223–226, 228, 235

as one of the aims in a shop chart, 34, 36, 38, 187, 224, 226

as one of the objectives in sampling inspection, 39, 187, 233–236, 274

as one of the objects of a designed experiment, 34, 91, 101, 112, 226

carried out by Quality Control Team, 33, 41, 71, 223–226

closing of, 226

cooperation of Shop in, 224, 225–226

examples of, 38, 71, 226

formal cases of (*See* Cases)

from unnatural patterns, 35, 54, 171

importance of, in a quality control program, 33–34, 226

opportunities for, 34, 36, 54, 62, 71, 120, 171, 188, 225–226

reports on, 224, 225–226

through decreased inspection, 34, 38, 39, 71, 188, 225, 226, 233–236, 246, 273–274

through process capability studies, 10, 34, 36, 54, 62, 66–71, 224, 226

through process control charts, 10, 36, 38, 41, 62, 64, 72, 224–226, 265

through process improvement, 34, 36, 38, 71, 224, 225–226, 233

Costs

affected by grouping of inspection items, 263

affected by inspection, 233, 236, 244, 245–246, 254–255, 260, 273–274

affected by quality rating, 273

associated with producer's and consumer's risks, 245–246

associated with unnatural variation, 35

conflict of, with quality requirements, 265

effect of, on inspection levels, 255, 265

Costs, *continued*
information on, 40, 46
of obtaining data, 17, 47–48, 77, 92, 116, 188, 189
of inspection, 33, 34, 35, 36, 39, 46, 71, 187, 233–236, 246, 260, 263, 273–274
of maintenance, 4
of manufacture, 10, 33–34, 35, 36, 38, 46–47, 54, 62, 64, 187, 193, 217, 226, 236, 244–246, 255, 262–263, 265
of process control charts, 38, 189, 190–192, 199, 223, 225–226
of selecting samples, 260
reduction of (*See* Cost reduction)
standard, 40, 46
Counts, 11, 20–21, 137, 191
Courses, vii, 23, 33, 97
Coverage (with control charts), 34, 38, 41, 72, 189, 224–225, 226
Cracked insulators, lugs etc., 270
Cracks, 12, 113
Criteria
change in, 31, 159, 268
for action, 208–209, 237
for classifying units of product, 157, 159
for inspection, 227, 237, 268, 269
for process control, 208, 227
Criterion I (Shewhart's), 25 (footnote)
Critical
defects, 198, 263
material, 262
Crossbar frames, 20
Cross-classification, 36, 55, 72, 85, 92–93, 101–103, 167–169
Cross-referencing of layouts, 205, 227, 267, 270
Cubing, as a cause of skewness, 57
Curing, 102, 104
Current
difficulties in the shop, 33, 187, 202, 224
electrical, 66, 68, 71, 152
level of business, 226
production, 225, 226
shop charts, 189, 199, 224–225, 227, 228–229
Curtailed inspection, in double or multiple sampling, 261
Curve
AOQ, 251
drawn by eye, 31, 59, 137, 144
fitted to a set of data (*See* Curve fitting)
operating characteristic (*See* OC curves)
representing a sampling plan, 238–239
slope of, 144–145, 164, 242

Curve fitting, 139–141
Customer's interests, 246, 254, 264, 270, 273
Cutting tool, 207
Cycles
causes of, 69, 70, 161–162
examples of, 69, 162
in production, 66
in the sense of electrical frequencies, 48
of steps in a process capability study, 34–35, 36, 47, 63
on control charts, 11, 31, 53, 54, 69, 70, 160, 175
short, 160
tracing of, 69, 70

D

d_2 factor, 56, 58, 71, 89, 98, 108, 131, 196
Damage, 113, 156, 163, 180, 246
Data
action on, in a process capability study, 61, 62
amount of, for checking distribution shape, 56
amount of, for designed experiments, 77, 78–79, 90, 92, 110, 111, 112, 113
amount of, for detecting unnaturalness, 9, 28, 112, 146, 170
amount of, for engineering studies, 50–51, 55, 62, 63–64, 66–72
amount of, for shop charts, 63, 64, 191, 192, 207, 209, 223, 228–229
amount of, for testing normality, 78–79, 82, 133–134
amount of, in study of correlation, 146
amount of, in study of skewness, 56
analysis of (*See* Analysis; Analysis of factorial design; Analysis of variance)
attributes, 11, 17, 18, 31, 38, 47, 48–49, 50, 54, 56, 59, 72–73, 74, 113, 144, 157–160, 188–189, 191, 194, 196–197, 198, 206, 210, 225, 227–228, 237, 262, 269
classification of, 36, 55, 56, 72–73, 85, 92–93, 117, 218
collection of, in a process capability study (*See* Collection of data)
division of, 36, 55, 72, 166, 175, 176
engineering, 34, 46, 49, 63–64, 76, 117
for a designed experiment, 76–77, 78, 84, 86, 90, 92, 113, 115–117

for a process capability study, 36, 41, 47–51, 66–67, 72–73, 223, 228
for a shop chart, 65, 190–192, 207–210, 214–216, 227, 228–229
for performance studies, 74, 228
freaks in, 52–53, 68, 70, 116–117, 162–164, 166, 179, 209, 214
identification of (*See* Identification)
identification of, in an experiment, 85, 92, 98, 117
inspection, 268–269, 271
modification of, in making estimates, 61
non-random patterns in, 116
obtaining of (*See* Obtaining)
percentage, 5, 7–8, 11, 17, 18, 19–20, 48–49, 74, 113, 144, 157–159, 189, 191, 194, 196–198, 206, 210, 213, 215, 221–222, 225–226, 227
plotted in an experiment, 82, 85–88, 99
rearrangements of, 36, 53, 55, 56, 72–73, 75–76, 85, 109, 117, 143–144
recording of, 207, 210, 227, 268–269, 271
reduced, in an experiment, 103, 106
realiability of, 41, 49, 62, 84–91, 111, 113, 117, 213–216
restrictions imposed on, 96, 106
semi-variables, 12, 49–50, 113
separation of, 36, 54–56, 75–76, 149, 166–167, 168, 179–180, 218–219
significant categories in, 55, 166
simple breakdown in, 36, 55, 75, 166
sources of, for simplification of patterns, 36, 54–55, 75, 160, 166, 168, 218–219
submitted by process checker, 229
suitability of, 10–12, 15, 41, 47, 49, 61, 72, 77, 84, 89–90, 113–114, 190
variables, in general, 6, 8, 9–10, 11, 12, 14, 21–23, 137–139, 152–156, 160–161
variables, in engineering studies, 15–16, 47–48, 49–50, 53–59, 66–72, 78, 82, 84, 86, 92, 107–111, 113, 119–127, 141, 144, 147
variables, in ship charts, 188, 189, 191, 194, 195–198, 203–206, 209, 210, 212, 215, 218, 225. 227–229
work sampling, 50, 277
(*See* Records)

288

Data sheets, 208, 210, 271
Date of samples, 207, 210, 271
Days
  between samples, 192, 207
  of the week, 49, 114, 162
Day shift, 72, 73, 161, 162
  (*See* Shifts)
Decibels, 12, 14, 138, 139, 140, 141
Decimal point, as a variable, 173
Decisions
  about control charts, 187–199,
    219, 223, 228–229
  about the job, 40, 62, 64, 202, 216,
    218–219, 220, 223–224
  engineering, 33, 34–36, 46–47,
    53–54, 56, 58, 61–64, 77, 83,
    87, 89, 92, 99–101, 119–127,
    141, 146, 192, 194, 196, 199,
    212, 219–220, 224, 233–236,
    263–265, 274
Defective units
  meaning of, 31, 159
  distinguished from "defects," 20,
    206, 239, 267
  reduction of 38, 46, 71, 233, 265
Defects
  causes of, 46, 72–73
  classification of, in inspection,
    263, 270
  classification of, in quality rating,
    263, 264
  classification of, on demerit
    charts, 198
  combination of, on a *p*-chart, 17,
    48, 59, 157, 159, 189, 196
  definition of, 20, 31, 159, 206,
    267
  failure to look for, 159
  level of, on a *p*-chart, 159
  number of, 20–21, 46, 191, 206,
    229, 233, 236, 239, 240, 265
  plotted on a *c*-chart, 20, 72–73,
    189
  prevention of, 35, 36, 187–189,
    201, 202, 217–219, 221, 225–
    226, 233, 235, 265
  reduction of, 10, 46, 71, 187, 189,
    225, 233, 235–236, 265
  vs. defectives, 20, 206, 239, 267
Definitions
  of technical terms associated with
    control charts, 12, 17, 20, 21,
    150, 151, 152, 197–198
  of technical terms associated with
    patterns, 24–25, 29, 160, 161–
    180
  of terms used in designed experi-
    ments, 76, 77, 78–80, 85, 86,
    89, 92–93, 96, 97, 98, 101, 103,
    104, 105, 106–107, 109
  of terms used in engineering
    studies, 124, 143, 144, 145,
    225

of terms used in inspection, 39,
    233, 234–236, 237, 238, 244–
    245, 247, 249, 251, 256, 259,
    260, 262–263, 267–269, 270,
    273, 274
of terms used in process capability
    studies, 35, 36, 45–46, 47, 49,
    56, 61, 74, 75
of terms used in quality control,
    3, 4, 9, 11, 33, 40, 50, 74, 89,
    90, 129–131, 134, 135, 137,
    139, 154
of terms used in shop control, 36,
    191, 194, 195, 205–207, 214,
    220, 221
used by statistical clerks, 229
Degreaser, 50, 178
Degrees
  associated with freaks, 162
  of assurance, 274
  of certainty (*See* Certainty)
  of completion, in engineering
    studies, 36, 47, 63, 64, 74
  of confidence, 273–274, 278
  of defectiveness, 159, 190
  of freedom, 79–81, 95, 96, 106
  of mixture, 179
  of protection, 273–274
  of significance, in an experiment,
    96–97, 99, 107, 109
  of skewness, 131, 156
  of training for operators, 46, 164,
    168, 204
  measurement by, 49–50, 113
Delays
  cost of, 217, 246
  in obtaining supplies, 246, 260
  in production, 33, 77, 187, 202,
    246
  in taking action, 190, 217, 219
  reduction of, in the shop, 33, 202,
    246, 260–262
  unnecessary, 246, 262
Demarcation, line of, 159
Demerits, 198, 263, 264, 270, 273,
    278
Demonstrations for operators, 202
Dented units, 214
Department of Defense
  (*See* U. S. Dept. of Defense)
Department of Navy
  (*See* U. S. Dept. of Navy)
Dependent variables
  (*See* Variables)
Depth of nicks and scratches, 113
Derivation
  of AOQL's for Final Inspection,
    264, 273, 278
  of plans for various inspection
    levels, 273–274

Design
  and development, 4, 10, 34, 35, 36,
    38, 46–47, 52, 54, 60–63, 75,
    76, 77, 83, 89, 91, 101, 141,
    119–122, 122–127, 140, 141,
    143–144, 198, 205, 219, 220,
    221, 224, 226
  "balanced block," 92–93
  capability of, 35, 46, 220, 224
  changes in, 46, 51, 69, 91, 198,
    212, 219
  comparison of, 35, 46, 224
  improvement in, 38
  new, 46, 47, 52, 224
  of a fixture, 62, 69, 164, 213, 219
  of a machine, 34, 35, 46, 47, 69,
    70, 83, 155, 171, 175, 213
  of a tool, 34, 35, 46, 47, 62, 63,
    121, 155, 169, 212, 219
  of process control charts, 63–65,
    189–192, 193–199, 211, 219,
    223, 227–229
  of product, 10, 34, 38, 40, 46, 47,
    52, 60–61, 76, 91, 101, 119–
    127, 140, 143–144, 193, 198,
    205, 219, 220, 224, 226
  of sampling plans, 263–265, 273
  quality control in (*See* Design
    problems)
  statistical, 76–77, 85, 92–93, 101–
    107
Designations on control charts, 65,
    207, 209, 228–229
Designed experiments, vii, 4, 28, 34,
    36, 41, 51, 55–56, 62, 75–117,
    120, 121, 122, 183, 187, 219,
    220, 224, 229
  advantages of, 75–77, 84–85, 91–
    93, 112, 187
  analysis of, 78–83, 87–89, 93–97,
    97–111
  assignable causes in, 83, 87, 89,
    111
  boxes in, 92, 97, 98, 101–103
  calculations for, 79–82, 86, 89,
    94–97, 97–98, 107–111
  combination of variables in, 89–
    90, 91–93, 94–98, 99–101,
    102–106, 114
  conclusions from, 75, 76, 80, 81,
    83, 87–89, 97, 100–101, 109,
    111–112
  control limits for, 83, 87, 89, 98,
    99, 100, 108–109
  diagrams for, 98, 109, 110–111
  effects in, 94–95, 98, 101–106
  error in, 103, 168
  examples of, 77–78, 84–85, 92–93
  factors in, 76, 77, 84, 90, 92–93,
    98, 99, 101–103, 106, 108,
    113–114
  five factor, 90, 110
  five percent level in, 100
  four factor, 90, 91–109

Designed experiments, *continued*
  guides for, 98, 99, 109
  higher order interactions in, 105–106
  identification of data in, 85, 98, 99, 100, 109
  inner control limits for, 99, 100, 107, 109
  interactions in, 36, 76, 77, 93, 96–97, 98, 104–106, 107, 168
  interpretation of charts in, 83, 84, 87–89, 100–101, 109, 111–112, 116–117
  levels in, 93, 94, 97, 102–103, 107
  limitations of, 76, 112
  main effects in, 93, 96, 98, 101–103, 104, 105, 107
  marking x's in, 100, 107, 109
  number of observations per box, 93, 107, 111, 113
  numerical effects in, 98, 99
  one factor, 76, 77–84
  one percent level in, 99, 107, 109
  plotting of, 82, 85, 87–88, 98–100, 107–109, 229
  potential effects in, 95, 98
  practical advice on, 112–117
  range chart in, 97–98, 100, 109
  related points in, 109
  residual in, 81, 93, 94, 96, 97–98, 100, 101, 103, 105, 106, 107, 110–111, 113, 168
  R points in, 100, 109
  shortcuts in, 97–98, 106, 110
  significance in, 80, 81, 83, 87, 89, 97, 100, 107–109
  significant points in, 87, 89, 97, 99, 100, 109
  simplification of data in, 102–103, 105, 106
  square root values in, 98
  symbols used in, 98, 99, 109
  tests for unnatural patterns in, 83, 100, 109
  three factor, 89, 90, 110
  three sigma control limits for, 82, 87, 88, 99, 100, 107–108, 109
  two factor, 84–91
  use of asterisks in, 97, 99–100, 107, 109
  use of question marks in, 99–100, 107, 109
  using attributes data, 113
  using variables data, 77–112
  variables in, 4, 76, 77, 83, 84, 88, 89–90, 92–93, 100, 101–103, 112, 113–114
  $\bar{X}$ points in, 100, 109
  (*See* Design of experiment)
Design engineer, 4, 10, 40, 46–47, 52, 60–61, 76, 91–92, 101, 119–127, 198, 219, 220, 224
  (*See* Design problems)

Design of experiment
  as related to process capability studies, 4, 34, 36, 41, 55–56, 63, 75, 76, 77, 83, 90, 91, 112, 114, 120, 121, 168, 218, 220–221, **224**
  in general, 4, 34, 36, 55, 56, 75–77
  meaning of "design," 76, 84–85, 86, 89–90, 92–93, 101–103
  references on, 101, 277–278
  (*See* Designed experiments)
Design problems, 4, 10, 46, 52–53, 119–122, 122–127, 167, 205, 224, 225–226
  (*See* Design; Design engineer)
Desired average, as basis for shop control chart, 64, 193
Destructive testing, 113, 188, 197, 254
Detail inspection (also called 100% inspection), 46, 188, 190, 226, 233–236, 249–251, 254, 256, 263, 265
Details (for a tool), 213
Deterioration of quality, 233, 273
Development
  expense, 226
  of a product (*See* Design and development)
  of a quality control program, vii, 10, 33–34, 41, 224–226
  of manufacturing methods, 34, 47, 226
  of new processes, 4, 36, 46, 47, 167, 180, 224, 226
  quality control during (*See* Design problems)
Deviations from authorized procedures, 45, 61, 158, 220
Diagnosis of production troubles, 11, 36, 188, 202, 217
Diagrams
  for calculating residual, 97, 110, 111
  for identifying data in an experiment, 92, 98, 101–102
  for plotting control charts in an experiment, 99, 108, 109
Diameter, as a variable, 6, 8, 10, 12, 47
Die, 162
Dielectric breakdown, 162
Differences
  as potential assignable causes, 6, 66, 151, 156, 162, 163, 167, 171, 180, 190, 215, 218–219
  between shop charts and process capability studies, 63
  due to natural variation, 6, 7, 62, 150
  in calibration, 53, 113, 153, 159, 165, 175
  in inspection levels, 246, 247, 264, 273
  in training of operators, 204

  in treatment of product, 155
  related to systematic variation, 175, 176
  significant, 6, 16, 25–28, 35, 36, 46, 61, 75, 78, 79–81, 82, 87–88, 96–97, 99, 103, 107, 109, 112, 145, 146, 150, 218–219
  (*See* Changes)
Difficulties in the shop, 15–16, 19, 36, 37–38, 159, 165, 188, 189–190, 202, 246, 254–255, 260–263
Digits, 116
Dimensions, 6, 8, 10, 12, 15, 46, 152, 177, 190
Directions
  for making control charts (*See* names of individual charts)
  for plotting, in an experiment, 82–83, 84–85, 98–99, 107–109
Dirt, 178, 212
Discriminating power
  of a measuring instrument, 87, 88–89
  of a sampling plan, 242
Discs (used in manufacture), 162, 165
Dispersion, **129–131**
  (*See* Spread; Standard deviation)
Disposal of product, 262
Distortion, 90
Distributions, 6, 46, 129–141
  addition of, 122–124, 124–127
  advantages of working with, 119, 202
  as an inspection requirement, 46, 119, 122, 265
  as related to fluctuations, 6, 23, 24
  associated with freaks, 163
  as statistical laws, 6–7
  center of, 30, 53, 56, 71, 120, 121, 129, 138, 139–140, 152, 160, 188
  center of, as an inspection requirement, 119, 122, 265
  changes in, 174, 180 (*See* Changes)
  characteristics of, 56, 63, 129
  combinations of (*See* Mixtures)
  compared with specifications, 30–31, 58–59, 71, 119–122
  component, 68, 122, 124–125, 127, 153, 155, 160
  double (*See* Bimodal)
  estimates of percentages in, 30–31, 56–59, 71, 127, 132–133, 135–136
  examples of, 15, 37, 57–59, 78, 137–138, 139–141, 152–179
  fitted to observed data, 139–141
  from a constant system of causes, 6, 45, 170–171
  in nature, 6
  interpretation of, 16, 61, 78, 140–141

location of, 62, 64, 65, 120–121, 171, 174, 179, 188, 193–196, 226

may look alike on a p-chart, 158

misuse of, 61, 78, 141

mixtures of, 58, 68, 160, 166

non-linear combinations of, 123 (footnote)

non-normal, 31, 56–58, 59, 69–70, 122, 134–136, 160–161, 182–183, 196

normal, 30–31, 56, 58–59, 78–79, 80, 82, 83, 127, 131–134, 138, 139–140, 154, 170, 180–182, 195–196

of ranges, 137, 181, 182

peaks in, 136, 158, 162, 166, 175

plotted from data in $\bar{X}$ and R chart, 16, 53, 138–139

plotting of, 15, 30, 78, 138–141

probabilities associated with, 132–136, 181–183

profile of, 131, 160 (See Shape)

proportions of, 153

requirements, 46, 119, 265

sampling, 23, 137–138, 151, 180–183

separation of, 68, 155, 165, 166, 169, 173, 179

shape of (See Shape)

shift in, 166, 174

should not be used for estimates, 61, 141

spread of, 9 (footnote), 30–31, 45, 56, 58–59, 62, 71, 83, 89, 119–122, 124–127, 129–132, 137–139, 154–156, 195–196

spread of, as an inspection requirement, 119, 122, 265

steep part of, 159

theory of, 6, 7, 23, 137–138, 151

truncated, 57

uses of, 15, 16, 53, 61, 78, 139–141 (See Frequency distribution)

Dividing line, in classification, 159

Dodge, H. F., 256, 262, 275, 277

Dodge-Romig sampling tables, 241, 242, 245 (footnote), 249, 250 251, 253, 254, 255, 256

Door of welder, 213

"Dot" charts, 198

Double centerlines (on shop control charts), 64, 65, 193–196

Double sampling, 238, 242, 259, 260, 261

Doubling of AOQL's, 273

Downtime on machines, 38, 226

Drawings, 16, 30, 119, 151, 153, 205 (See Blueprints; Specifications)

Drift
  as a source of error in measurement, 90
  of a process, 67, 90, 153, 175
  of a test set, 46, 113, 153, 178, 218

Driver on a highway, 216

Drop (in a level or curve), 159, 164, 174

Dropouts
  charts on, 38, 48, 189, 225, 227
  minimized by process control charts, 38
  records of, 224–225, 227, 264
  reduction of, 225

Drying time (as a variable), 91, 92, 93, 100, 101

Dullness of a tool, 178

Duncan, A. J., 79, 133, 134, 148, 277, 278

Duplicate
  conclusions, in an experiment, 111, 112
  measurements, 6, 84–86, 90, 93, 111, 113

Durability of charts, 192

Duties
  of engineers, 34–36, 39–41, 45–74, 75–77, 119–127, 187–192, 198–199, 201, 202, 212, 219, 220, 223–227, 236, 244–246, 254–255, 263–265, 273–274
  of inspectors, 39, 216, 218, 219, 227, 234, 235, 236, 237, 267–271
  of management, vii, 33–34, 41, 226
  of process checkers, 41, 159, 192, 205–212, 213–216, 217, 227
  of product engineers (See Duties of engineers)
  of quality control engineers, 33, 39–41, 45–74, 75–77, 112–117, 120–121, 183, 187–199, 201–202, 213, 216, 218–222, 223–229, 233–236, 254–255, 263–265, 273–274
  of statistical clerks, 216, 228–229
  of supervisors, 39–41, 190–192, 201–216, 217–222, 223–227, 236
  of suppliers, 39, 224 (See Piece parts)
  of the Quality Control Team, vii, 33, 39–41, 45, 64, 66, 187, 189–192, 198–199, 201–202, 213, 219, 220, 223–229, 236 (See Responsibilities)

E

E_2 factor, 196

Early operations
  effect of, 167, 171, 180, 189, 202, 218
  importance of, 37–38, 46, 48, 51, 63, 64, 114, 187, 188

Earnings, 11, 22, 203

Eccentricity, 57, 162, 198

Economical state of control (See Control)

Economic centerlines, 64–65, 192, 193–194, 195–196

Economic considerations
  in choice of sampling plan, 239, 245–246, 254–255, 263–265
  in inspection, 39, 187, 233–236, 246, 260–262, 263, 264, 265, 273–274
  in process capability studies, 34–36, 46, 54, 61–65, 71
  in setting up shop control charts, 37, 38, 64–65, 188, 189–190, 199, 227
  in specifications, 34, 36, 64–65, 71, 122
  in the quality control program, 4, 10, 33–34, 34–46, 38, 41, 46–47, 187, 224–226, 233, 273
  on p-charts (in the shop), 196–197
  on $\bar{X}$ and R charts (in the shop), 63, 64–65, 193–196
  related to OC curves, 242–246, 255, 265
  (See Costs; Cost reduction)

Economic control limits, 64–65, 194, 195–197

Economic decisions, 36, 62, 64–65, 188, 190, 192, 193–194, 199, 220, 223

Economic gains, 10, 33–34, 36, 38, 54, 61–63, 71–72, 101, 187, 199, 202, 217, 219, 220, 225–226

Economic stopping point, 33–34, 35, 36, 45, 47, 55, 61–63, 166, 194

Effectiveness
  of maintenance, 155, 162, 164, 167–169, 175, 178, 180, 204, 206, 219, 227
  of process controls, 16, 19, 34, 37–38, 62, 64, 155, 164, 167, 177, 178, 187, 226, 233, 235, 265

Effects (in an experiment)
  calculation of, 93–97, 98, 102–103
  removal of, 103, 105, 106

Efficiency
  in the shop, 10, 21, 33, 37, 38, 71, 158, 202–203, 224, 226 (See Output)
  in tracing causes, 261 (See Active causes)

Electric current, 68
  (See Current)

Electrical characteristics, 6, 8, 9, 10, 66, 71, 77, 90

Electrical properties
  (See Electrical characteristics)

Electrical signals, 14, 67

Electrodes, 10, 37, 212

Electrons, 6

Electron tubes, 3, 4, 224, 225

Elements
  in a process, 35, 36, 53, 54–56, 155, 158, 164, 166, 176, 218–219
  of a machine, 3, 151, 161, 207
Elimination
  of an adjustment, 67
  of assignable causes, 9, 35–36, 37, 53, 54–56, 61–63, 66–72, 122, 150–151, 153, 217
  of gaging, 71, 72
  of interference in a circuit, 67
  of lines of identification (in an experiment), 108
  of a major variable, 55, 67
  of noise, 67
  of 100% inspection, 234–236
  of operations, 34, 47
  of possible causes, 69, 153, 218
  of unnatural variations, 34, 35–36, 37, 75
  of unstable mixtures, 68–69, 166
  of variables in an experiment, 76, 114
  of variables in a process capability study, 34, 55, 66–68, 166, 171
Emergencies
  in shop and engineering, 40, 187, 202
  inspection plans for, 233, 246, 263, 273–274
Emphasis
  in a quality control program, vii, 33, 34, 41, 226
  on control charts, vii, 4, 9, 10, 33, 38, 75, 84, 187–190, 201–203, 217, 223
  on cost reduction, 33, 34, 36, 38, 224, 225, 226
  on demerits, 198
  on designed experiments, 4, 34, 76, 77
  on Engineering, vii, 10, 34–36, 38, 39–41, 45–47, 53–56, 61, 63–65, 69, 70, 75, 77, 122, 188, 192, 219, 220, 223–226, 233, 236, 245–246, 260–265
  on Inspection, vii, 39, 233–236
  on Operating, vii, 10, 33–34, 38, 39–41, 45, 63–65, 67, 72–73, 114, 120–121, 187, 190, 201–204, 216–219, 220, 223–224, 233, 236, 246, 255, 260–262, 263, 265, 274
  on process capabilities, vii, 33–34, 36, 62, 64, 75–76, 112, 124, 125, 127, 187, 235
  on Quality Control Teams, vii, 39–41, 187, 223
End
  of parts, 90
  of process capability studies, 36, 45, 47, 61, 62, 63, 71, 74, 75, 221
  of month or week, 189

  of rods or strips of stock, 156, 163
End product, 46, 48, 51, 171, 233, 264–265, 270, 273
Engineering
  comments on a control chart, 53, 212
  cooperation with shop, vii, 33–34, 38, 39–41, 45, 49, 63–65, 66–72, 74, 114, 117, 120–121, 124–125, 127, 187–199, 204, 209, 212, 213, 214, 219, 220, 223–229
  courses (See Engineering training)
  data, analysis of, 46 (See Process capability studies; Designed experiments)
  decisions, 33, 34, 36, 46–47, 53–54, 61–63, 64, 99, 192, 194, 196, 199, 212, 265
  effort, 63–64, 77, 246
  for inspection, 46, 224, 226, 233–236, 242–246, 254–255, 260–265, 267–271, 273–274
  for process control, 33–38, 39–41, 45–46, 61–65, 66–72, 74, 76, 83, 101, 112, 119–127, 187–199, 201–202, 205–211, 212, 219, 220–229
  for quality control program (See Development of a quality control program)
  information, 34, 35, 46–47, 54, 75–77, 177, 219, 220
  judgment (See Engineering decisions)
  knowledge, 35, 40, 46, 54, 75, 77, 114, 159, 177, 219
  layouts, 25, 192, 199, 205–209, 213, 214, 217, 218, 224, 227, 236, 262, 263, 265, 267–271
  problems, 3, 4, 10, 33–34, 35–36, 46–47, 61–63, 66–72, 75–77, 84, 91, 112–113, 119–127, 187, 188, 204, 219, 220, 223–224, 225–226, 233–236, 242–246, 254–255, 262, 263–265, 273, 274
  questions, 4, 34, 46–47, 75, 220
  responsibility, 46, 204
  studies, 4, 10, 55, 63–64, 188, 190, 191, 212, 226 (See Process capability studies)
  studies in the shop, 34, 36, 38, 39–41, 51, 63–64, 66–72, 75, 77, 162, 167, 188, 220, 226
  time, 63–64, 77, 92, 246
  training, vii, 23, 33, 97
Engineering experiments
  conducted in the shop, 77, 117, 220
  effect of, on patterns, 167, 180
  examples of, 77–78, 84, 91–93
  importance of, 36, 62, 75–77, 120–121, 219, 220

  interpretation of, 46, 76–77, 78–117
  made inconclusive by unnatural variation, 35, 38, 75, 220
  results of, 46, 112, 224
  used for cost reduction, 226
  (See Designed experiments)
Engineers
  (See Design engineers; Product engineers; Wage incentive engineers; Quality control engineers)
Equipment
  as a process variable, 3, 35, 38, 46, 51, 53, 67, 70, 89, 90–91, 158, 159, 164, 167, 180, 203, 204, 206, 215, 216, 217, 219, 235
  changes in, 47, 53, 70, 113, 174, 215
  complex, 3–4, 21, 189, 191
  held up unnecessarily, 246
  unreliable, 180
Equipment engineering
  (See Wired equipment)
Equivalence of variances
  assumption of, 78, 80, 82
  hypothesis of, 82
Erratic
  causes, 150, 155, 166
  controls, 167
  fluctuations, 53, 68, 72, 166, 167, 174
  performance of a machine, 15–16, 166
  variables, 37, 69, 166–167, 179–180
Erratic patterns, 31, 53, 54, 166, 167, 174, 179, 204
  estimating from, 59–60
  meaning of (See examples on pages 60, 67 and 72. See also the names of specific patterns such as Instability, Mixtures)
  simplification of, 54–56, 66–72, 72–73, 166
Error
  experimental, 103 (See Residual)
  in calculating, 162, 163, 180, 214–215
  in plotting, 163, 166, 180, 215
  in substraction, 163
  normal distribution of, 88
  of estimate (in correlation), 145
  of first kind, 25 (footnote), 99–100, 107
  of second kind, 25 (footnote)
  (See Error of measurement; Trial and error methods)
Error of measurement, 46, 49, 50, 53, 61, 62, 75, 76, 84–91, 111, 113, 163, 215, 219
  (See Precision of measurement; Accuracy of measurement)

Establishment of standards, 46, 54
Estimates
    based on R chart, 156
    from a pattern out of control, 54–
        56, 59–60, 60–61
    from a sample, 50, 278
    of costs, 34, 35, 38, 46–47, 62, 233,
        236, 245–246, 260, 263, 273–
        274
    of current production, 226
    of expenditures for cost reduction,
        226
    of operator capability, 35, 46, 73,
        170
    of percentage outside of limits,
        30–31, 58–59, 119, 120, 127,
        132–133, 135–136
    of process capability, 45, 56, 58–
        59, 71, 73, 127, 235
    of process spread, 56 (See Spread)
    of random variation, 103
    of residual, 95–96, 97–98, 103, 105,
        106, 107, 110
    of savings, 224, 226
    of skewness, 53, 56–58, 61, 122,
        196
    of standards and allowances, 34,
        35, 36, 46, 53–54, 61, 122,
        125, 235, 265
    of ultimate number of charts, 38,
        189, 225
    to be based on a natural pattern,
        35, 53–54, 61
    wrong, 60–61, 141
Etching solution, 178, 218
Evenness of plating, 156
Evidence
    obtained from control charts, 9,
        10, 83, 100, 218
    of an effect, in an experiment, 103
    of the Law of Large Numbers, 6
    on an R chart, 66, 67, 68, 154–156,
        168, 194 (See R chart)
    statistical, 8, 9, 10, 45, 75, 103
Examination of units, 163, 218
Examples
    of calculations, 14, 18, 22, 58–59,
        71, 78, 79–82, 86, 89, 94–97,
        98, 103–106, 107–109, 124–
        127, 130, 147–148, 180–183,
        196, 229, 240, 242, 251–252
    of c-charts, 72–73
    of chart for individual measure-
        ments, 22, 23
    of designed experiments, 82, 87,
        88, 92, 99, 100
    of marking of charts, 212–213
    of patterns, 5, 8, 15, 16, 19, 23,
        24–30, 52, 60, 67–71, 72–73,
        74, 82, 85, 87–88, 99, 120–
        121, 144, 146, 153–154, 161–
        180, 203–206, 212, 221
    of pattern simplification, 66–72,
        72–73

of p-charts, 8, 19, 74, 144, 194
of process capability studies, 66–
    73
of shop charts, 65, 203–206, 211,
    212–213
of $\bar{X}$ and R charts, 15, 16, 31, 65,
    67–71, 82, 85, 87–88, 99, 120–
    122, 144, 203–206
Exhaustion of degreaser, 178
Existing processes, 34, 226
Expansion
    as a variable, 153
    of plotting scales, 190
Expense
    of certain operations, 34, 47, 122
    of development, 226
    of obtaining data, 48, 77, 92,
        116, 188
    of sorting, 122, 226, 234, 236, 263,
        265
Experience
    as a means of interpreting control
        charts (See Job knowledge)
    as a variable, 38, 55, 72–73, 158,
        167, 204
    gives evidence of the Law of Large
        Numbers, 6, 10
    in using control charts, 10, 40, 66–
        67, 201–206, 219
    of operators, 6, 30, 73, 158, 167,
        204
    results in conflict with, 77, 218,
        219
Experiment, steps in, 47, 75–77
    (See Designed experiments)
Experimental
    error, 103
    units, 92, 163, 180
    work, 167, 180
Experimental control charts
    headings on, 84, 99, 108–109
    identification on, 99, 108–109
    interpretation of, 83, 87–88, 89,
        99–101, 111–112
    plotting of, 82, 84–85, 87–88, 97,
        98–99, 107–109, 116
    used in the shop, 38, 63–64, 74,
        188, 220, 228
Experiments
    affected by state of control in the
        shop, 10, 38, 67, 75, 112, 188,
        220
    compared with process capability
        studies, 4, 34, 36, 47, 75–76,
        112
    complicated designs for, 77
    conduct of, 112–117
    containing more than one meas-
        urement per box, 93, 111,
        113
    importance of, 34, 36, 41, 55–56,
        62, 75–77, 120, 121, 219, 220,
        224

interpretation of, 77, 78–84, 87–
    89, 92, 93–101, 107, 109, 111–
    112
involving a number of variables,
    77, 89–90, 91–111
meaning of terms in, 76, 103, 104,
    106–107
on a going process, 76–77, 191,
    220, 224, 228
planning of, 41, 84–85, 92–93,
    112–117
types of, 76–77
using attributes data, 113
using variables data, 77–111
without statistical design, 77, 84,
    91–92, 220
(See Designed Experiments.)
Exponential scale, 163
Extraneous causes, 6, 9, 10, 45, 53,
    150, 166, 171

F

Facilities
    as a variable, 158, 175
    breakdown of, 163
    for handling product, 5, 40, 246,
        260
    for testing (See Test sets)
    inspection of, 227
    maintenance of (See Mainte-
        nance)
    need for productive work, 246
    reduction of, 38
    (See Equipment)
Factorial design, 75, 92–93, 101–107
Factorial experiment
    (See Factorial design)
Factors
    for calculating control limits on an
        $\bar{X}$ and R chart, 12
    for estimating σ', 131
    for limits on experimental control
        charts, 107–108
    in an experiment, 4, 36, 76–77, 84,
        89–90, 92–93, 97, 98–99, 101–
        103, 106, 110–111, 113–114
    to be plotted in an experiment,
        108, 109
Factual reports, 226
Failure
    to look for defects, 159
    to meet requirements, 15, 19, 20,
        66, 121, 189, 204, 205, 206,
        234
Fatigue, 161, 162, 178, 180, 219,
    236
Feeding of parts, 19, 83
Feeler gage, 270
Ferrell, E. B., 198, 277
Files of charts and layouts, 192, 207,
    227, 228–229
Filter, 67

Final inspection
AOQL's for, 264, 273
made compatible with quality rating, 263, 264, 270, 273
reduction of, 10, 38, 39, 46, 71, 120, 187, 188, 234, 236, 246, 260–263, 273–274
relations with shop, 37, 202, 224, 226, 227, 236, 254–255, 262, 263, 265, 269, 274, 278
sampling plans for, 39, 255–263, 264, 265, 273–274
use of results of, 39, 234, 269, 270
Final tests of product, 48, 51, 167, 217, 233, 234, 260–262, 264, 270, 273
Finish, 102
First order interactions, 93, 94, 98, 105, 106
First shift, 72, 73, 161, 162
(*See* Shifts)
Fisher, R. A. 101, 277
Fit of parts
(*See* Clearances)
Five factor experiment, 75, 90, 110–111
Five percent limits, 97, 99, 100, 107, 109
Five week month, 191
Fixtures
as a variable, 3, 10, 35, 53, 55, 69, 156, 158, 162, 168, 176, 203, 207, 212, 219
changes in, 53, 69, 83, 164, 175, 212, 213, 215, 219, 235
clogging of, 178
design of, 62, 69, 164, 213, 219
for holding charts, 192
play in, 55, 68, 155, 162, 167, 180, 219, 235
re-design of, 62, 69
used by Operating as essential equipment, 216
Flatness of spring, 270
Flattening of reeds, 213
Flaws, 20
Flexibility of control chart method, 83, 91, 97, 106
Flow of product, 260
Fluctuating patterns, 5, 6, 9, 24, 66, 72, 160, 175, 176, 178, 190, 219, 237–238
Fluctuations
abnormally large, 11, 24, 66, 68, 166–167
abnormally small, 11, 24, 29, 172–174
as related to distributions, 6
causes of, 6, 150, 152–180, 217–219
effect of, on a shop chart, 190
erratic, 53, 60, 68, 72, 166, 167, 174
evidence of, in the world around us, 5–7

in a pattern, 5–6, 7, 9, 24–25
in a process, 8–9, 30, 35, 37, 56, 60, 61, 62, 64, 65, 67, 122, 193, 195, 196, 203, 220
in voltage, 10, 162
limits of, 7–9 (*See* Control limits)
magnitude of, 6, 11, 24, 29, 68, 160, 166, 172–174, 190
natural, 6, 24, 150
normal to a process, 203
on an R chart, 67, 69, 154–156, 168
on an $\bar{X}$ chart, 67–68, 69, 152–154, 166, 168
on a p-chart, 173, 196–197
random, 8–9, 24, 46, 103, 149, 150, 156, 161, 172, 173, 175, 176–177, 203, 237–238
sampling, 5–6, 7–8, 24–25, 46, 103, 112, 145, 146, 203, 237, 238
statistical, 5–9, 46, 173, 203
unnatural, 6, 9, 24–25
(*See* Patterns)
Follow (of a control chart)
(See Tendency to follow)
Forecasts, 278
to be based on a natural pattern, 35, 46–47, 53–54, 59–60
(*See* Predictions)
Foreign particles, 20, 270
Formal
control chart audits, 227
cost reduction cases, 34, 36, 224, 226
inspection audit, 227
study of interactions, 4, 36, 75, 94–97, 167–168
Formal analysis (other than control chart)
analysis of variance by the sum of squares method, 78, 81, 82, 83, 93–97
Bartlett's test, 78, 79, 80, 82, 83
Chi-square test, 78, 82, 133, 140, 278
comparison of averages, 78, 80–81, 83
correlation, 143–148
F-test, 78, 79, 81, 82, 83, 96–97
other tests of significance, 134, 278
regression, 144–145
test for significance of correlation coefficient, 146
tests for constancy of cause system, 78, 79
tests for equivalence of variances, 79–80
tests for normality, 78–79, 133–134
t-test, 78, 80, 82, 83
Formation
of patterns on a control chart, 4, 149
of samples in an experiment, 82, 85, 108, 109

Forms for recording and charting, 41, 192, 227
(*See* Control chart forms; Inspection forms)
Formulas
for addition of distributions, 123
for AOQ, 251
for AOQL, 251
for arithmetic mean, 12, 129
for calculating control chart tests, 180–183
for c-charts, 20
for charts of individual measurements, 8, 21–22
for correlation coefficient, 146
for error of measurement, 88, 89
for estimating percentage outside of limits, 31, 58–59, 133, 135, 136
for estimating sigma, 56, 58, 130, 131
for estimating sigma from a sample, 131
for estimating the spread of a normal distribution, 56, 61, 122, 132, 195
for estimating the spread of a skewed distribution, 56, 61, 122, 196
for line of regression, 145
for modified control limits on shop charts, 195–196
for np-charts, 20
for p-charts, 7–8, 17
for range, 11, 12, 131
for removing the effects of a variable, 102–103
for residual, 97, 106, 110
for sigma of averages compared to sigma of parent, 138
for standard deviation, 130
for standard error of estimate, 145
for u-charts, 21
for variance, 130
for $\bar{X}$ and R charts, 12, 14
to be used in designed experiments, 98, 104–106, 107–108, 110
Four factor experiment, 75, 90, 91–109
Four week month, 191
Fraction defective, 17, 20, 191
(*See* Percent defective)
Freaks
apparent, 52–53, 58, 116–117, 162, 164
as a pattern, 11, 161, 179
in designed experiments, 83, 111, 116–117
in process capability studies, 52–53, 54, 58, 68
in shop data, 192, 209, 214, 215
interpretation of, 155–156, 160, 162–164, 179

on a chart for individual measurements, 160, 163
on *p*-chart, 11, 163
on *R* chart, 68, 70, 153, 155–156, 163, 166
on $\bar{X}$ chart, 11, 70, 153, 163
treatment of, 52, 53, 117, 192, 209, 214, 269
Freedom, degrees of, 95, 96, 97, 106
Freeman, H. A., 277
Frequency
electrical, 48, 90, 164
known, used as a standard, 90
of checking, 41, 192, 209, 214, 227
of defects (on a *p*-chart), 159
of re-grinding, 203
of re-setting, 16, 67, 166, 188, 203–204
of sampling, 219, 262
of trouble associated with certain characteristics, 188
Frequency distributions
addition of, 68, 122–123
affected by error of measurement, 89
comparison of, with specification, 30–31, 119–122
for comparing machines, 15
for comparing methods, 78
specified as a requirement, 119, 265
study of, in engineering, 45, 46, 53–54, 56, 61, 68, 70, 83, 152–180, 220
study of, in the shop, 16, 30–31, 37, 188, 195–196, 202, 220
theory of, 23
(*See* Distributions)
Fresh copies of shop control charts, 192, 207, 228
Front insulator, 270
Fry, T. C., 134, 277
F-test, 78, 79, 81, 82, 83, 96–97
Fully reduced data, 106
Furnace, as a variable, 21, 51, 114, 189

G

Gages
as a process variable, 3, 10, 46, 49, 113, 158, 162, 167, 168, 171, 203, 218, 219, 224
checking of, 153
correct use of, 216, 227
insertion of, 155, 216
inspection of, 219, 227
master, 91
provision of, 192, 270
specification of, 227, 270
wear of, 178
Gaging, elimination of, 71, 72
Gain in db., 14

Gas composition, 21
General instruction
for inspection, 267–271
for process control, 205–211, 213, 215
Generalization (to be based on a natural pattern), 35, 53–54, 59, 61, 62
General purpose tubes, 224, 225
Glass, 224, 225
Glow lamps, 224, 225
"Going through the mill," 164
Gold plating, 156
Goode, H. P., 242, 262, 277
Good or bad? 35, 54, 57, 62, 63, 150–151, 189
Good will of customer, 246
Good work done by operators, 202, 203, 223, 226
Government inspection, 119, 247–248
Government Printing Office
(*See* U. S. Government Printing Office)
Gradual
breakdown in process controls, 273
changes in a process, 11, 53, 54, 161, 164–165, 177–179
extension of maintenance program, 164
shift in level, 11, 53, 54, 161, 164–165 (*See* Trends)
Grand average, 12, 21, 107, 129
Grant, E. L., 182, 239, 242, 277
Graph paper, 13, 17, 22, 79, 133, 211, 215
Grease on a control chart, 216
Grids, 224, 225
Grinding, 57, 203
Groove, 119
Group leaders, 202, 213, 217
Grouping of inspection items, 263, 265, 270, 271, 274
Grouping or "bunching" of measurements, 11, 54, 68, 160, 161, 165–166, 179
Growth of program, 33–34, 41, 224–226
Guidance by management, 33, 41, 224–227
Guided missiles, 4
Guides for plotting, in an experiment, 99, 108, 109
Guiding mechanism, 19

H

Habits of operators
(*See* Work habits)
Hald, A., 116, 275, 277
Handbook
history of, iv, v

purpose of, v, vii
treatment of topics in, vii, 4, 9, 23, 25 (footnote), 33, 34, 36, 38, 45, 49, 75, 77, 78, 84, 110, 148, 149, 151, 153, 187, 201, 216, 233, 239, 264, 270
Handling of product, 38, 156, 163, 246, 260–261, 263, 265
Handwriting, 7
Haphazard arrangement of data, 116
Hardness of stock, 153
Hartley, H. O., 275, 277
Hawthorne Club Evening School, Western Electric Co., 147–148, 275
Headings
on control charts used in experiments, 99, 108
on shop charts, 65, 228
Heads (on a machine), 55, 66, 71, 72, 151, 161, 202, 207
Heat treating, 35, 47, 50, 114
(*See* Chemical operations)
Heiland, R. E., 50, 277
Helps for operators, 4, 37, 188, 201, 202, 203, 204, 217
Hidden
pattern, 67–68, 75, 218
variables, 36, 48, 66–68, 75, 76, 77, 219
Higher order interactions, 93, 94, 98, 105–106
High points on a control chart, 70
Highway, 216
Histogram, 15, 139, 140, 141
(*See* Frequency distributions)
History of a job, 188, 192, 228, 229
(*See* Progress reports)
Hit and miss
data, 116
experimentation, 76, 220
Hoel, P. G., 277
Holders
for control charts, 192, 228
for product, 156, 167, 178, 180
Holding devices, 69, 175, 235
Holes, 162, 176, 178
Homogeneity, 150, 151, 178, 262
(*See* Consistency; *R* chart)
Hook for control charts, 217
Hours
between samples, 192, 207, 209
required for making product, 71, 203
Housekeeping, 10, 50, 178
Human variables, 3, 4, 6, 30, 35, 40, 45, 62, 63, 72, 114, 116, 158, 162, 166, 178, 202, 219, 227
Humidity, 21, 153, 162, 178
Humps (in a distribution), 162
(*See* Peaks)
Hypergeometric equation, 239, 242
Hypothesis
in a process capability study, 47

Hypothesis, *continued*
  of constancy, 47, 82
  of equivalent variances, 82
  of normality, 82, 132
  rejected by a control chart, 82, 83

I

I_b, 229
Ideas for interpreting charts, 55, 75,
    161, 218
Identification
  of boxes in an experiment, 98
  of causes, 11, 56, 111, 146, 166,
    176
  of causes of trouble, 217–219
  of duplicate measurements in an
    experiment, 85, 111
  of product, 209, 218, 261, 270
  of unnatural disturbances, 9, 36,
    54–56, 217–219
  of variables, 36, 37–38, 55, 75–76,
    168, 218–219
  of variables in an experiment, 93,
    99, 100, 103, 108, 109, 111
Identification of data
  in a designed experiment, 76, 84–
    85, 92, 98, 109, 117
  in a process capability study, 49,
    51, 52, 53, 54–56, 72–73, 76
  in inspection, 261, 269, 270
  on a chart for individual measure-
    ments, 160
  on a data sheet, 210, 271
  on a layout, 209, 269–270
  on shop charts, 207, 208, 212–213,
    215, 218–219, 227, 229
Importance
  of AOQL's, 274
  of dimensions, etc., 46, 48, 51,
    187, 202
  of fluctuations, 190
  of patterns, 4, 6, 9, 11, 35, 36, 39,
    45, 47, 53–56, 60, 61, 66–71,
    72–73, 74, 83, 87–89, 91, 97,
    99–101, 144, 145, 149–180,
    203–206, 215, 218, 219, 221,
    223
  of process control, 33, 34, 36–38,
    41, 62, 63–64, 77, 122, 187,
    201–202, 217, 219, 220, 226,
    233, 274
  of R chart, 11, 15–16, 55–56, 66–
    69, 89, 91, 125, 127, 144, 153–
    154, 154–156, 168, 171, 195,
    196, 204
  of simplicity, 91, 97, 189–190
  of specifications, 36, 62–63, 65,
    119, 122, 187, 188, 224
  of taking action, 61–63, 190, 217,
    219, 221
  of variables in an experiment, 4,
    91–101, 103, 112, 114

of variables in a process capability
    study, 35, 36, 51, 53, 54–56,
    62, 66–73, 76, 112
of x's, 23, 25, 27, 52, 168, 195, 218
Impregnating operations, 64
Impressions, visual, 10, 46, 67, 78,
    99, 103, 160, 161, 164, 173–
    174, 178, 179, 190 (*See* Ap-
    parent)
Improvement
  due to control charts, 37–38, 62,
    64, 155, 164, 167, 177, 178,
    187, 226, 233, 235, 265
  in alignment, 69
  in design, 34, 38, 46–47, 69, 187,
    212, 224
  in equipment, 47, 70, 174, 175
  in maintenance, 178, 204, 206
  in methods, 34, 46–47, 175, 178,
    187, 224, 226
  in piece parts, 219 (*See* Piece
    part quality)
  in positioning, 69
  in process average, 265
  in quality ratings, 226
  in reliability, 72
  in specifications, 10, 35, 36, 38,
    46, 48, 61–63, 65, 122, 125,
    188, 219, 224, 226
  of existing processes, 34, 46, 226
  of operators, 4, 167, 188 (*See*
    Training)
  of process, 10, 11, 19, 33–34, 35,
    36, 38, 41, 46–47, 54, 61–63,
    64, 67–71, 74, 76, 83, 101,
    112, 120–121, 122, 164, 187,
    188, 190, 198–199, 202, 206,
    219, 220, 221, 222, 223–226,
    228, 229, 234, 236, 246, 265
  of products, 16, 19, 72, 83, 101,
    112, 121, 187, 220, 233, 265
  of quality, 10, 19, 33–34, 35, 36,
    46, 54, 63, 72, 83, 187, 225,
    226, 233, 234–236, 246, 265
  on paper, 187
  opportunities for, 35–36, 54–56,
    66–71, 76, 120–121, 220, 226
  real, 36, 187, 225–226
  reflected on charts, 74, 199, 228,
    229
  shown by R chart, 71, 168, 195
Inattention, 235
  (*See* Carelessness)
Incomplete operation, 163, 180, 270
Inconclusive
  pattern, 28, 62, 64, 112, 146
  results in an experiment, 62, 77,
    81, 91–92, 97, 112, 117
Inconsistency
  as one of the meanings of assign-
    able causes, 150
  as shown by R chart, 30, 154
"In control"
  good or bad? 35, 54, 150–151,
    171, 189–190, 221

importance of, 36, 38, 45, 47, 53–
    54, 56, 58, 59, 61, 87, 91, 119–
    122, 127, 131, 141, 187, 188,
    189, 190, 195, 196, 204, 219,
    233, 246, 265, 273–274
  meaning of, 9, 16, 19, 24, 30, 71,
    74, 149, 150, 159, 170–171,
    172, 204, 205, 220–221, 262–
    263
  (*See also* "Out of control")
Incorrect
  calculations, 162, 163, 173, 214–
    215, 219
  control limits, 52, 153–154, 173–
    174, 219
  frequency of check, 219, 227
  measurements, 49, 113, 215–216,
    219, 227 (*See* Error of meas-
    urement)
  plotting, 163, 166, 215, 219
Increase
  in cost reduction effort, 226
  in emphasis on engineering, 34, 41
  in number of charts, 189, 224–225
  in production, 71, 178 (*See* Sched-
    ules; Efficiency)
Independent variables
  (*See* Variables)
Indexing of a machine, 155
Indicators
  of capability, 45, 63, 71, 74
  of progress, 225–226 (*See* Progress
    reports)
Individual
  errors, in measurement, 88, 89
  heads, positions etc., 66, 70, 72,
    151, 172, 176
  machines, 3, 10, 15–16, 19, 46–47,
    48, 49, 54, 55, 66–69, 70, 114,
    221
  motors, 70
  points on a control chart, 7, 24,
    70, 149, 156, 176, 177
Individual layouts
  for inspection, 236, 262, 263, 267,
    269–270
  for process control, 199, 201, 207,
    209, 213, 214, 217, 219
Individual numbers or measure-
    ments
  as used in control charts, 6, 8, 11–
    12, 50–51, 188, 189
  control limits for, 8, 12, 21–22, 196
  distribution of, 6, 16, 31, 137, 138,
    139, 140–141, 195
  interpretation of, 9, 10, 31, 160–
    161
  plot of, 6, 8, 12, 16, 22–23, 137,
    144, 198
  relation of, to average, 16, 30–31,
    137, 138
  spread of, 16, 30–31, 53, 56, 58,
    62, 88, 89, 122, 131, 137–138,
    151–152, 160, 195, 196

use of, in checking calculations, 215

(*See* Charts for individual measurements)

Individual operators

benefits for, from quality control, 201, 202, 203

charts for, 4, 5, 8, 16, 17, 38, 48, 49, 72–73, 188, 204, 218, 221

training of (*See* Operators)

Individuals, in the sense of individual measurements

(*See* Individual numbers)

Individuals, in the sense of individual people

(*See* Human variables; Individual operators)

Individual samples

estimates from, 50, 278

in correlation, 146

in inspection, 39, 237

in the shop, 16, 167, 190, 203–204

on a *p*-chart, 197

Individual units, 6, 115–117, 119, 153, 156, 163, 165, 172, 173, 175, 218

(*See* Freaks)

Industrial Quality Control Magazine, 277

Inflation

due to hidden variables, 66–68

due to interactions, 66–68, 105, 168

in control limits, 173–174

in estimate of σ, 131

on an R chart, 66–68, 168

reduction of, 66–68, 168–169, 195

removal of, 55, 67

Informal cost reduction, 226

Informal analysis

by frequency distribution, 56, 78, 140–141

by observation of data, 78

of interactions, 167–169

Information

for management, 224, 225, 226, 227 (*See* Progress reports)

from a *p*-chart, 159

from out-of-control patterns, 35–36, 37, 54–56, 66–72, 72–73, 159, 161–180, 218–219, 221, 223

from patterns in general, 53–54, 97, 159, 171, 189

from process capability studies, 34–36, 46, 53–61, 66–73, 75, 76, 112, 187

given to shop, 65, 158, 192 (*See* Layouts)

needed for control, 190

obtained from control charts, 9, 10, 34–36, 37, 46–47, 72, 83, 84–89, 101, 202, 203–206, 218–219, 223–224

on Head No. 6: 66, 72

on process variables, 4, 11, 33, 35, 46, 54, 66–72, 75–77, 114, 159, 202, 215, 218–219, 223–224

reliability of, 46, 61, 75–76, 112, 141 (*See* Apparent)

to be plotted, 209, 215, 270

to be recorded, 209, 270

which may be needed in the future, 192, 228

Ingenuity in separating data, 55

Initial capability of a process, 34–35, 45, 47, 75–76

Initials on a shop chart, 70, 212, 217, 218

Initial variation in a process, 35, 75

Initiation of action, 208–209, 217–218

Injury, personal, 234

Inner control limits, 99, 100, 107, 109

Inner third of a control chart, 25, 27, 181, 182, 183, 208

Insertion of gage, 155

Inspection

amount of, 4, 23, 35, 39, 46, 188, 225, 226, 233–236, 254, 260, 262, 273–274

areas, 260

as an auditing operation (*See* Minimum inspection; Quality rating)

as a process variable, 46, 49, 159, 218, 236

as related to process control, 10, 37, 38, 39, 187, 202, 233–236, 273–274

audit of, 227

characteristics covered in, 265 (*See* Inspection items)

charts for, 39, 225, 246, 262–263, 265, 274

cost of (*See* Costs)

definition of, 233

detail (also known as 100%), 46, 188, 226, 233–236, 249–251, 254, 256, 257, 263, 265

economy of, 10, 39, 46, 71, 187, 233–236, 273–274

emergency (*See* Emergencies)

fatigue in, 236

forms used in, 270–271

general instruction for, 267–271

included in control chart audit, 227

lots, 196, 227, 259, 260–262, 267

layouts, 227, 236, 260, 261, 262, 263, 267–270, 274

load, 260

methods, 227, 267–271

need for, 38–39, 233–234

normal amount of, 46, 235–236, 273–274

of final product, 264, 273

of gages, test sets etc., 227

of piece parts, 264

of purchased supplies, 39, 158, 254, 264

of raw materials, 39, 158, 264

of sub-assemblies, 264

one hundred percent (*See* Detail inspection)

piece rates, 260, 263

planning, 39, 233, 236, 242–246, 254–255, 260–262, 263–265, 267–270, 273–274

principles, 38–39, 233–236, 273, 274

problems, 3, 4, 39, 46, 202, 216, 217, 218, 224, 227, 233–236, 273–274

product rejected by, 37, 46, 203, 217, 226, 246, 254, 261, 265, 269, 270, 273

protection in hands of, 273

quality levels for, 263–265, 273

records kept by, 39, 226, 227, 260, 261, 263, 268–269, 271

reduction of, 4, 10, 23, 33, 34, 35, 36, 38, 39, 46, 71, 120, 188, 225, 226, 233–236, 246, 252, 254, 260, 273–274

relations with shop, 37, 201, 202, 203, 216, 217, 219, 224, 233, 234–236, 263, 265, 273–274

requirements, 265, 273 (*See* Inspection standards)

responsibilities, 233–234, 235, 236 (*See* Responsibilities; Duties)

results, 39, 269, 270

standards, 264, 265, 268, 270, 273, 274

treatment of, in Handbook, vii, 233

types of, 264

(*See* Final inspection)

Inspection items

grouping of, 263, 265, 270, 274

selection of, 265, 270, 271

Inspection levels

explanation of, 273–274

in Mil. Std. tables, 247

need for, 246, 264, 273

shifting of, 273–274, 278

(*See* Normal inspection; Reduced inspection; Minimum inspection; Tight inspection)

Inspection plans, 34, 187, 224, 227, 246–263, 265, 273–274

Inspection supervisors, vii, 23, 33, 236, 267–271

Inspectors

advice given by, 40, 216, 219, 234, 236

affected by fatigue, 155, 236

as a variable, 30, 152, 155, 168, 174, 215, 218

charts plotted by, 39, 216, 225, 234, 262–263, 247

Inspectors, *continued*
  duties of (*See* Duties)
  gages used by, 162
  instructions for, 267–271
  number of, 23, 38, 226
  results reported by, 173, 269, 271
  sampling plans used by, 4, 237, 238, 242, 246–263
Instability
  causes of, 27, 68–69, 150, 166–167, 179–180
  of product, 46, 67, 90, 175
  on a p-chart, 19, 159, 167, 180, 194
  on an R chart, 16, 67, 69, 155, 156, 166, 167, 179, 180, 204, 206, 212
  on an $\bar{X}$ chart, 15, 16, 66, 67, 153–154, 166, 167, 179, 180, 203, 204, 206, 212
  patterns of, 11, 25, 54, 68–69, 72, 83, 87–89, 161, 166–167, 179–180
  recognition of, 66, 67, 68, 72
  statistical, 25, 155, 156
  tests for, 25–28, 180–183
Installation
  of a quality control program, 33–34, 41
  of control charts, 39–41, 72, 187–199, 201–202, 223, 224–225, 234, 265
  of timer, etc., 70, 235
Instantaneous samples, 192
Instructions
  for inspection, 267–271
  for machine setters, 66, 67, 203–204, 217, 218
  for making control charts (*See* Directions)
  for plotting designed experiments, 82, 85–86, 99–100, 107–109
  for process checkers, 41, 205–211, 213–216, 227
  for process control, 205–213
  for statistical clerks, 228–229
  given to operator, 158, 212 (*See* Training)
Instruments
  calibration of, 165
  comparison of, 84–91
  use of, 84, 87, 89, 227
Insulation resistance, 163
Insulators, 17, 270
Insurance companies, 7
Intangible human elements (*See* Human variables)
Intangible results (*See* Results; Savings)
Integration of quality control techniques, 33–34, 39–41, 75–76, 187, 233, 265, 274
Interactions
  as a source of variability, 168
  calculation of, 94–95, 98, 104–106

capable of affecting the main effects in an experiment, 95, 96, 105, 106
  explanation of, 11, 77, 93, 104–106, 167–169
  first order, 93, 94–95, 98, 104–105, 106
  higher order, 105–106
  in a designed experiment, 36, 75, 76, 77, 81, 91, 93, 94–96, 98, 101, 104–107,
  in a process capability study, 53, 54, 161, 167–169
  introduction of, in an experiment, 104–105
  meaning of, 11, 93, 104, 107, 167
  on the R chart, 11, 68, 155, 156, 168–169, 179
  on the $\bar{X}$ chart, 11, 167, 168
  removal of, 105, 106
  second order, 94–96, 98, 105–106, 110
  third order, 105–106
  used as a guide in plotting control charts, 98–99
Interest
  shown by management, 33, 34, 41, 225, 226, 227
  shown by Quality Control Team, 190, 199, 219, 223–229
Interference
  due to assignable causes, 47, 149
  fits, 126, 188
  in an electrical circuit, 67
  with productive work (*See* Interruptions)
Intermittent behavior
  of a process, 46, 60, 187, 194
  of relay, timer etc., 154
Intermittent operations, 3, 37, 46, 51, 160, 175, 189, 192, 221–222
Interpretation
  in analysis of variance, 81, 82, 83, 97
  of a control chart in a designed experiment, 97, 100–101, 109, 111
  of a distribution, 15, 16, 56–58, 59, 61, 78, 137, 141
  of an AOQL, 254–255
  of an F-test, 79, 82, 83, 96–97
  of an OC curve, 238–239, 242–244
  of a scatter diagram, 143
  of a specification, 119
  of assignable causes, 149–151
  of asterisks in an experiment, 97, 100, 107, 109
  of averages, 61, 78, 83, 153–154
  of Bartlett's test, 79, 82, 83
  of capability studies, 34–36, 45–46, 52–53, 53–56, 56–63, 66–73, 189

of c-charts, 21, 30, 72–73, 160, 191 (*See* Interpretation of p-charts)
of charts for individual measurements, 9, 10, 12, 22–23, 31, 160–161, 191 (*See also* appropriate portions of pages 161–180)
of coefficient of correlation, 146, 148
of complex patterns, 54–56, 66–73, 166–167, 179–180, 218–219
of control charts (*See* Interpretation of patterns; Control charts)
of control limits, 7–9, 16, 24–25, 30–31, 51–52, 72–73, 87–89, 100, 107, 109, 137–138, 151, 153, 161, 173–174, 189–190, 194–195
of demerit charts, 198
of designed experiments, 76–77, 78–84, 87–91, 92, 97, 100–103, 109, 111–112, 115–117
of error of measurement charts, 84, 87–88, 89
of freaks, 52–53, 54, 117, 162–164
of inspection results, 39, 274
of np-charts, 20, 31, 160, 191 (*See* Interpretation of p-charts)
of p-charts, 9, 10, 11, 17, 19–20, 31, 48–49, 53–56, 59–60, 61–62, 73, 157–159, 183, 188–189, 190, 191, 194, 196–197, 198, 215, 217–219, 221, 223 (*See also* appropriate portions of pages 161–180)
of question marks in an experiment, 100, 107, 109
of R charts, 11, 15–16, 30, 48, 53–59, 61–63, 66–72, 83–84, 87, 88, 89, 90–91, 100, 153–156, 182–183, 191, 195, 204, 212 (*See also* appropriate portions of pages 161–180)
of regression lines, 145
of shop charts, 37–38, 40, 41, 63, 65, 171, 189–190, 194, 199, 202–206, 208–209, 212–219, 221, 223–224, 227
of t-charts, 197
of trend charts, 144, 177–179
of t-test, 80, 82, 83
of u-charts, 21, 31, 160, 191 (*See* Interpretation of c-charts)
of verification points on a control chart, 274
of $\bar{X}$ and R charts, 15–16, 30–31, 66–72, 152–156, 170, 176, 177 (*See* separate entries under $\bar{X}$ and R)

of $\bar{X}$ charts, 11, 16, 30–31, 47–48, 53–59, 61–63, 66–72, 82–84, 87–91, 100, 109, 152–154, 156, 180–182, 212 (*See also* appropriate portions of pages 161–180)

of x's in an experiment, 83, 87–89, 100, 107, 109, 111

Interpretation of patterns

  by a Quality Control Team, 219, 223–224

  by machine setters etc., 202–206, 212–213, 217

  by process checkers, 208–209, 215, 217, 227

  in designed experiments, 83–84, 87–89, 100–101, 107, 109, 111–112, 116–117

  in general, 6, 9, 10, 11, 23–31, 149, 152–180, 180–183

  in process capability studies, 35–36, 52–56, 59–60, 62, 66–73, 171

  in the shop, 37–38, 63, 65, 171, 189–190, 192, 194, 195, 217–219, 221

  (*See also* the names of individual patterns and charts)

Interruptions

  in the shop, 33, 77, 187, 202, 220, 225

  of a pattern, 60, 194

  of production, 33, 37, 38, 246, 254–255, 263, 265

Intervals

  between cycles, 162

  between samples, 41, 192, 199, 227, 233, 274

  confidence, 100, 107, 109, 278

  in a frequency distribution, 138

  required for processing, 218, 223

  (*See* Checking intervals; Checking frequency)

Introduction

  of a quality control program, vii, 33–34, 39–41, 233–234

  of control charts in the shop, 39–41, 62, 63–65, 72, 187–192, 201–216, 223

  of sampling plans in the shop, 224, 236, 254, 263

  to control chart theory, 4, 5–10, 11, 23–25, 149–151

  to designed experiments, 75–77, 101–107

  to statistical quality control, 3–4

Intuitive impressions from data, 10, 46, 61, 78, 123, 160, 161, 178–179, 190

  (*See* Apparent)

Invalid methods of estimating, 60–61, 122, 141

Inverted image, 156

Investigations

  based on R chart, 15–16, 48, 55, 66–70, 83, 87, 88–89, 153, 154–156, 163, 167, 168, 171, 173, 179, 195

  cost of, 77, 246

  in a process capability study, 34, 35–36, 45–47, 54–56, 59, 61, 62–63, 66–73, 74, 75–76, 120–121, 122

  of assignable causes, 6, 9, 10, 11, 15–16, 19–20, 27, 30–31, 34–36, 38, 45–46, 48, 52–53, 54–56, 61–63, 63–64, 66–73, 83, 87, 89, 91, 113, 116–117, 122, 141

  of proper conduct of process controls, 227

  of shop control charts, 9–10, 37–38, 41, 64, 74, 217–219, 221, 227

  of shop troubles, 34, 202, 217–219, 223–224, 235

  to verify control chart, 10

  when chart goes out of control, 158, 190, 192, 217–219, 221

Ireson, W. G., 277

Irregular shape of distribution, 131, 138, 166

Isolated points (on an R chart), 156

J

Jamming of locating device, 83

Jigs, 212, 216, 235

Job knowledge

  for interpreting a p-chart, 11, 19, 31, 48, 59, 72–73, 158–159, 218

  for interpreting engineering data, 53, 54–55, 61, 75, 77

  for interpreting shop charts, 40, 71, 201, 202, 212, 219

  importance of, in a process capability study, 34–36, 40, 49, 52, 54–55, 56, 61, 62–63, 64–65, 67–70, 75

  importance of, in the shop, 10, 11, 37, 40, 63–64, 219, 236

  supported by control charts, 38, 91, 101, 219

  (*See* Shop experience)

Jo-blocks, 90

Jobs

  chronological record of, 192, 228

  covered by process control, 202, 226

  decisions about, 40, 223, 224

  effect of charts on, 202–203

  history of, 192

  knowledge of (*See* Job knowledge)

  made interesting, 203

  on sampling inspection, 226

  time on, 73

training for, 204

Job setters

  (*See* Machine setters; Layout operators)

Job shop (*See* Intermittent operations)

Joint

  action, 39–41, 62, 187, 189, 199, 201, 218, 219, 223–224, 236 (*See* Cooperation; Quality Control Teams)

  cost reduction cases, 224, 226

  interpretation of $\bar{X}$ and R charts, 16, 156, 176–177

  reaction of charts, 64, 121, 176, 177, 218, 223

Jumps in a test set etc., 171

Junking of product, 254

Juran, J. M., 277

K

"k," 134

Keeping, E. S., 148, 277

Kendall, M. G., 277

Kenney, J. F., 148, 277

Key found in R chart, 67

Knowledge

  about process variables, 11, 16, 19–20, 33, 34, 35, 49, 54, 55, 59, 157, 189, 202, 212–213, 215, 218–219, 221, 224–225

  affording protection, 273

  gained by process capability studies, 4, 34, 35, 36, 46–47, 53–73, 75–77, 112, 187, 223, 224, 228, 235

  gained through unnatural patterns, 35, 36–37, 54–56, 66–71, 72–73, 159, 161–180, 221

  needed by inspectors, 273

  needed by shop, 71, 202, 217–219

  needed by Team in a process capability study, 38, 40, 66, 67, 75, 112, 220

  needed to interpret patterns, 31, 38, 40, 55, 66–68, 71, 218–219

  not available to people on job, 10, 68 (*See* Unsuspected; Unknown)

  of control charts, 31, 40, 55, 67, 218–219

  of job, 38, 61, 219 (*See* Job knowledge)

  of people, 40, 201–202, 203 (*See* Human variables)

  of process controls, 233, 273

  reflected in shop charts, 199, 212–213, 219, 223, 228 (*See* Notes)

  results in conflict with, 77

  shop, 38, 40, 71, 114, 217–219

  technical, 40, 54, 75, 114, 177, 218, 219, 223–224

Known frequency, used as a standard, 90
Known sources of complexity, 36, 55, 69, 75, 114, 166, 218.
   (*See* Production paths)
Kurtosis, measure of, 134

L

Labor, 57
   (*See* Shortcuts)
Laboratories, 10, 91, 93, 100, 101
Lack of alignment, 69, 155, 167, 180
Lag in chart reaction, 218, 223
Lapping, 167, 168
Large samples, for inspection, 242, 260, 273
Later operations
   (*See* Subsequent operations)
Law of Large Numbers, 5–7, 170, 171
Laws
   of chance, 24, 116
   of nature, 6
   statistical, 6–7, 23–25, 123–124, 214
      (*See* Randomness)
Layout operators, 202, 213, 217
Layouts
   as a process variable, 158, 224
   changes in, 40, 192, 199, 219
   for inspection, 227, 236, 260, 261, 262, 263, 267–270, 274
   for process control, 25 (footnote), 192, 199, 201, 205–209, 223, 227
   manufacturing, 205, 227, 262, 267
Lead wire, 209
Least squares, method of, 145
Leeway (in running a process), 64, 65, 122, 193–197
Length
   as a variable, 12, 119
   of life, 7 (*See* Life test)
   of lines in a pattern, 160, 169
   of process capability study, 36, 45, 47, 50–51, 63, 72, 76
   of service, 72, 73
   standard of, 90
Leptokurtic distribution
   (*See* Symmetrical non-normal distributions)
Lettering on shop charts, 65, 228
"Level Four" inspection (minimum), 263, 264, 273, 274
"Level One" inspection (tight), 264, 273, 274
Levels
   for inspection (*See* Inspection levels; Quality levels)
   in a designed experiment, 92–93, 94, 96–97, 102–103, 105, 107, 110, 112
   in terms of percent defective, 265

of a process, 62, 120, 121, 194, 220 (*See* Centering)
of a variable, 168
of quality, 265 (*See* Quality Levels)
of significance, 97, 100, 107, 109, 180–183
on a control chart, 11, 51–52, 60, 61, 62, 64, 71, 152, 154–155, 156, 159, 164–165, 168, 174–175, 176, 177, 194
on an *R* chart, 71, 168, 175
on a *p*-chart, 159, 194
optimum, for a process, 64, 193
simple shifts in, 55, 72, 152, 174–175
"Level Three" inspection (reduced), 264, 273
Level-to-level correspondence on a control chart, 156, 176, 177
"Level Two" inspection (normal), 264, 273
Life
   of a person, 7
   of a tool, 23 (*See* Toolwear)
Life test, 113, 197
Limits
   confidence, 278
   control (*See* Control limits)
   maximum or minimum, 57, 58–59, 64, 66, 71, 119, 125, 126, 127, 132, 133, 135, 136, 193, 195–196, 202, 204, 205, 206 (*See* Arrows)
   narrowed, for inspection, 262
   natural, 5–9, 16, 53–54, 61, 122, 151–152, 170
   percentage outside of, 30–31, 53–54, 56, 58–59, 61, 64, 71, 119, 127, 132–133, 135–136, 189, 194, 225, 235
   product outside of, 66, 71, 120–121, 160, 189, 195, 204, 254
   specified, 13, 15, 16, 30–31, 54, 58–59, 61, 62–63, 64–65, 119–122, 124–127, 132, 151, 160, 224 (*See* Specifications; Specification limits)
   statistical, 5–9 (*See* Control limits)
Line
   of best fit, 144–145
   of demarcation, 159
   of regression, 144–146, 147, 148
   of standard length or width, 90
Liquid, 189
Liquor, 146
List of variables, 91, 113
Lloyd, B. H., 101, 277
Loading, 246
Locating devices, 19, 83, 176
Location
   in the sense of manufacturing plant (*See* Western Electric)

of distributions, 62, 64, 65, 120–121, 171, 174, 179, 188, 193–196, 226, 228
of jobs, 51
of parts, 55, 68, 69, 83, 167, 176, 180, 235
of trouble, 51, 188, 190, 202, 217–219
   (*See* Early Operations.)
Locator (for a relay), 19
Locking device, 10, 68, 162
Logarithmic scale, 163
Long drying, 91, 92, 100, 101
Long-term capability, 34–35, 36, 45–46, 61–63, 64, 122
Loose connections, 20, 191
Looseness
   of a mechanical device, 19, 69, 155, 178, 180, 219
   of inspection plans, 273
   of spoolheads, 5, 7, 8, 64
Losses
   affected by inspection practices, 246, 254–255, 261, 263
   charts on, 4, 21, 23, 38, 48, 188, 225, 227
   minimized by process control charts, 36, 38
   normal amount of, 46
   reduction of, 4, 10, 16, 19–20, 33, 34, 35–36, 38, 46–47, 61–63, 71, 120–121, 122, 187–188, 217, 226, 265
Loss of data, unit etc., in an experiment, 116, 117
Lot-by-lot sampling plans, 255, 259–261, 262, 265, 268, 269, 270
Lots
   as a process variable, 55, 156, 163, 164, 167, 175, 178
   definition of, in inspection, 229, 259, 267
   disposition of, 227, 254, 269
   given a "second chance," 260
   in continuous sampling, 255, 256
   may be used as "samples," 17, 191
   rejection of, 227, 249–250, 254–255, 265, 269, 273
   sampling from, in inspection, 227, 255, 256, 260, 261, 265, 267, 269, 270
Lot size
   affected by process control, 262
   disregarded, 262, 263
   in calculating AOQ, 251
   in Dodge-Romig tables, 250, 253
   in lot-by-lot inspection, 227, 247, 250, 251, 253, 259, 260–262, 265, 267, 270
   in Mil. Std. tables, 247
L-shaped distribution, 163
LTPD, 249, 250, 253

LTPD sampling plans, 249, 250, 264, 265
Lubricating oil, 23
Lugs, 270
Lunch periods, 70, 162

M

Machine operations, 15–16, 66–72, 203–204
Machines
  adjustment of, 16, 30, 37, 67, 153, 166, 188, 202, 203–204, 212 (*See* Overadjustment)
  age of, 168
  as a variable, 3, 36, 45, 114, 158, 169, 174, 215, 217, 218–219, 224
  capability of, 33, 35, 46, 170, 172, 175, 202, 204, 207, 224, 235
  centering of, 30, 188
  comparison of, 36, 46, 49, 54, 90, 159, 171, 172–173, 175, 202, 215, 224
  construction of, 66, 151, 161
  design of, 34, 35, 36, 46, 47, 69, 70, 83, 155, 171, 175, 213
  downtime on, 38, 226
  improvement of, 69, 70, 83
  maintenance of, 10, 15–16, 19, 30, 35, 48, 167, 168, 175
  needing repair, 10, 16, 30, 48, 69, 155, 167, 180
  number of (for identification), 49, 207
  overhauling of, 16, 219
  purchase of, 47, 121
  sampling from, 66, 151, 214
  setup of, 150, 151, 174, 188, 202 (*See* Machine setting)
  trouble with, 15–16, 19–20, 48, 66, 202
Machine setters, 201, 202, 223, 226
  adjustments by, 6, 16, 67, 150, 152, 166, 174, 190, 202, 203–204, 219, 220
  as a variable, 10, 180
  control exerted by, 48, 66, 67, 188, 202, 203–204
  instructions to, 16, 66, 67, 217, 218
  investigations by, 209, 212, 213, 217–218
  notes by, 66, 67, 212, 213
Machine setting, 6, 16, 30, 48, 50, 62, 150, 151, 152, 163, 202, 203, 204, 219
Magnet, 125, 235
Magnetic alignment, 69
Main effects
  corrected, 105, 106

in a designed experiment, 75, 92–93, 94–97, 98, 99, 103, 104–105, 106, 107
  meaning of, 104, 107
  removed from an experiment, 102–103, 106
Maintenance
  amount of, 168, 175
  considered as a process variable 53, 113, 167, 168, 175, 178, 180
  cost of, 4
  improvement in, 164, 204, 219
  of a quality control program, 4, 33–34, 39–41, 223–229, 236
  of fixtures, 35, 219
  of machines, 10, 15–16, 19, 30, 35, 48, 167, 168, 175
  of shop charts, 36, 38, 41, 65, 199, 205–209, 213–216, 219, 223–229
  of soldering tips, 219
  of test sets or gages, 159, 178, 219, 227
  organization, 16, 202, 219
  problems, 15–16, 19, 38, 206, 219, 227
  program for, 46, 155, 162, 164, 180
Major
  components, 55
  defects, 196, 263
  variables, 55, 66–68 113–114, 187–188
"Make operations," 216, 235
Management
  courses, vii, 23, 33
  guidance of program, 33–34, 41
  interest in results, 10, 33–38, 41, 225–227
  problems, 3, 4, 10, 22, 23, 33–41, 46–47, 77, 187, 233–236, 273–274
  reports, 33, 225, 226, 227, 229
Manual operations, 3, 4, 5, 8, 9, 10, 30, 38, 45, 48–49, 55, 57, 61, 62, 70, 72–73, 158, 162, 164, 167, 169, 170, 172, 175, 188, 203–204, 218, 219, 221, 235, 265
Manuals
  for Final inspection sampling plans, 264, 273, 278
  for statistical clerks, 229
  for training (*See* Training)
Manual skill, 168
Manufacturing
  costs, 34, 35, 36, 236 (*See* Costs)
  engineers (*See* Product engineers)
  layouts (*See* Layouts)
  problems, 3, 4, 46, 47, 75–77, 187–189
Margin, arrows in, 13–14, 16, 30–31, 65, 67–71, 120–121, 190, 205–206, 212
Markings (on control charts)

designed experiments, 82–83, 87–88, 99, 100, 107, 109, 111
engineering charts, 52, 53, 66–71, 72–73, 188, 212
shop charts, 25(footnote), 192, 194–195, 208–209, 212–213, 215, 217, 218, 221, 227, 229
Marking x's
  importance of, in general, 13, 18, 19, 20–21, 22, 23, 25 (footnote), 25–29
  on engineering charts, 23, 52, 53, 83, 99, 100, 107, 109, 111, 168, 170
  on shop charts, 23, 65, 192, 194–195, 202, 208, 209, 213, 215, 216, 217, 218, 221, 227, 229
Masking
  of a pattern, 66–67
  of cycles, 69
  of parts during spraying, 165
  of variables, 55, 66, 67, 69, 168
Master charts in the shop, 65, 228
Master gage, 91
Materials
  as a variable, 3, 5, 6, 30, 45, 55, 69, 152, 155, 158, 164, 167, 168, 169, 171, 174, 175, 176, 178, 179, 180, 218
  capability of, 35, 46, 224
  changes in, 30, 62, 63, 174, 176
  critical, 262
  for assembly, 10, 37, 61, 64, 219, 254
  for progress reports, 225–226
  physical limits of, 57
Mavericks, 156
Maximum
  limit, in specifications, 13, 15–16, 30–31, 57, 58–59, 61–65, 66, 71, 119–122, 124–127, 132–133, 135–136, 193, 195–196, 205, 206, 212, 220
  values plotted on control chart, 197
Mean
  as an average (*See* Averages)
  squares, 81, 91, 95, 96, 98, 130
Mean deviation, 198
Meaning
  of "individual," "month," etc., 191
  of "same essential conditions," 85, 90
  (*See* Definitions)
Measurements
  accuracy of, 49, 89, 90–91
  at end or sides of part, 90
  attributes, 5, 6, 17, 18, 20–21, 47 (*See* Attributes data)
  considered as a process variable, 49, 53, 62, 87, 89, 111, 113, 116–117, 165, 166, 215–216, 219, 227

Measurements, *continued*

error of, 46, 49, 50, 53, 61, 62, 75, 76, 84–91, 111, 113, 163, 215, 219 (*See* Accuracy; Precision)

identification of, 49, 51, 52, 53, 54–56, 72–73, 84–85, 92, 98, 99, 100, 109, 111, 117, 208–209, 212–213, 215, 218–219, 227

incorrect, 215–216, 219 (*See* Error)

in inspection, 270

may occur in non-random clusters, 160, 164–165 (*See* Grouping)

may reflect either process or product, 47

number of, 6, 50, 66, 90, 92, 93, 110, 111, 113 (*See* Amount)

of things which "cannot be measured," 12, 49–50, 113

randomized, in an experiment, 93, 113, 114–116

scale of, 138, 139, 216

scatter of, 129–131, 138, 143 (*See* Spread)

semi-variables, 12, 49, 50, 113

suitability of, 49–50, 51, 62, 84–85, 89–90, 113, 114, 116–117, 146, 190–192, 214, 215–216, 219

taken by process checker, 41, 49, 192, 201, 207, 209, 210, 213, 214, 215–216, 223, 228, 229

treated as separate factor in an experiment, 111

variables, 6, 8, 12, 14, 21–22, 47, 78, 84, 92, 139, 147 (*See* Variables data)

Measuring instrument, 84–91, 165

Mechanical devices, 69

Medians

chart of, 197

meaning of, 129, 132

used in life testing, 197

used with midranges, 198, 277

Medical data, 6, 21

Meetings

of the Quality Control Team (*See* Quality control meetings)

with machine setters, 201–202, 218, 223, 226

with operators, 201–202, 223, 226

Members of the Team, 39, 40, 201–202, 223, 226, 234, 236

Mental activity, as a system of causes, 4

(*See* Human variables)

Mental arithmetic, 4, 215

Merchandise losses, 4, 23, 34, 46, 50 (*See* Losses)

Mercury switch, 209

Metallurgists, 40

Meter, 67, 71

Methods

as a variable, 3, 4, 45, 158, 164, 167, 217, 219, 227

capability of, 35, 46 224

changes in, 30 46–47, 62, 63, 68–70, 121, 165, 174, 175, 218, 219, 226

comparison of, 35, 46, 53, 55, 63, 72, 75, 76, 77–84, 90, 91–92, 93, 100–101, 112, 141, 175, 202, 218, 220, 224

development of, 34, 47, 226

of analysis, 36, 53, 54–56, 75–76, 77–84, 91–92, 93, 101, 141, 143–148, 149–183, 217–219, 220

of calculating residual, 94–95, 97, 103, 106, 107, 110–111

of changing inspection levels, 273–274, 278

of randomizing data, 93, 114–116

of selecting samples, 15, 49, 51, 82, 84, 113, 116, 149, 151, 190–192, 207, 209, 213, 214, 219, 227, 237, 239, 257, 259, 260–262, 267–268

of testing (*See* Testing; Test sets)

unreliable, 180

variability in, 83

Methods of measurement

changes in, 165, 180, 218, 219

errors in, 49, 53, 62, 84–91, 113, 215–216, 219

for engineers, 49, 53, 62, 113

for inspectors, 268, 270

for process checkers, 192, 209, 214–216

(*See* Error of measurement)

Methods of processing

general, 47, 48, 54, 114, 158, 218, 226

units for an experiment, 93, 113, 114–116, 117

Micrometer, 91

Middle

of a pattern, 24–25, 29, 160, 169, 171, 172–174

third of a control chart, 25, 27, 181, 182, 183, 208

Midpoint of cell, 130, 131, 154

Midranges and medians, 198, 277

Milling (on a welder), 213

Millivolts, 119

Mil. Std. sampling tables, 242, 247, 248, 278

Miniature tubes, 224, 225

Minimum

limit, in specifications (*See* Maximum)

values plotted on control chart, 197

Minimum inspection

as an inspection level, 246, 247, 262–263, 264, 273–274

provision for, in Dodge-Romig tables, 254

Minor defects, 198, 263

Minutes

between samples, 192, 207

of quality control meetings, 224, 226

spent on repairs, 225

Mishandling

of data, 16, 49, 52–53, 61, 66–67, 76, 78–81, 84–85, 112, 117, 125, 131, 141, 145, 146, 153–154, 159, 163, 172, 173–174, 175, 178, 190, 194, 214–216, 219, 227, 254

of product (*See* Damage)

Misinterpretation

of AOQL, 254–255

of chart for individual measurements, 160, 161, 173–174, 179

of control limits, 16, 151, 173–174, 190

of data (*See* Mishandling; Wrong conclusions; Apparent)

of instructions, 213

of p-chart, 59, 157, 159

of R chart, 67

of scale, 163, 190, 215

of $\bar{X}$ chart, 153, 154

Missile systems, 4

Mistakes

associated with specification limits, 16, 151, 190

in calculation, 162, 173, 215 (*See* Calculations)

in estimating 60–61 (*See* Wrong conclusions)

Misunderstanding

of drawing, 153

of procedures, 67, 213, 227

of process controls, 227

Mixed product, 36, 54–55, 150, 155, 156, 164, 166, 167, 171, 172–173, 179–180, 218–219

Mixtures

as a pattern on a control chart, 11, 29, 53, 54, 67–68, 83, 111, 161, 166–167, 169–170, 171–174, 175–176, 179–180, 219

of distributions, 57–58, 68, 136, 156, 158, 163, 165, 166, 169–170, 171, 173, 176, 179

of product (*See* Mixed product)

on a chart for individual measurements, 160, 167, 171, 176, 180

on an R chart, 11, 66–68, 154–156, 161, 167, 168, 171, 172–173, 176, 178, 179–180

on an $\bar{X}$ chart, 11, 153–154, 161, 167, 171, 173, 175, 179–180

on a p-chart or c-chart, 11, 72, 73, 157, 158, 159, 161, 167, 171, 173, 176, 180, 190

Mode, 129, 131, 132

Moderate degree of defectiveness, 190

Modification
of a machine, 68–70, 83, 212, 213
of a requirement, 38, 48, 61–63, 65, 122, 153, 187–188, 198, 219, 224, 226
of data, 61, 141
of layouts, 192, 199
of process control charts, 38, 41, 65, 189–190, 198–199, 219, 223, 227–229
of specifications, 61–63, 65, 122, 198, 219
of statistical conclusions, 61, 83, 101, 141, 145
of test sets, 174, 218, 224
of tools, 62, 63, 121, 155, 158, 169, 179, 203, 212, 213, 219, 224
Modified control limits
for c-charts, 196–197
for charts of individual measurements, 196
for p-charts, 196–197
for $\bar{X}$ and R charts, 64, 65, 120, 195–196
Moisture, 153
Mold, 152
Molina, E. C., 239–242, 277
Money saved in experiments, 77, 92
Monthly samples, 191, 192
Moroney, M. J., 145, 275, 277
Motion patterns, 61, 158
(See Work habits)
Motivation of operators, 158, 174, 188, 201–203, 223, 226, 235, 265
Motives, 4
(See Human variables)
Motors, 70–71
Mounting of charts in the shop, 192, 209, 217, 218, 228
Movements
of a machine, 151, 161
of a pattern, 9, 29, 160, 177, 178, 179
Moving range charts, 21–23
(See Charts for individual measurements)
Moving range limits
for individual plotted points (See Charts for individual measurements)
for p-charts or c-charts, 196–197
for summary control charts, 222
Multifactor experiments, 75, 77, 97, 110–111
Multi-modal distributions, 136, 166, 173 (See Non-normal distributions; Bimodal distributions)
Multiple spindles, positions, heads etc., 66, 72, 151, 161, 172, 176, 219
Multiple sampling, 238, 242, 259–261
(See Sequential sampling)

Multiple tests
for interpreting control chart patterns, 25 (footnote), 25–30, 53, 100, 107, 109, 180–183, 208, 218–219
probabilities associated with, 25 (footnote), 180–183
"Multi-vari" charts, 198
Mundel, A. B., 262, 278
Munitions Board, 278
(See U. S. Dept. of Defense)
Mysterious troubles, 4, 35, 38, 51, 54–56, 66–67, 75, 76, 77, 91–92, 155, 157, 159, 166, 187, 188, 202, 206, 217, 218, 219, 220
(See Unknown causes of trouble)

N

Narrowed limit sampling plans, 262, 278
Narrowness
of control limits, 72, 73, 150, 166
of process, 62, 120, 121
of specified limits (See Tightness)
Natural
behavior of a process, 34, 36, 45, 150, 171
limits, 46, 61, 64, 122, 124–127, 151–152
tolerances, 61, 152
(See Natural spread of a process; Natural variation)
Natural pattern
amount of data required for, 9, 150, 170, 171
causes of, 6, 9, 24, 53, 150, 171
characteristics of, 8, 9, 24, 161, 170, 175
conclusions from, in a process capability study, 35, 36, 53–54, 56, 58, 59, 61–63, 71, 119–122, 127
explanation of, 6–7, 9, 24–25, 149, 150, 170–171
importance of, 34–35, 36, 45, 47, 53–54, 56, 61, 71–72, 87, 119, 122, 125, 127, 141, 145, 189–190, 217, 219
not necessarily desirable, 35, 54–56, 61, 112, 171, 189, 205
Natural spread of a process, 9, 16, 30–31, 45, 56, 58–59, 61, 62, 71, 83, 89, 119–122, 124, 131, 151–152, 156, 170, 195, 196, 205
Natural variation
importance of, 35, 36, 53–54
meaning of, 6, 9, 24, 35, 53, 149, 150, 170–171
(See Variability; Variation; Natural pattern)
Neatness of shop charts, 216

Negative correlation
(See Correlation)
Negative skewness
(See Skewness)
Neglect
of charts, 217, 221, 227
of process controls, 227
New
capability studies, 40, 62, 228
characteristics created by assembly, 122
designs, 34, 46, 47, 52, 188
jobs in the shop, 188
operator or inspector, 49, 73, 152, 155, 167, 174, 175, 180, 202, 204, 218
performance studies, 74, 227
plant expense, 226
process checker, 41, 192, 212, 213, 218, 223
processes, 34, 38, 47, 52, 76, 220, 226
products, 47, 188
supervisor, 51, 169, 178
Nicks, 113
Night shift, 72, 73, 161, 162
(See Shifts)
Noise, 10, 12, 68, 138–141
"Nominal" dimension
moved to another place, 63, 121
working on one side of, 64, 167, 204, 220
Non-assignable causes, 6, 150, 152, 171
"Nonconforming" material, 269
Non-homogeneous product
(See Mixed product; Homogeneity)
Non-linear
behavior of a variable, 164
combinations of distributions, 123 (footnote)
correlation, 148
scale, 163
Non-normal distributions, 131, 134–136, 138
causes for, 56–58, 83, 136
compared with specification, 56, 122
detected on a control chart, 69–70, 83, 156
estimating shape of, 30–31, 56, 59, 141
estimating spread of, 31, 56, 59, 61, 122, 134–136
"modified" limits for, 196
not properly allowed for, 125, 153, 160
percentage outside of limits in, 31, 59, 122, 134, 135, 136
probabilities associated with, 56, 134–136, 182–183, 239, 242
related to chart of individual measurements, 160–161, 170

Non-normal distributions, *continued*
(*See* Skewed distributions; Bimodal distributions; Multi-
modal distributions; Sym-
metrical non-normal distributions)
Non-normal sampling distributions,
132, 138, 182–183, 191, 239,
242
Non-random arrangement of points
on a control chart, 36, 55–56,
72–73, 75, 99, 108–109, 149
(*See* Grouping or bunching)
Non-randomness
in haphazard data, 116
in measurements, 116, 165–166
in patterns, 24–25, 149, 153, 156,
160, 161, 165, 172, 173, 175,
176–177
in sampling, 167, 171, 173, 180,
214, 239
Non-standard control charts, 198
Normal capacity, losses, yields etc.,
35, 45, 46, 54
Normal distribution
assumption of, 78, 80, 82–83, 88,
124–125, 127, 154
behavior of samples from, 156
compared with specification, 30–
31, 58–59, 119–121, 132–133
description of, 131–134
equation for, 132
estimating percentages for, 30–31,
58–59, 132–133
estimating spread of, 56, 71, 119–
120, 122
fitting data to, 139–141
importance of, 78, 80, 82–83, 88,
124–125, 126–127, 132, 138
"modified" limits for, on a shop
chart, 195–196
not necessarily desirable, 57
not necessarily present in the case
of a natural pattern, 170
of errors, 88
probabilities associated with, 132–
133, 180–182
sampling distributions from, 138,
181, 182
tables for, 133
tests for, 78–79, 83, 133–134
theoretical description of, 131–
134, 139–141
Normal inspection
as an inspection level, 246, 264,
273–274
as normal amount of detailing
etc., 46, 120–121, 226, 233–
236, 246, 254–255, 256, 257,
263, 265
Normality
assumption of, 78, 80, 82, 83, 88,
124–125, 127, 154

hypothesis of, 82
(*See* Normal distribution)
Normal lot size, 262
Normal product
accepted by a sampling plan, 233,
244, 255, 264, 265, 273, 274
rejected by a sampling plan, 246,
254–255, 265, 273
(*See* Process average; Process
capability)
(*See also* OC curves)
Notes
by a machine setter, 66, 67, 213,
217
recorded in a process capability
study, 49, 51, 53, 66, 67, 70,
71
recorded on a shop chart, 206,
208, 209, 212, 213, 215, 217,
218, 221, 227
np, 20
np-Charts, 20, 160, 191, 229
Number
of a gage, test set etc., 49
of a machine or shift, 49, 207
of causes affecting one chart, 190
of characteristics covered by inspection, 265, 270
of characteristics covered on a p-
chart or c-chart, 17, 48, 59,
157, 159, 160, 189, 190, 196
of characteristics covered on a
sampling plan, 263
of charts, 34, 38, 41, 72, 187, 189,
190, 199, 219, 223, 225, 226,
227
of complaints, 38, 62, 226, 246,
264
of defects, 20–21, 46, 191, 206, 233,
236, 239, 240, 265
of defects missed by 100% inspection, 236
of defects per unit (as an inspection requirement), 265
of inspection items, 263, 265, 270
of inspectors, 23, 38, 226
of jobs on sampling inspection, 226,
233–236
of jobs under process control, 226
of measurements in an experiment, 77–78, 84–85, 90, 93,
110, 111, 113 (*See* Amount of
data)
of measurements in a process capability study, 50, 66–72
of operations, 225
of operations charted, 190, 225,
226
of operations not requiring process
control, 190, 225
of operations still to be studied,
225
of operations studied, 225, 226
of operators, 23, 38, 71, 226

of operators working with process
control, 226
of process control charts (*See*
Number of charts)
of samples taken in a process
capability study, 66
Number of units
in a sample, 12, 17, 18, 19, 20, 50–
51, 66, 83, 84, 85, 98, 107,
111, 160, 189, 191 (*See*
Sample size)
in an experiment, 78–80, 84, 85,
91–93, 110, 113, 116
Numbers in general, 3, 4, 5, 6
Numerical effects in data, 75, 94–
97, 99, 100, 102–106

O

Objectives
in separating data, 36, 55, 59, 75,
157, 159, 218–219
of a cost reduction case, 226
of a quality control program, vii,
3–4, 10, 33–41, 45–47, 53–54,
61–63, 71–72, 75, 77, 119,
122, 125–126, 169, 187–189,
201–203, 217–226, 233–236,
273–274
of designed experiments, 4, 34,
36, 62, 75–77, 84, 91, 92,
101, 112–113, 219, 220
of inspection, 38–39, 233–236, 264,
273–274
of process capability studies, 34–
36, 45–47, 66, 72, 159, 187,
221
of process control charts, 10, 36–
38, 62, 63–64, 125, 187–189,
190, 201–206, 224, 225–226,
233, 262, 265, 273–274
of the Quality control team, 33,
39–41, 45–47, 66, 75, 187,
223–226, 236, 274
Obscure patterns (in a process
capability study), 66, 67
Observational standards, 268
Observations (*See* Measurements
Data)
Observed average, frequency etc.,
78
Observed data
informal analysis of, 5, 6, 9, 78
theoretical distribution fitted to,
139–141
Observers, 50
Obsolete shop charts, 41, 199, 219,
223, 227
Obtaining data
cost of, 17, 47–48, 116, 188, 189
difficulty of, 17, 47, 188, 189
for experiments, 76, 77, 84, 85,
91–92, 93, 113–117

for performance studies, 74, 188, 228

for process capability studies, 47–51, 55, 63–64, 66–67, 223, 228

for shop charts, 41, 190–192, 205–210, 213–215, 223, 228

Obvious defects, 209, 269

Occasional checks, 190, 224

Occasional disturbance in a process, 16, 51, 53, 67, 150, 203–204 (*See* Overadjustment)

OC curves

as basis for selecting sampling plans, 242–246, 247, 249, 252, 254–255, 256, 264, 265

compared to process, 244, 255, 264, 265

costs associated with, 245–246

economic importance of, 242–246, 254–255, 264–265

examples of, 239, 243, 246, 249, 252, 256

explanation of, 238–239, 239–242, 242–246

for continuous sampling, 241, 256

for single, double and multiple sampling, 239–242, 243, 244–255

for variables sampling, 242

importance of, 242–246, 255, 264, 265

plotting of, 240–241

used in comparing sampling plans, 242–245, 246, 249, 252, 256, 260

uses for, in estimating risks, 244–245

Odd points in a test, 26, 181

Offcenter

contacts on a relay, 19

distributions, 62, 64, 121, 160, 167, 220

parts, assemblies etc., 5, 8, 155, 167, 175, 180

Offcenter processes

as shown on a chart for individual measurements, 160

deliberately run close to one side of specification, 64, 220

effect of, on yields, 62, 64, 121

in trouble with specification, 31, 62–63, 64, 121, 122

Official quality rates, 264, 270, 273

Ohms, 119

Oil, 216, 270

Olmstead, P. S., 277

Omission

of operation, 163, 180, 270

of x's, 23, 218

"One best place" (for a distribution), 193

One factor experiment, 76

One hundred percent

gaging by shop, 72

good or bad (said of product), 173, 180, 190

inspection, 46, 188, 190, 226, 233–236, 249–251, 254, 256, 257, 263, 265

sorting, 46, 71–72, 120–122, 190, 191, 226, 235, 246, 252, 255, 257, 263, 265

One percent limits, 97, 99, 100, 107, 109

One-sided

process, 62, 64, 121, 160, 220

tests, 28, 182

One year report, 225

"Opens," 209

Operate current, 66–71

Operating organization

action by, on control charts, 16, 19, 202, 203–204, 217–219, 221

cooperation of, with Engineering, 33, 38, 39–41, 45, 65, 74, 188, 190, 202, 219, 220, 223, 224, 226

emphasis on, vii, 187, 201, 216

problems of, 3, 4, 10, 15, 19, 22–23, 33–38, 40, 46–47, 61, 62, 63–65, 66–73, 91, 101, 120–127 151, 168, 187–226, 234–236, 246, 254–255, 260–265, 273–274

rejection of product to, 4, 37, 46, 66, 71, 226 227, 237, 244–246, 254–257 261, 263, 265, 269

relations of, with Inspection, 37, 38–39, 126, 187, 201, 202, 233–236, 246, 257, 260–262, 269

responsibility of, for plotting charts, 36, 41, 65, 187, 192, 197, 201, 205–216, 217, 219, 221, 223, 227, 228, 234

responsibility of, for quality, 233–236

responsibility of, for results, 46, 48, 188, 201, 203, 216, 217, 235

routines in, 33, 38, 65, 77, 202, 220, 246 (*See* Bottlenecks)

should not aim at AOQL, 254–255

sorting by, 46, 120–122, 226, 234–236, 246, 254–257, 260, 263, 265

(*See* Shop experience; Shop troubles)

Operating supervisors, vii, 4, 5, 23, 33, 38, 39–41, 162, 168–169, 201–226, 236

Operational sorting

(*See* Sorting)

Operations

breakdown by, 33, 36, 55, 166, 224–225

categories for, 225

continuity of, in the shop, 36, 46, 187, 202, 217, 219

definition of, 225

difficult, 34, 47

effect of, on other operations, 187, 202 (*See* Early operations; Subsequent operations)

expensive, 34, 47, 71–72, 122, 235, 265

found to be free from trouble, 264

nature of, in the shop, 38, 46, 47, 190, 224, 225

number of, in the shop, 224, 225

sequence of, 209, 267

shortcuts in, 57, 70

studied and charted, 190, 224–226

Operations research, 40, 77, 277

Operators

acting as process checkers, 190, 213

acting on control charts, 4, 155, 158, 164, 167, 177, 178, 188, 203, 221, 235, 265

advantages of quality control for, 201, 202, 203

as a variable, 5, 6, 17, 30, 36, 55, 62, 69, 72, 73, 152, 171, 172, 178, 202, 214, 215, 217

capability of, 35, 46, 73, 170

charts for, 201–203, 221–222

comparison of, 36, 49, 55, 159, 171, 175, 204, 215, 218

control by, 30, 48, 57, 70, 188, 203

covered by process control, 226

encouragement of, 4, 33, 174, 188, 201–203, 223, 226

equipment given to, 155, 158,, 164 167, 169, 174, 175, 176, 179, 180, 203, 217, 218

experience of, 6, 73, 158, 164 (*See* Training)

explanation of control charts to, 201–202, 223, 226

habits of (*See* Work habits)

importance of, 38, 201, 202, 203–204, 223, 226

instruction of, 37, 158, 202, 212, 217, 219

meetings with, 201–202, 223, 226

motivation of, 174, 188, 201, 202, 223

names of, for identifying data, 49, 207, 218, 271

number of, required for building product, 23, 38, 71, 226

of an instrument, 87, 88, 89

sorting by, 122, 234, 235, 246, 257, 260, 263, 265

training of, 31, 35, 37, 46, 55, 70, 72, 73, 155, 158, 162, 164, 167, 168, 169, 175, 180, 202, 203, 204, 212, 217, 219

Opportunities
  for cost reduction, 34, 36, 46–47,
    54, 187–188, 226
  for finding defects, 20
  for improvement, 35–36, 54–56,
    66–71, 76, 120–121, 220, 226
Optimum
  balance between cost and quality
    (*See* Balance; Economic
    stopping point)
  level for a process, 37, 62, 64, 120–
    121, 188, 193, 264–265
  number of control charts, 34, 38,
    41, 62, 63, 189, 199, 219, 223
Optional calculations, 49, 53, 98, 110
Order
  absence of, in a natural pattern,
    7, 24, 149, 160, 161–162, 175,
    176 (*See* Arrangement)
  of measurement, 78, 82, 83, 84, 85
  of plotting, in experiments, 82–83,
    84, 85, 99, 108–109
  of production or testing, 5–6, 15,
    49, 61, 66, 82, 84–85, 151, 176,
    192, 207, 214 (*See* Sequence)
Orders (for work done etc.), 40
Ordinary
  control limits, on a *p*-chart, 19
  variables, 37–38, 61, 62, 71, 150–
    151, 217 (*See* Shop-type
    variables)
Oscillator, 90
Other departments, 223, 224 (*See*
  Suppliers)
Ott, E. R., 101, 113, 262, 277
Outer control limits, 99, 107–109
Outer third of a control chart, 25,
  27, 181–183, 208
"Out of control"
  examples of, 9, 10, 15–16, 19, 37,
    59–61, 66–71, 72–73, 82–83,
    87–89, 99–100, 196–197, 203,
    204, 206, 212–213
  good or bad? 6, 35–36, 54–56,
    150–151, 189–190
  importance of, 35–36, 37–38, 45,
    52–53, 54–56, 61, 74, 91, 111,
    113, 122, 131, 141, 145, 189–
    190, 196–197, 217–219, 221,
    223, 227, 262–263, 273–274
  meaning of, 9, 25–28, 30–31, 37,
    63, 65, 66, 72, 74, 83, 87, 89,
    100–101, 116–117, 149–151,
    159, 160, 172, 189–190, 217–
    219, 220–221, 222
  synonymous with trouble, 189,
    190, 223
  tests for, 23–30, 79, 180–183, 192,
    208–209, 215, 218, 227, 229
Out of limits, 37, 46, 54, 56, 66, 71,
  121, 160, 189, 204–206, 254
  (*See* Percentage)
Out of order, 156, 171, 180

Out of parallel, 198
Out of round, 89–90, 198
Out of specification
  (*See* Out of limits)
Out-of-the-ordinary, 150
Output, 4, 10, 33–38, 46–47, 62, 64,
  66, 71, 91, 101, 122, 187–189,
  198, 202, 203, 217–219, 220,
  224, 225, 235, 255
  (*See* Quantity; Production; Ef-
    ficiency)
"Outside limit" material, 254, 269
Outstanding causes, 38, 63, 70, 190
Oven, 47, 55, 102, 104, 114, 152
Overadjustment, 16, 67, 166, 180,
  188, 190, 203–204
Overall
  capability, 46, 48, 59, 157, 159
  cost of control charts, 10, 34, 35,
    38, 62, 225–226
  estimates, 47, 48, 59
  p-chart, 17, 48, 59, 157, 159, 188–
    189, 190, 196–197, 198, 218
  quality standards, 264, 270, 273
  savings, 10, 33–34, 38, 46–47,
    225–226 (*See* Cost reduction)
  shifts and trends, 196–197
Overhauling of machines, gages etc.,
  16, 53, 113, 219
  (*See* Maintenance)
Overlapping tolerances, 54, 124–126,
  188
Oversize parts, 71, 155, 214

P

p, 17, 18
Pairs
  alternate (*See* Alternate pairs)
  measurements occurring in, 160
  of measurements, used in analy-
    sis, 83, 85, 108, 109
  successive (*See* Successive pairs)
Panels, wired, 72, 73, 191
Pans, 167, 171, 214
Paper
  and pencil, in the shop, 215
  graph, 13, 17, 22, 79, 133, 211, 215
  improvements on, 187
  probability (*See* Probability
    paper)
  products, 20
Parameters of a product
  (*See* Characteristics)
Parent distribution
  as related to sampling distribu-
    tion of averages, 16, 30–31,
    138
  as related to various other sam-
    pling distributions, 138, 181,
    182

information on, 6, 16, 53–54, 56,
  61, 119–120, 122, 131, 137,
  138–139, 141, 170 (*See also*,
  appropriate portions of pages
  161–180)
  (*See* Universe; Individuals)
Parent population
  (*See* Parent distribution)
Part numbers, 196, 209, 269, 270
Parts
  alignment of, 5, 8, 19, 68, 69, 155,
    167, 175, 180
  positioning of, 68, 69, 167, 175,
    176, 180
  (*See* Piece parts)
Patterns
  analysis of, 9, 11, 23–32, 34–37,
    52–56, 62, 66–73, 82–84, 87,
    89, 100–101, 107, 109, 111–
    112, 116–117, 149–183, 189–
    190, 199, 203–206, 208–209,
    212–219, 223–224, 227, 229,
    237–238
  apparently worse than others, 67
  as source of assurance, 9, 274
  breakdown of, 36, 55, 66–68, 72, 166
  changes in, 55, 66–72, 73, 153, 155,
    164–165, 166, 168, 174–175,
    177–179, 203, 206, 218
  complex, 54, 67, 72 (*See* Complex
    patterns)
  continuous movement of, 9, 29,
    160 (*See* Trends)
  edge of, 24–25, 29, 160, 169, 171,
    172–174
  erratic, 8, 19, 31, 54–56, 60, 67, 68,
    72, 162–163, 166, 169, 179–
    180, 204, 206
  fluctuating, 5–6, 7–9, 24, 66, 72,
    160, 175, 176, 178, 190, 219,
    237–238
  hidden, 67–68, 75, 218
  importance of, 4, 6, 9, 11, 35–36,
    39, 45, 47, 53–56, 60, 61, 66–
    73, 74, 83, 87–89, 91, 97, 99–
    101, 144, 145, 149–180, 203–
    206, 215, 218, 219, 221, 223
  inconclusive, 28, 62, 64, 112, 146
  in control, 9, 35, 36, 38, 45, 47,
    53–54, 58, 59, 61, 71, 74, 91,
    119–122, 127, 131, 141, 149–
    151, 159, 170–171, 187, 188,
    189, 190, 195–196, 205, 221
  information from, 4, 11, 15–16,
    19–20, 35–36, 37, 53–56, 66–
    73, 83, 87, 89, 97, 100–101,
    152–180, 189, 217–219, 221
  interpretation of, in designed ex-
    periments, 82–83, 84, 87,
    89, 100–101, 107, 109, 111–
    112, 116–117
  interpretation of, in process capa-
    bility studies, 35–36, 52–56,
    59–60, 62, 66–73, 171

interpretation of, on shop charts, 37–38, 41, 63, 65, 171, 190, 192, 194–195, 199, 201–216, 217–219, 221, 222, 223–224, 227

interrupted, 60, 194

length of lines in, 160, 169

list of, 11, 54, 161

marking of (*See* Markings on control charts; Marking x's)

middle of, 24–25, 29, 160, 169, 171, 172, 173, 174

natural (*See* Natural pattern)

non-random, in data, 24–25, 116, 149, 153, 156, 160, 161, 165–166, 172–173, 175, 176, 177

obscure, 66–67

of instability, 11, 25–28, 54, 68–69, 72, 83, 87–89, 161, 166–167, 179–180

out of control, 9, 10, 15–16, 19, 25–32, 35–38, 52–53, 54–56, 59–61, 63, 65, 66–73, 74, 79, 82–83, 87–89, 91, 99–101, 111, 113, 116–117, 122, 131, 141, 145, 149–151, 159, 160, 172, 189–190, 192, 196–197, 203, 204, 206, 208–209, 212–213, 215, 217–219, 220–222, 223, 227, 229, 237–238, 262–263, 274

produced by unnatural variation, 6, 9, 35, 54–56, 159, 218, 221

reading of, 66–67, 69

recognition of, 11, 54, 66–70, 161, 213, 218–219

repetition of, 29, 69, 84–85, 156, 160, 161, 175, 176–177

shift in, 11, 54, 55, 72, 152, 161, 164–165, 173, 174–175, 177–179

significant, on a control chart, 35, 54–56, 60, 66–73, 75–76, 82, 87, 88, 99, 149–180, 203–206, 212, 217–219, 220, 221

simplification of, 17, 36, 38, 48–49, 53, 54–56, 59, 63, 66–73, 75, 106, 157–160, 166–167, 179, 190, 197, 199, 218–219, 221–222, 223

tests for, 9, 23–30, 100, 107, 109, 180–183, 208

types of, 6, 11, 23, 54, 152–160, 161

uninterpretable, 17, 48, 49, 59, 66–67, 72, 157, 159, 190, 219

unnatural (*See* Unnatural patterns)

used by Inspection, 39, 262–263, 274

(*See* Control chart patterns; Tests for unnatural patterns)

Pay group, 22, 203, 222

p-Charts

advantages of, 11, 17, 19–20, 48, 59, 157, 188–189, 196–197

amount of data required for (in engineering studies), 28, 50–51, 113, 191

as one of the measures of process capability, 45, 54, 56, 59, 62, 157

assignable causes on, 11, 159, 189, 190, 218

breakdown of, 48, 59, 157, 159, 190

calculations for, 7–8, 17–18, 20, 162, 196–197, 215, 229

centerlines for, in the shop, 62, 63, 192, 193–195, 197

characteristics to be plotted on, 11, 17, 48–49, 59, 157–159, 189, 190

compared with np-charts, c-charts and u-charts, 11, 20–21, 31, 49, 160, 189, 191

comparisons between, 51, 159

complex patterns on, 17, 48, 59, 73, 157, 159, 190, 198, 218, 223

components of, 59, 157, 159

construction of, 7–8, 17–18, 20, 196–197

control limits for, 7–8, 17–19, 191, 194–195, 196–197, 229

data sheets for, 207, 209, 210

difficulty in interpreting, 11, 17, 48, 59, 72, 157–159, 190, 198, 218

economic stopping point for, 194

examples of, 7–8, 18–20, 51, 74, 144, 194, 204

explanation of, 7–8, 11, 17, 48, 157–159, 188–189

frequent defects on, 159

importance of, 11, 45, 48, 54, 56, 59, 158–159, 196, 198

in engineering studies, 48–49, 50, 51, 54, 59, 62, 73, 157–159

instability on, 159, 167, 180, 194

interpretation of (*See* Interpretation)

levels on, 62, 194, 228

lower limit for, 17, 18, 20, 194–195

measurements for, 17, 18, 50, 157, 203–204, 209

modified limits for, 196–197

overall, 48, 59, 159, 197

samples for, in the shop, 191

sample size for, 17, 50, 113, 191

scales on, 17, 51, 53, 159

sensitivity of, 11, 48–49, 59, 158, 159

stairstep limits for, 18–19

stratification on, 157, 173

substitutes for, 11, 49–50, 113, 198, 218

symbols for, 17

tests for, when control limits are unsymmetrical, 28, 182, 183, 191

theory of, 137, 151

used for correlation, 144

used in designed experiments, 113

used in routine inspection, 262–263

use of decimals in calculating, 18, 20

uses in the shop, 62, 63, 64, 188–189, 190, 194, 196–197, 204, 227

variations of, 11, 20–21, 49, 160, 189, 191, 198, 204

varying sample sizes for, 18, 191

where to use, 48–49, 188–189, 191

Peaks

in a cycle, 69–70, 161, 162

in a distribution, 131, 136, 153, 155, 158, 162, 163, 165, 166, 169, 170, 173, 174, 176, 179

Pearson, E. S., 275, 277

Peculiarities in a distribution, 16, 140–141, 156, 160, 161

Pencil and paper (in the shop), 215

People in the shop, 201, 202, 203, 217 (*See* Operators; Layout operators; Machine setters; Supervisors)

Percent

good, lost, spoiled etc., 11, 17, 38, 48, 157, 189

of product rejected, 37, 46, 66, 71, 226, 227, 235, 237–239, 244–246, 254–255, 264, 265 (*See* OC Curves)

Percentage

as a measure of capability, 45, 48, 54, 56, 59, 127, 157, 159, 194, 197

as a statistic, 137, 151, 196, 198

calculation of, 17, 18, 213

data, 5, 11, 17–20, 31, 48, 50, 54, 59, 113, 157, 183, 188–189, 191, 194, 196–197, 198, 229

defective (*See* Percent defective)

determined by process capability studies, 54, 56, 58–59, 71, 126–127, 235

differences in, 31, 159

for non-normal distribution, 30–31, 56, 59, 134–136

for normal distribution, 30–31, 54, 58–59, 132–133

from an $\bar{X}$ and R chart, 56, 58–59, 126–127

from a p-chart, 56, 59, 157, 159

of defectives, 11, 17, 59, 157, 189, 235, 237–265

of dropouts, 38, 48, 189, 225, 227, 264

Percentage, *continued*
of points out of control, 221–222, 226
of product outside of limits, 30–31, 54, 56, 58–59, 61, 64, 66, 71, 120–121, 127, 132–136, 189, 204, 225, 234–235
Percent defective
as an inspection requirement, 265
calculation of, 17, 18, 215, 229
in a process, 61, 63, 66, 71, 127, 235
in inspection, 39, 234–235, 237, 238, 239, 243, 254–255, 263–265
in inspection planning, 244, 255, 264, 265
on a *p*-chart, 8, 11, 59, 63, 74, 157, 159, 189, 194, 215, 227
reduction of, 19, 31, 159, 167, 175, 178–179, 224–225, 233–235, 236, 265
related to operational sorting, 120, 121, 122, 235, 236, 265
Performance
as distinguished from capability, 45, 61, 66, 74, 187–188
current, 39, 227, 264 (*See* Process average)
of a machine, 16, 19, 66, 71, 83, 202, 203, 204
on shop charts, 65, 74, 194, 206, 212–213
in the past, 61, 65
study of, to keep shop charts up to date, 74, 227, 228
(*See* Capability)
Performance studies, 34, 74, 187, 188, 227, 228
Periodic
adjustment of a process, 16, 67, 203
control chart audits, 227
disturbance in a process, 67, 150, 203–204 (*See* Overadjustment)
follow-up on audits, 227
patterns (*See* Cycles; Systematic variables)
review of cost reduction cases, 224, 226
review of layouts, 227
review of progress, 33, 41, 226
selections from shop control charts, 229
summaries of results, 33, 74, 221–222, 226, 228–229
Periods of trouble, 187, 202, 233, 246, 273
Permanent
control of process, 62, 224, 226
cost reduction, obtained by control charts, 36, 38, 226
effect of process changes, 62, 72, 228

file of charts, 228
location of process, 62, 121, 228
results of engineering work, 38, 61, 62, 63–64, 101, 112, 187, 220
Permissible average
as basis for choice of sampling plans in inspection, 264
as basis for shop control charts, 64, 65, 193–194, 195–196, 196–197
Personal injury, 234
Personnel, changes in, 227 (*See* New operators)
Physical
abnormalities, 52, 116–117, 163 209, 214, 268, 269
differences between units, 214, 268
laws, 6, 7
limits of materials, 57
measurements, 6
Piece parts
abnormal, 156, 214 (*See* Set-up parts)
as a variable, 10, 31, 55, 64, 71, 167, 171, 196, 202, 212, 213, 215, 217, 220
difficulty in making, 15
ends or sides of, 90
needed for assembly, 220, 246, 260–261
positioning of (*See* Positioning)
positions on, 90 (*See* Taper; Out of round; Positional variability)
quality of, 37, 39, 47, 64, 71–72, 155, 169, 175, 180, 202, 217, 219, 220, 264
specifications for, 119
suppliers of, 174, 207, 260
Piece rates, 203, 260, 263
(*See* Efficiency; Wage incentives)
Pileup of metal, 209
Pillars, walls etc., 192
Pilot runs, 46, 76–77, 91–92, 220
Pin projection, 123
Pipes, 192
Planned experiments, 76–77
(*See* Designed experiments)
Planning
for a process capability study, 46–51, 66
for inspection, 233–236, 263, 264–265, 273, 274
for process control, 61, 62, 63–65, 187–199, 265
of quality control program, 33, 39–41, 223–226
of shop charts, 36–38, 40–41, 187–189, 190, 192, 223–224
Plate current, 229
Plates (for assembly, lapping etc.), 167, 212

Plating
as a variable, 4, 35, 37, 152, 156
solutions for, 23, 153, 178
thickness of, 91, 93, 100, 101
(*See* Chemical operations)
Platykurtic distributions
(*See* Symmetrical non-normal distributions)
Play (in a fixture etc.), 55, 69, 155, 162, 167, 180, 219, 235
Plotting
diagrams for, 99, 108, 109
errors in, 163, 166, 180, 219, 227, 228–229
guides for, in an experiment, 99, 109
of charts used by inspectors, 39, 262–263, 270, 274
of control charts in general, 5–6, 13–14, 18–19, 20, 21, 22, 143–144, 145, 149
of designed experiments, 82–83, 84–85, 87–88, 97, 98–100, 107–111, 116–117, 229
of process capability studies, 51–52, 53, 66–72, 72–73
of shop charts, 190, 192, 197, 201, 208–209, 213, 214–216, 219, 223, 227, 228–229
of verification samples on shop charts, 274
order of, in a designed experiment, 84–85, 99, 109
Plotting guides
for use by statistical clerks, 229
for use in designed experiments, 99, 108, 109
Plus or minus tolerances, 119, 122, 202
(*See* Limits)
Points
calculation of, for an experiment, 85–86, 108–109
considered as part of a statistical pattern, 24, 149, 175, 176, 177, 274
for selecting samples, 51, 190–192, 207, 227, 267
out of control, 70, 71, 212, 213, 221–222, 226, 227
plotted by inspectors on shop charts, 274
plotting of, on control charts (*See* Plotting)
Point-to-point correlation, 16, 29, 69–70, 156, 176–177
Poisson distribution, 239–240, 242, 252, 277
Pole piece assembly, 125
Pooling
of effects with residual, 96–97, 106
of job knowledge (*See* Quality control teams)
of residual, 96–97, 106, 110–111

Population, 137
  (*See* Parent distribution)
Positional variability, 89–90
Positioning of parts, 69, 167, 175, 176, 180, 213
Positions
  on a machine, 55, 70, 151, 161, 172, 176, 207
  on a part, 90
Positive
  correlation (*See* Correlation)
  skewness (*See* Skewness)
  stop on a machine, 57
Possible causes, 69, 161–180, 218–219
Potential
  effects in an experiment, 95–97, 98
  electrical, 164
  improvement, 35–36, 54–56, 66–71, 76, 120–121, 220, 226
Powder, 189
Power
  in the hands of Inspection, 273, 274
  of a control chart, 9, 11, 61, 83–84, 141, 149 (*See* Sensitivity)
  of a designed experiment, 76, 112
  of an instrument, 87, 88, 89
  of a sampling plan, 242, 246
  output, 164, 177
  supply, 48
Practical wisdom, 40, 64, 114, 219 (*See* Job knowledge)
Practices
  of Inspection, 233–236, 264–265, 267–271, 273–274
  of Inspection (affecting Operating), 236, 246, 254–255, 263, 265
  questionable, 45, 61, 73
Precision
  in detecting out-of-control conditions, 11, 47, 48, 160, 161, 165, 189
  of control limits, 52, 100, 107, 109, 161
  of tests for unnatural patterns, 180–183
Precision of measurement, 49, 50, 61, 62, 75, 84–91, 113
  (*See* Error, Compare with accuracy of measurement)
Predictability
  as one of the concepts associated with a natural pattern, 59–61, 150, 170–171
  of a distribution, 6–7, 141
  of a process, 34, 35, 36, 45–46, 53–54, 64, 71
  of points on a control chart, 7, 24, 149, 161, 175, 176
  of results, 40, 53–54, 61–63, 71, 194

Predictions
  engineering, 34, 35, 36, 38, 46–47, 50, 53–56, 59–61, 62, 63–64, 71, 73, 91, 101, 112, 122, 125–127, 236, 244, 265, 274
  from an unnatural pattern, 35, 54–56, 59–61, 194
  should properly be based on a natural pattern, 36, 53–54, 59–61, 149–150, 170, 171
  statistical, 7, 24, 149–150, 170–171
  (*See* Allowances; Forecasts; Estimates; Standards)
Pressures
  due to work loads, 227
  for production, 73, 155
  of gas etc., considered as a process variable, 6, 11, 21, 114, 164, 189
Prevention
  of defects, 37–38, 233, 265
  of shop troubles, 33–34, 36–38, 187, 202–206
Previous knowledge
  contradicted, 10, 68, 76
  needed for interpreting patterns (*See* Job knowledge)
  reconciled with results, 77, 218
Pride
  in improvement of job, 202, 203, 223, 226
  of operators, in control charts, 203
Prior operations
  (*See* Early operations)
Probabilities
  associated with multiple tests, 25 (footnote), 180–183
  associated with normal distribution, 31, 132–133, 181
  associated with R charts, 137, 151, 181, 182
  associated with sampling plans, 38, 237–242
  associated with skewed distributions 135–136, 183
  associated with various control chart tests, 183
  associated with $\bar{X}$ charts, 137–138, 151, 180–182
  Binomial, 183, 239, 242, 252, 278
  calculation of, in control chart tests, 180–183
  for ranges of samples of 2: 181–183
  Hypergeometric, 239, 242
  Poisson, 183, 239–242, 252
  tables of, 239, 242, 277, 278
  used in tests for unnatural patterns, 25, 25 (footnote), 181, 183
Probability
  limits (*See* Statistical limits)
  paper, 79, 133
  theory of, 237, 239–240

Probability of acceptance
  calculation of, 239–242
  examples of, 237–238, 240–242, 244–245
  explanation of, 237–238, 240, 244–245
  for other than single sampling plans, 242
Probability of rejection, 239, 240, 244–245
Problems
  engineering (*See* Engineering problems)
  isolated, 15, 19, 33, 66, 72, 125–127, 143–146, 187–189, 203–206
  lists of, 3, 10, 33, 34, 46–47, 112, 114, 187
  shop (*See* Operating organization, problems of)
  solved by process capability studies, 4, 10, 34, 36, 46, 47, 63, 66–72, 72–73, 75–76, 112, 187–188, 220, 235, 265
  solved by quality control program, 3, 4, 5, 10, 33, 34, 35, 38, 46–47, 75, 77, 187, 233–236, 265, 273–274
  solved by shop charts, 10, 16, 19, 36–38, 62, 64–65, 71–72, 187–189, 202–206, 220, 221, 223–226, 235, 265
  solved by studying R chart, 66–68
Procedures
  as a variable, 61, 114, 158, 162, 167, 171, 178, 180, 218–219, 224, 227
  in designed experiments, 78–81, 82–83, 84, 85–89, 91–92, 93–97, 97–101, 107–112, 112–117
  in process capability studies, 36, 41, 45, 47–63, 63–65, 66–72, 74, 75, 112, 220, 228
  in process checking, 41, 190–192, 201, 205–216, 217, 223, 227–229
  in sampling inspection, 267–271
  in setting up shop charts, 64, 65, 190–192, 209
  unsystematic, 171, 180
Process
  action on, in a process capability study, 36, 61–63, 66–72
  adjustment of, 30, 37, 67, 153, 188, 202, 203–204, 265
  centering of, 30, 62, 64–65, 120–121, 167, 170, 188, 202, 220
  changes in (*See* Changes)
  checked for unstable mixtures, 68, 166
  compared to OC curve, 244, 255, 264, 265
  control of, 217, 226 (*See* Process control)
  definition of, 3–4, 45

Process, *continued*

drift of, 67, 90, 153, 175

fluctuations of (*See* Fluctuations)

immediate check on, 37, 190, 212–213, 217

improvement of (*See* Improvement)

manually controlled, 3, 16, 30, 57, 70, 72–73, 219, 221, 235, 265 (*See* Manual operations)

new knowledge of, from unnatural patterns, 35, 36–37, 54–56, 159, 161–180, 221

optimum level for, 37, 62, 64, 120–121, 188, 193, 264–265

permanent changes in, 62, 72, 228

predictability of, 34, 35, 36, 45–46, 53–54, 64, 71

relation of, to specification, 13–14, 16, 30–31, 34, 35, 46, 48, 53–54, 58–59, 61–65, 66, 71, 119–122, 124, 125, 127, 140, 151, 157, 158, 160–161, 170, 187–189, 195–196, 198–199, 204–206, 219, 220, 223, 224, 226

spread of (*See* Natural spread of a process; Process spread)

stability of (*See* Stability)

where checked, in the shop, 51, 151, 190–192, 207 (*See* Early operations)

(*See* Processes)

Process average

as basis for choosing sampling plans, 244, 245, 250–253, 264, 265

as basis for estimating costs, 245–246, 265

as basis for evaluating product of suppliers, 39

as basis for minimizing inspection, 39, 246, 250, 252, 253, 273–274

as used in Dodge-Romig tables, 250, 253, 254, 255

Process capability

approach to, 36, 47, 63, 64, 71, 73, 74, 83

as used in the shop, 65, 187, 202, 203–204, 217, 221–222

compared with specification, 61–65, 71, 119–122, 124, 125–126, 127, 195

definition of, 34, 35, 36, 45, 47

dependent on a natural pattern, 35, 53, 56, 59–61, 141

evidence of, 36, 63, 71, 149–152, 170–171

importance of, 34–36, 45–47, 53–54, 56, 76, 112

long-term, 61, 64, 196–197

meaning of, 4, 34–36, 45, 56, 61, 71, 74, 75–76, 122, 131, 149–152, 170–171, 234–236, 244, 246, 264–265

numerical estimates of, 45, 56, 58–59, 71, 73, 127, 235

related to OC curve, 244–245, 255, 264–265

related to operational sorting, 120, 121, 235, 265

satisfactory and unsatisfactory, 34–35, 45–47, 61–63, 71, 121, 122

short-term, 61, 64

shown by natural patterns, 53–54, 59–61, 71, 122, 125–127, 170–171

two ways of expressing, 45, 56

use of, in engineering, 34–36, 45–47, 61–65, 119–127, 145, 224–226

use of, in inspection, 234–236, 244, 246, 250, 252, 253, 255, 264–265

wrong estimates of, 60–61, 141

Process capability studies vii, 4, 28, 34–36, 38, 40, 41, 45–74, 75–76, 112, 113, 116, 119–122, 125–127, 187, 195, 199, 219, 220, 223, 228, 235, 265

abnormal data found in, 49, 52–53, 61, 62, 116–117

action based on, 61–63, 67–72, 73, 235, 255, 265

advantages of (*See* Advantages)

amount of data in, 28, 47, 50–51, 61, 62, 63–64, 66–72

analysis of, 47, 51–63, 66–73

as proper basis for sampling inspection, 36, 235, 244, 246, 250, 252, 253, 255, 264–265

as proper basis for shop control charts, 33–34, 36, 38, 40–41, 45, 62, 63–65, 71–72, 187, 193–195, 199

as related to operational sorting, 120, 121, 122, 235, 265

assignable causes in (*See* Assignable causes)

average of long period not a substitute for, 61

characteristics plotted in, 47, 66, 72

collection of data for, 36, 41, 47–51, 55, 62, 63–64, 66, 67, 74, 223, 228

complex patterns in, 54–56, 66, 67–73

complexity of, 36, 45, 47, 63, 72

conclusions from (*See* Conclusions)

control limits for, 51–52, 53

covering entire jobs, 224–225

data for (*See* Collection of data)

decisions in, 47–53, 66, 72

definition of, 3–4, 34, 36, 45–46

description of, 35–36, 47, 75, 76

distribution not a substitute for, 16, 61, 141

economic basis of, 34–36, 45–47, 61–63, 265

effect of skewness on, 56–58, 61, 122

elimination of variables in, 55, 66, 67, 68

end of, 36, 47, 63, 66, 71

examples of, 66–72, 72–73

for cost reduction, 34–36, 41, 46, 62, 64, 71, 223–224, 225–226, 228, 235, 265

for process improvement, 4, 34, 35, 36, 41, 46–47, 62, 63–65, 66–72, 120–121, 235, 265

growing out of shop charts, 40, 199, 223, 228

identification of data for, 49, 51, 52, 53, 54–56, 72–73, 76

ignoring patterns in, 66, 91, 153

importance of, vii, 4, 33–34, 34–36, 38, 40, 41, 45–46, 61–63, 120–121, 125–127, 187, 223, 225–226, 235, 244, 246, 265

importance of R chart in, 55, 66, 67, 68 (*See* R Chart)

inflated patterns in, 55, 66, 67, 168, 173

instructions for collection of data in, 49, 66, 67, 223, 228

interpretation of, when patterns are in control, 53–54, 56, 61–63, 71–72

interpretation of, when patterns are not in control, 54–56, 59–61, 66–71, 72–73, 189 (*See also* appropriate portions of pages 149–180)

introduction of shop chart before study is completed, 36, 63–64, 71–72, 74, 188, 198–199, 221, 228

knowledge needed in, 38, 40, 54–56, 66, 67, 71, 72, 75, 112, 220

leading to the need for other studies, 34–35, 36, 40–41, 45–47, 63, 83, 223, 228

leading to the need for shop charts 36, 40–41, 45, 62, 63–65, 66–72, 187, 188

length of, 34–35, 47, 63, 66, 72

long and short term estimates from, 61, 64

made by a Quality Control Team, 40, 41, 45, 66, 74, 220, 223, 228

new, as needed, 40–41, 62, 65, 190, 194, 199, 220, 223, 228